Bard   FICTION PRIZE

Bard College invites submissions for its annual Fiction Prize for young writers.

The Bard Fiction Prize is awarded annually to a promising, emerging writer who is a United States citizen aged 39 years or younger at the time of application. In addition to a monetary award of $30,000, the winner receives an appointment as writer-in-residence at Bard College for one semester without the expectation that he or she teach traditional courses. The recipient will give at least one public lecture and will meet informally with students.

To apply, candidates should write a cover letter describing the project they plan to work on while at Bard and submit a C.V., along with three copies of the published book they feel best represents their work. No manuscripts will be accepted.

Applications for the 2023 prize must be received by June 15, 2022. For further information about the Bard Fiction Prize, call 845-758-7087, or visit www.bard.edu/bfp. Applicants may also request information by writing to the Bard Fiction Prize, Bard College, Annandale-on-Hudson, NY 12504-5000.

Bard College PO Box 5000, Annandale-on-Hudson, NY 12504-5000

COMING UP IN THE FALL
Conjunctions:79
ONWORD
Edited by Bradford Morrow

This issue of *Conjunctions*, which might have been our last but for the passionate support of many people far and near, will feature as many themes as there are writers in its pages. A gathering of fiction, poetry, essays, and all manner of hybrid ingenuities, *Onword* will celebrate moving forward with our words and visions, imagining paths ahead where there seem to be nothing but obstacles. While the issue will explore unities and continuities, having faith, showing strength, rising up, it will also peer into the darker, meaner, harder side of human experience, the everyday catastrophes each of us has the ability to provoke—sometimes by the use of "mere" words that can and do break bones.

China's great innovative writer Can Xue contributes one of her most moving stories, "Smog City," about three aging citizens who narrate their tales of isolation, patience, and tiny triumphs in a city sunk under a mysterious toxic smog. Bonnie Nadzam makes her debut in our pages with two lyrical monologues of longing and privation, one beginning, "Everything promises you to me. Certain stainless mornings, certain lonely farmhouses, certain bent trees." *Conjunctions:79, Onword* will also include new work by Fred Moten, Carmen Maria Machado, Peter Gizzi, Elizabeth Hand, Rae Armantrout, Peter Orner, and many others both emerging and established, along with a selection of previously unpublished poems by the late C. D. Wright, selected by Forrest Gander.

One-year individual US subscriptions to *Conjunctions* are only $30 (two years for $50) for today's most innovative fiction, poetry, and narrative nonfiction. To read dangerously, subscribe or renew at conjunctions.com, or mail your check to *Conjunctions*, Bard College, Annandale-on-Hudson, NY 12504. For e-book editions of current and selected past issues, visit openroadmedia.com/conjunctions. If you have questions or wish to request an invoice, e-mail conjunctions@bard.edu or call (845) 758-7054.

CONJUNCTIONS

Bi-Annual Volumes of New Writing

Edited by
Bradford Morrow

Contributing Editors
Diane Ackerman
Martine Bellen
Mei-mei Berssenbrugge
Mary Caponegro
Brian Evenson
Peter Gizzi
Elizabeth Hand
Robert Kelly
Ann Lauterbach
Carmen Maria Machado
Dinaw Mengestu
Rick Moody
Fred Moten
Karen Russell
Joanna Scott
David Shields
Peter Straub
Quincy Troupe

Published by Bard College

EDITOR: Bradford Morrow
INTERIM MANAGING EDITOR: Melynda Fuller
SENIOR EDITORS: Jedediah Berry, Benjamin Hale, A. D. Lauren-Abunassar, Linnea Marik, Edie Meidav, Michael Sarinsky, Pat Sims
COPY EDITOR: Pat Sims
ART EDITOR: Jessica Fuller
ASSISTANT EDITORS: Sarah Ahmad, Shadiyat Ajao, Megan Brien, K Chiucarello, Kate Monaghan, Magali Roman
PUBLICITY: Mark Primoff
EDITORIAL ASSISTANTS: Celeste Flahaven, Ari Mackoff, Wyatt Reu

CONJUNCTIONS is published in the spring and fall of each year by Bard College, Annandale-on-Hudson, NY 12504. This project is supported in part by awards from the National Endowment for the Arts, the New York State Council on the Arts with the support of Governor Kathy Hochul and the New York State Legislature, Community of Literary Magazines and Presses, and the Whiting Foundation.

SUBSCRIPTIONS: Use our secure online ordering system at conjunctions.com, or send subscription orders to CONJUNCTIONS, Bard College, Annandale-on-Hudson, NY 12504. Single year (two volumes): $30.00 for individuals; $50.00 for institutions and non-US. Two years (four volumes): $50.00 for individuals; $80.00 for institutions and non-US. For information about subscriptions, back issues, and advertising, contact us at (845) 758-7054 or conjunctions@bard.edu. *Conjunctions* is listed and indexed in JSTOR and Humanities International Complete and included in EBSCO*host*.

Editorial communications should be sent to Bradford Morrow, *Conjunctions*, 21 East 10th Street, 3E, New York, NY 10003. Unsolicited manuscripts cannot be returned unless accompanied by a stamped, self-addressed envelope. Simultaneous and unsolicited email submissions will not be considered. Do not send work via any method requiring a signature for delivery. If you are submitting from outside the United States, contact conjunctions@bard.edu for instructions.

Copyright © 2022 CONJUNCTIONS.

Cover design by Jerry Kelly, New York. Cover art by Henry Glover: *To Touch You*, 2019, oil, soft pastel, and charcoal on canvas, 39 x 39 inches. Courtesy of the artist.

Conjunctions e-books of selected past issues are distributed by Open Road Integrated Media (openroadmedia.com/conjunctions) and available for purchase in all e-reader formats from Amazon, Apple, B&N, Google, Indiebound, Kobo, Overdrive, and elsewhere.

Retailers can order print issues directly from *Conjunctions*.

Printers: Maple Press, Puritan Capital Press

Typesetter: Bill White, Typeworks

ISSN 0278-2324

ISBN 978-0-941964-89-0

Manufactured in the United States of America.

TABLE OF CONTENTS

FEAR ITSELF

Edited by Bradford Morrow

what mask do you wear, wearing your animal haunches
preparing for your human performance

Pan, the child of Hermes and a wood nymph, lord of the woods
His name means "all"—*all* delight, *all* forest, *all* things
and his name gives rise to "panic"

—*Eleni Sikelianos*

EDITOR'S NOTE

WHETHER FOUNDED IN TRUTH or imagination, fear has a toxic genius for pervading our lives. It has many faces and many means of forcing itself upon us. War, inequality, abandonment, an evolving climate catastrophe born of the relentless degradation of our planet, this tenacious pandemic, the unknown—such are only a few realities that daily generate existential fear. A staggering array of phobias challenge some of us as well, from all-too-common derangements like xenophobia and homophobia to rarer disorders like hypnophobia, the fear of falling asleep, and optophobia, the fear of opening one's eyes. Many of us find ourselves fearing fear itself, dreading to examine the fears we harbor. Yet fear is ubiquitous in our myths and fairy tales, songs and theater, art and literature, and the historical legacies of every culture. Fear and its many nemeses—confidence, bravery, faith among them—are locked in a mortal dance in every narrative humans create, both in life and on the page.

Fear Itself gathers the work of some thirty contemporary writers willing to interrogate the wide spectrum of apprehensions, terrors, and dread we humans experience. In these pages readers will find a devastating poem on the fraying memories of a black man kidnapped as a child by his white grandparents, and another that explores the defiant fears of a dying woman and a man terrified he will not succumb to death "efficiently." Here, as well, is a classic nightmare tale of a father who loses his daughter in a bustling airport while trying to catch a flight home, along with an alphaphobiac novella that traces the metamorphosis of a retired tennis pro named Ben into a mythic amphibious creature known as the Botusfleming Hedwigkraken.

Being alive is an iffy business, and unwelcome fears await us with open arms at every turn. Once in a while, however, as *Fear Itself* further confirms, we witness instead the grace of courage and the cool of fortitude.

—Bradford Morrow
April 2022
New York City

Two Stories
Bronka Nowicka

—Translated from Polish by Katarzyna Szuster-Tardi

THE SENSE OF LACK

MEMOIRS, SURVIVING FRAGMENTS:

Here, they combine the knowledge of choosing words with the art of touch. Before somebody utters *soft fur*, they keep their hands on a dog's head for years.

From granaries, they dispense hunger, a spice that stimulates the sense of lack. The king trusts that absence is the saltpeter of things susceptible to nonexistence: what doesn't keep in salt will be preserved in hunger. No myth can be cut like the fabric for a coat, the halves of which will be dragged through life. Thanks to the spice, the subjects of the kingdom don't know stale love, only unfulfilled. The professed religion is apnea. All maturing is mutiny. Red fruit get a visit from hangmen.

The menstruating queen is transported to snow-covered fields. She is stripped naked, her legs and wrists tied. They abandon her. Returning—exhausted at that point—she must crawl. Then she leaves a trail of blood on the snow. From the castle tower, the king admires this female trail.

He decreed that her belly would never be bloated by a child. He said: Wear all precious stones except this one. If you ever bring this stone to me, I will tie another to your neck and send the two of you to the river. Sometimes the queen tries a child on in front of the mirror. She puffs up the draped dress. It takes only a moment. Too short to put on a basting stitch.

—Extinguish me or unleash me—says the queen.
  —I only grow concerns—replies the king.

He waits for the procession to pass: he throws his head, hip, hand. Head, hip, hand. When he walks, his tic has the same rhythm. That's how his insanity introduces itself—without having to tilt its hat. The local madmen receive sweet communion. The king is generous—he skillfully targets the sugar cubes at overgrown tongues.

Dinner is served at the mouth. She gets bony syllables; he, sentences stuffed with sense. The king eats with his hands. Later, he demands water. Then he gets up. Other kings stroke their queens' necks, crushing their lips with the mortar of their tongues. When this king gets up, he just leaves. Now the queen can wring her face. Dogs' tongues are working on the puddle on the floor. Nothing is wasted in the bloodstream of the kingdom.

When the king got bored with the senselessness of the rituals, he instituted bestiaries: the court, herded to the city slaughterhouse, ridicule each other. People deride, point their fingers at someone else's ugliness, fear, and defects. The king also appears. He parodies animals that are led to death: sneering by the slaughterhouse.

The decaying books read: a woman should have her hands busy, otherwise her thoughts are busy. The court honors old sentences. Every evening, they send a lacemaker to the queen. Bent over spools, they work on the royal mistress. Intricate work—to crochet a good body. When the last loop is pulled, the lacemaker leaves. If the queen manages to create a golem out of chenille, the king wakes up happy. They serve him tea—it cools down more slowly than the woman lying next to him. Before she stretches, she's back to being a bundle of thread.

The sentence has been passed: such a dream could not arise in this man, it was stolen. Pulling a dream out of a thief with horses or oxen is the most severe torture inflicted in the kingdom. Animals yoked to the consciousness tear it apart and drag its scraps around the market. Children play with them despite their mothers' warnings: they poke them with a stick, rub them in with their soles.

—Put on another one—says the king.—This one looks as if dogs had chewed it up, have it ironed.
The queen takes her face off and sits bald until breakfast is over.

The king checks the results of battles and lotteries. Courtiers spit into the moat.

At lunchtime, the queen's face is ironed.

The king recognizes illegitimate children—it takes several hours. After dinner, he goes to the queen's bedroom.

—Can you lend me the love I once gave you?

—Yes—replies the queen.—Let me remember where I put it.

She searches until she pulls out something small wrapped in parchment from under the bed.

—Don't forget to give it back—she pleads.

The king can't hear her. He rushes through the chambers and upstairs to the attic. He hands over the bundle to a washerwoman who's hanging out the queen's face between the sheets.

THE ONEIRISTS

The resources of tabularia—maps of stone and clay, woven *mappae mundi*—document the existence of areas inhabited by nimrods who tried to explore the essence of time in order to control it. Rotuli texts and engravings testify to hunting practices, some of which were to inflict wounds or death on time, others to capture it. It was believed that only something that possessed a body could be comprehended, and, in the case of invisible things, the body supposedly manifested itself after being wounded, trapped, or postmortem.

What later researchers thought to be the anticipation of clocks was, in fact, time snares whose sprockets, dials, cords, weights, and pendulums were designed to cut, bond, stun, and squash the captive. They wanted time to bleed, expire, struggle, thrash against the walls of crates stuffed with iron. Similarly, rods and arrowheads stuck in the ground, wrongly taken for the first gnomons, were the primitive tools of hunters going after the animal running ubiquitously. What was intended to drown and crush the victim was mistakenly considered by those who came afterward as sand and water hourglasses. In fact, all the time traps along with their mechanisms were organ donors for the first clocks, not their prophecy.

Manuscript artifacts mention Ichneumons, who, having reflected on the figure of time, came to the conclusion that it was either time or the observer that moved and based their ritual on this thought. They believed that it would be possible to see time if one stopped striding it and gave up all activities related to movement. So they abandoned their crops, neglected their animals, extinguished the fire, bolted the door, and affixed themselves at the windows. Hired solely for looking, they toiled with their eyes day and night, expecting remuneration in the form of a picture of time made present. But all they saw was landscapes. In the end, they quit practicing stillness and reached for ceremonies intended to force the invisible to appear. They wanted to offend time, deny its effects, merge the spheres it separated. Remembering and planning were banned. Verbs describing past, present, and future activities were made indistinguishable. They removed the boundaries between the living and the dead. They dug up the deceased, perched them on platforms erected in the market square, and forced them to pretend aliveness in public—bodies waved their hands around, raised by balloons tied to their wrists with string. Thanks to these rites, the Ichneumons provided their posterity with a stage, a puppet, and a prop, but no knowledge about the nature of time.

Oneirists, the first transplantologists of an idea from dream to reality, who built their cities, systems, and mythologies sleepwalking, knew: time, like sleep, would never be matter, but they sensed that it could inscribe itself into a manufactured object, cocreating a souvenir of its own presence.

Oneirists dreamed of fishlike membranes containing reflections of the real world. Plates with miniature figures. Caskets that could trap matter, light, and time. In somnambulistic studios, they put together boxes similar to birdhouses. They called these constructions cameras and put them outside at dawn. They hoped that at dusk, they would reach into the boxes, with the same gesture they used to pick eggs from nests, to find a picture of the past, but all they took out was empty hands.

Tireless in their search, they lay in groups on loosened soil. Once they posed in the horizontal atelier, the gardeners sowed this strip of ground with grass. If the sun was good, after a week, the Oneirists got up and, from the scaffoldings brought into the field, they looked at the black doubles of their own shapes lying amidst the green. This is how the first photographs were created, still impermanent and lacking in detail.

Another oneiric invention for studying the relationships between time and object were anatomical theaters. They were used for autopsying old things. Stripped of their shells, their inner layers, organs, and cavities were studied to find a way to revisit the past. Musical

11

instruments, laid on the autopsy table, gave up the hair of their former users while pieces of walls and rocks hiding paintings or writing were examined.

Explorers, propelled by the content of their own dreams, used them to drag the prototype of a museum into reality. That was because they dreamed of edifices erected in honor of time, full of objects gathered for it, so it could play with them—destroying some, saving others.

With the advent of museums—places where people came to worship time—many visions of its embodiments froze up, fossilized into sentiment.

The Nature of the Beast
Stephen Graham Jones

TINA HAS BEEN WATCHING the place between the wall and her couch for either three minutes now, or for her whole entire life. It's two thirty in the morning—2:34, actually, which feels like fate, like either a really lucky or a really terrible number—and she's on her way back from checking the sliding glass door, because she couldn't remember if she'd locked it or not, and who could sleep like that? But what she can't remember *now* is if there's a tall, broad-leafed rubber plant on the far side of the couch or not, making that for-sure-there shadow fall against the pale wall in that . . . she doesn't want to commit to "wrong way," but a way she's not sure she can look away from, as it might twitch closer in that instant. Maybe she can wait it out, though? Maybe she can think it through, reduce it to the nothing it surely is, that it would have been if she hadn't traipsed down here to check the sliding glass door that she'd already checked before bed, last thing. *But,* another part of her argues—and she hates that part of herself—wouldn't a plant's leaves be sighing the least little bit in the gentle breeze from the ceiling fan? At least one of them, which is in a different state of maturity than the rest, meaning it's looser or tighter? Less attached to the main stalk, or more attached? Plants don't go still when someone walks into the room, anyway, like she's ninety percent certain this one just did. That would be stupid. Also, there's no plant there anymore, Tina knows. The pot it had been in, it's even out on the balcony, turned upside down so it won't collect water, become a mosquito incubator. Tina specifically remembers setting a glass of iced tea on it a few hours ago, and joking to herself about how this was the perfect coaster at the absolute perfect height, that she was going to miss this wonderfully comfortable *coaster* when she finally took a chance on another needlessly large house-plant. So, if this is the shade of a plant she's seeing, then it's the after-image of the plant she killed in February, it's the memory of the plant that *was*, it's . . . it's her guilt made manifest, even though it wasn't really even her fault, plants die all the time, it's completely natural, and guilt over a plant has got to be stupid, doesn't it? Still she does

the calendar math from February until now—February to June, five
months, depending how you count—but it doesn't soothe her, it
doesn't explain what she's pretty sure is standing over there in the
darkness. It just makes it worse. If the pot really is on the balcony
like she knows it is, and if this really is a plant, then how's it even
standing, right? Meaning—do the math, Tina, face the facts—meaning it's probably not a plant, is it? And it's not some made-up childish "plant *ghost*" either, get real, grow up. Plants don't have ghosts.
Only people do. Unless, of course, this is just her mind playing tricks
on her. Isn't that what ghosts are anyway? Projections? Imagination
run wild? Something fake that you choose to believe in, to scare yourself with? All the same, Tina knows—she knows knows knows—
that if she keeps walking through to the entryway to go back upstairs, then she's going to see that carbon monoxide detector by the
couch from an angle she doesn't want to. An angle that blips that little
green light into darkness for a moment, because there's something or
someone standing between Tina and that light. Something that wasn't
there before, that shouldn't be there at all. And if she *doesn't* see that
light blip out, then she doesn't have to know, she doesn't have to
acknowledge, she won't have to start screaming, she won't have to run
up the stairs with her back swayed in because those are for sure and
for certain footsteps behind her, clomping in. "You're being stupid,"
she whispers to herself out loud. Then, more like a chide, "The sliding door was locked, you're alone in here." But . . . what's the history
of this apartment, after all? This land? That couch? And, just because
the sliding door *was* locked doesn't mean it was locked two minutes
before she crept down here, when she didn't even have a real reason
to be creeping at all, other than that it felt wrong to *crash* through
darkness, to blunder through this kind of unsuspecting silence. At
night, everything is made of the thinnest, most breakable glass, isn't
it? Everything's made of glass, and there are doorways opening with
each step you take, doorways that can deliver you places you don't
want to be, and can't find your way back from. "Said the dramatic
girl," Tina adds, her lips thin, teeth bared, eyes surely flashing, giving her exact location away. But she has to acknowledge that what
could be happening here is that the animal part of her brain is whispering truths her more rational side doesn't want to listen to. Because
animals know. But Tina doesn't. Or, rather, she does, but what she
knows is that, even though the sliding glass door was locked, that
doesn't necessarily mean she's alone right now either. So she stands
there caught, waiting like all of us—all of us except that presence in

the corner by the couch, either staring back through the darkness at Tina, or not really there at all. Which doesn't mean it can't hear what her animal brain is telling her, is insisting on, is promising is the temporary solution to this moment. Run? Scream? Wait this out? Laugh at herself, and hope it doesn't turn into uncontrollable sobs? Say something out loud again, hoping her voice won't crack down the middle, revealing her soul, cringing smaller and smaller? Or maybe it's nothing. Maybe there's nothing there on the other side of the couch at all. That's the best answer, really. It's always nothing, it's always just Tina's nerves getting the better of her, like happens with all of us in our weaker moments, at two thirty in the morning. Or, at 2:34 on the digital clock on the component under the television, actually, a dimply, glowing-green number that really should have advanced already, Tina's pretty sure, if the world could just be a place that makes sense again, please, she's ready for the moment after this one, the next minute of all the minutes she has coming, she doesn't want to have see into that darkness on the other side of the couch, because what if it's *her* over there, right? What if it's the version of herself that walks the floors at night, barefoot, running the hungry pads of her fingers over the back of the couch, over that line of trim in the wall, because people can have ghosts, she has to admit, but if she sees her own, then she'll lose track of which is who, until she's the one caught over there, thinking that if she can just stand still enough, then this will all be over, it'll all be done, and she can go back to pacing the hall, the kitchen, stopping every few steps to cock an ear upstairs, listen for footsteps approaching, but otherwise just returning again and again to the sliding glass door like home base, to move that lock up and down, exhilarating in the space between but also falling headlong into it, and rushing away from her reflection if she happens to see it, because you can't get caught in that back and forth, nosiree. If you get stuck in that loop, in a moment like that, then an important part of you never quite makes it all the way out, like you're made of thread and running from where you snagged on the slightest, most invisible burr in the wall, or your life, only each step leaves you thinner, less substantial, until, at some point in the night, the thread runs out, and you just snap into nothing, keep going.

15

Like a Disease Whose Threshold No One Can Cross, She Says

Coral Bracho

—Translated from Spanish by Forrest Gander

1.

Someone nodding, and the light pressing down
as though it had weight.
And right in the middle of what I want to say
there's a long row of chairs. There are green,
red, yellow arches that gradually contract
and close, like doors.
Like a disease whose threshold no one can cross,
she says.

2.

It's OK. Nothing more for these three.
A recurring character materializes in the center.
She appears in a painting
and then
becomes the painting. As if someone
were cheating
and she hadn't even shown up.

3.

The light moves like a current
or skein of threads.
There's a wooden boat, a small plane,
and the current rocks them now and then.
Inside, there's a crab.
There's also a heart.

4.

She approaches me wanting to tell me
that I. And then she stops telling me.
You never know the story, someone explains.
One sparrow, and suddenly they all descend
swarming the root of everything.

5.

There are precipices that they refashion
to match the sketch of a flume.
Don't pen tedium in that same circle;
free it from its cage. The hoop was spinning
and spinning.
But don't go on and on, because that's what confounds you.

6.

With their curious manners, they see me like this,
And me, how do I see them?
What do they expect?
And she takes a swipe. I don't want to.
And that's it.

7.

I don't know, don't know what they are.
I don't know what's happening to you all,
she comments.
Is she getting better? There's something
they altered, but no one knows what,
no one ever knows.

8.

A person no longer submerged in the water.
Just a little frame freighted with glitter.
Footprints in the batter.
Like a duck's. Little plastic ducklings.
On the trashcan it says:
"They tossed out something."

9.

And I'm not so sure I understand.
But do you know when they get to kindergarten? Yes,
it's like a triangular window,
long, orangish. Behind it, someone's there.
But as far as I can tell, it's another girl.

10.

Is she getting better?
You have to put her in the shower.
She's wearing an apron. You were working?
Yes I was. It must be a misunderstanding.

11.

Don't be late. I think someone thinks.
A pink roof strewn with many pipes
and someone blots out her face
with some ink.
The left side of her face smiles.
That's the end. And you're granted the option.
But as far as I can tell, it's another girl.

12.

Don't come back, she says.
No one knows the story.
The window gets closer and closer
and behind it, someone's there
but she's been erased, and only the light remains,
that yellow light.

Flying

Julia Elliott

AT FIRST YOU THINK THE MONSTER is old, all skin and bones and rancid rags, crimped hands resembling bird claws, talons that snatch babies up by the scruffs of their necks. She whisks the plump squallers to her woodland hut and slits them throat to groin, savoring the steam they give off. She siphons their blood, sorts organs, pickles some, pounds others into porridge, grinds delicate skeletons into bonemeal. She boils and ferments and stocks her rough-hewn shelves. Though her bottles are old, chipped, and marked with scabby fingerprints, the wine she makes gives off a pomegranate glow. It looks delicious, and when you gaze through her sooty windows, you forget about killing her: you want to drink the wine and see where it takes you.

Her hut, ringed round with bones, buzzards dozing in the fungus-blasted trees, is never in the same place twice. Every time you find it, you fall asleep, wake up freezing in the middle of nowhere, a fox nosing your rucksack. You go back to your cottage at the edge of the village, back to the hearth, the wife, the plow, the children who eat you out of house and home. When the cows' hooves turn to jelly, when the green wheat spikes go pale, when well water comes up muddy and your wife laughs at your soft cock, you go back into the woods to kill the witch.

This time you wander through a sun-dappled forest, butterflies thick in the late summer haze. Crickets chirr in the brush, a sleepy silver sound that makes you wonder if you're dreaming. You eat wild fruit so ripe it gives you a buzz. By the time you find her in an afternoon glade, you're stumbling and muttering, starved and thirsty, dumbfounded by the opalescent pallor of her skin. Her hair is the red of wrens, braided and coiled—fake, you think, for you have seen the Lady of the Manor cavorting in a flame-colored wig. When the Lady laughs, her teeth are black and jagged. She hides them behind a silk fan.

But the monster's teeth are white, her gums pink as peonies, her lips a shame to roses. Her eyes, the color of sun-lit mead, look you over. She smirks. A beautiful sweet evil flickers between you. Perhaps she's not a monster after all, you think, fingers loosening around the haft of your knife. She takes you deeper into the woods, where the path thins and strange birds call. When she pulls the bottle of glowing wine from her willow basket, you know it's the same stuff the hag made. Same stained cork. Same dark fingerprints on the glass. Pushing this knowledge down into the cellar of your mind, you lick your lips.

You've dreamed of this wine, dreamed that the hag landed on your thatched roof, that you slipped out a window, lifted your wooden cup, and begged for a taste of it. You screamed when she flew away, waking your youngest, who squalled until the sun came up. That's when you found the blighted wheat. That's when you found the blasted cows. Mud in the well. The whole land kissed with curses.

But everything is different now. The woman speaks an old language, a tongue your grandmother muttered in bits and bobs, words children sometimes babbled around secret fires when you were small and the world still amazed you. Some of it comes back to you now.

"Eat," she says.

Braided barley cakes glazed with honey. Six roasted birds on a stick. Mushroom tarts. A salad of herbs and flower petals. You've never tasted food like this, food that makes your eyes water, food that makes you stare too long at the moon. How did it get to be night so fast?

The glow of the woman's skin ought to scare you. The coppery taste of the wine ought to give you pause. But you pass the bottle, quaff and laugh and hang on to her every word, the guttural dips of her voice that make you wonder if she's a wolf in disguise.

She goes on about stars and planets, solstices and equinoxes, the sun and moon. You sigh as you slide a hand up her smooth thigh. She takes a long pull from the bottle, sets it aside, and leaps upon you. Crouching, she husks your pants, slides a long tongue up your throat, and huffs hot breath into your face. She's astride you before you can say *jackrabbit*, her hair wind whisked, wild and lovely. Her bony rump chafes your skin as she rides you. Everything changes except her eyes, shining like twin yellow moons in the wreckage of her face.

As she screeches with pleasure, a cold wind whips through the forest, carrying her hair away like pale dandelion seeds, leaving her scalp pocked and bald. Whooping, the hag hops off you, scampers away in the moonlight, her fox's tail bobbing as she goes.

Drained, dreading the curse she's left upon you, you hobble back to your village. You bathe in the creek, sleep for two days, and then: back to grueling work and scant crops, back to shrill children and scolding wife. You bury another cow. Your oldest child collapses in the turnip field and suffers a lavish fit. Sniffing some taint upon you, your wife eyes you with suspicion, stiffens when you stroke her wrist. She whispers with the village holy man, rifles through your rucksack, scrutinizes the moist, plump mole that recently sprouted on your inner thigh. *It looks like a baby toad,* she says, *or the kind of mushroom that grows from dung.* She claims you smell peculiar— like sour whey, like tripe and barley soup, like a nest of newborn mice.

When autumn comes, the village granary is half full, your lard supply low, your cupboards stocked with misshapen gourds, bags of feed-grade peas and moldy grain. You remember the feast the beautiful monster fed you—tarts and cakes, mushrooms and flowers, tender songbirds with edible skeletons. You remember the crunch of crispy skulls, the sweet pasty meat within. When you tasted it, you heard nightingales and felt a delicious terror.

Against all reason, you want to see her again: fuck her, kill her— you don't know. You imagine yourself kissing her, lapping at the nectar of her mouth. The second you taste bile, you'll whip out your knife, stab her in the heart. Death, you think, will show you what she really is—stringy crone or luscious girl, harpy or siren, some diabolical hodgepodge of human and animal parts. You'll hack off her goat-horned head, carry the fanged and snake-tongued trophy home, toss it at the feet of the pompous priest, the man who has his clammy hands all over the hot, quaking soul of your wife.

Stomach aflutter, you leave before daybreak, stale bread in your rucksack, your leather bottle full of murky water, your knife fresh sharpened. You're already a mile in when sunlight floods the forest— red and gold leaves, butterflies to match, the last of the season. You spot a russet fox, plumped for winter, memories of the last frost faint in its mind. Or maybe the fox can already smell the misery of January, chilled bones and pinched stomach. You know nothing of the minds of foxes. You've never really thought about their lives though you've trapped them, cut their throats, made slits in their fur, and peeled off their stunning hides.

Another mile in, you realize you're following the fox. You understand that deep inside yourself—the self with name and deeds, wife and children—there's a secret self that has known this all along. Each time the fox loses you, it scampers back, catches your eye, coaxes you down another trail—trails tramped by boar and deer, faint foot-paths etched by wildcats and hares. You think of all the bustling animals, hunting and foraging, prepping winter burrows. You imagine the smell of their lairs—musk and milk and earth. You hear strange birds again, the ones that moan and titter in turns, birds you've never heard in your village or in the shallows of the woods. The fox leads you to a cluster of gnarled oaks, sits to rest, and then slips off into the forest.

The woman emerges in a spruce-green velvet gown, her skin pale as poison mushrooms. Her hair is loose, her eyes luminous, her belly blown and high, impossibly huge. She moves toward you, so light on her feet you think her belly is a trick, a feat of sorcerous puffery—something stuffed under her dress, a balloon made from the inflated bladder of a prize sow.

She takes your hand, plants your palm on her stomach, holds it there until you feel the kick and squirm of life within her. When you pull your hand away, it tingles with pins and needles.

"My time has come," she says.

"This has nothing to do with me," you say, but you remember the day in the woods, the lovely girl astride you, howling and withering and spitting out teeth. You remember how her laughter rang in the air after her body had shifted away. You fear you've cooked up something diabolical, a creature that will reveal the vilest depths of yourself.

Trembling, you let her pull you deeper into the woods, into a forest of stunted trees, moss-covered boulders, mist so thick you can barely see her. But when she shucks her gown, her skin gives off a sickly green light. She drops to her knees and wails, a sound you recognize, a howl you once mistook for a wolf as a boy.

The monster hunkers. Arches her back. Squats and pants.

Her thigh muscles bulge.

Glimmering with blue veins, her great belly pulses.

Grunting and shrieking, heaving and grimacing, she pushes a warm, steaming creature out into the world. A limp, cloven-hoofed thing, slicked with blood curd—dead, you think. But the monster scoops it up, licks it clean, sets it prancing onto the ground. A perfect little goat kid, frisky and curious, it nibbles your sleeve and trots off into the woods.

Next, the monster births a shoat, wobbly and matted with gore. But soon it's clean and prancing, snuffling and snorting, a tawny striped creature so soft and fluffy you long to pet it, to let it lick your hand. But you know better. Fingering the handle of your knife, you kick the creature away, imagining poison in its mouth, spit that will strip off a man's skin.

The monster births a fawn, a bear cub, a wildcat that paws at your shoes.

The monster births a badger, a dormouse, a mink—blind, half-bald creatures that squeak for milk. But soon they are on their feet, sniffing and sporting.

The monster births rabbits and voles, shrews and mice.

The monster births bats that unfold new wings and flit around your head.

The monster births live birds, sparrows and hawks, crows that shake dampness from their feathers and flutter up into the trees.

By the time a litter of newts slithers from her, the hullabaloo of beasts is so loud you can no longer hear the monster keening. The air is heavy with the sweet, musky smell of new animal bodies. You doze off, drop your knife, startle awake to bees and butterflies thick in the air, the clatter of beetles on the forest floor, worms writhing on mossy stone. You fear they'll close in on you, press their tingling, damp lives against you, and smother you to death.

By now the monster's flaccid belly droops like an apron past her knees. Still, she squats, grits her teeth, rocks on her haunches, pants in a rhythm that seems to pulse through your bloodstream, driving your own life.

The last creature comes out with a sputtering of frog spawn; a gush of brine and silver minnows; soft, fleshy blobs that look like oysters. A human infant, mottled and pink, frog eyed and puffy—a boy. The monster catches it before it slips out onto the rocks. She flips it over, gnaws through the cord that yokes it to her, and ties the boy's belly knot. Holding the baby by the feet, she shakes it until it gasps. The boy has her eyes, amber and shiny, a thatch of hair as black as your own. The monster smacks the child to her left breast, sighs as it suckles.

Night falls. A sickle moon rises. All the little animals hide in the forest, watching with shining eyes. As the baby sucks, the monster withers, shrinking from maiden into crone—baggy eyed, sinewy. She places the sleeping infant between two rocks. Hooting, she shrivels down to skin and clacking bones, dissolves into dust, whisks away on a gust of wind.

The fog clears. The moon sits high.

You poke the baby with a twig, expecting it to lapse into mist or shrink to a bundle of tiny bones.

23

But the naked infant screams and pants, eyes bulging—a creature of splotchy flesh, pissing itself and writhing.

"Come back," you scream, "and get your baby."

You hear wind and laughter, trilling nightingales.

You pace around the infant with your hand on your knife, ready to slay the monster once and for all. You're an idiot, you think. You should have stabbed her in the heart while she was stunned by pain and spurting rodents.

"I'm leaving now," you yell, marching off into thorny brush, westward, you think, judging by the constellations. You find a creek, follow its winding path until the baby's cries grow faint and your heart stops pounding. You reach a clearing, hunker amid wild fennel to study the stars. Now you hear whimpering again. You smell piss and sour milk. Look down to find the infant right under your nose, squirming in a willow basket, white froth oozing from its mouth. Though it looks like a normal baby, you imagine misshapen organs inside it, eyes that shoot infectious curses, snake fangs nestled in soft, pink gums.You flee, splash through the creek, run into an oak trunk and bash your nose. There, hanging from a bough, is the willow basket, rocking in the breeze. No matter which way you run, you find the baby, spitting up hag milk.

You think of the village holy man, who claims that a woman's first milk is poison, who advises new mothers to drain their breasts by suckling puppies. You picture him, constipated with piety, placing the host on your wife's pink tongue.

When a wolf howls in the forest, the baby quiets.

You creep closer, peer at his face, revel in the infant's beauty, a flattering mirror that reflects your own features: arched eyebrows, large forehead, pointy chin. The baby smells of apricots and sun-dried flaxen cloth. The baby gurgles and coos. Smacks his perfect pink lips. You suffer a vision, a fantasy, perhaps—the child as a young man, shapely and strong, waving a sickle in the air. You lift the boy from his basket, cradle him, sniff his fragrant neck.

You carry the baby back to the village, tell your wife you found him in the woods—a poor creature abandoned by a hapless girl, or worse, snatched by a witch intent on butchering him.

"We can barely feed the children we have," your wife says, eyeing the baby's features.

"Should I take him back to the forest," you say, "leave him to starve, be devoured, perish from frost?"

Your wife grunts and sucks her teeth.

"It has weird eyes," she says.

"Think of Moses, mewling in the rushes."

"I don't want it."

Your wife walks back to the hearth, back to pickling turnips and stirring cabbage soup. In the cramped cottage, your four-year-old feeds your two-year-old boiled groats. Your eight-year-old gives your shrieking six-year-old a wedgie. Your ten-year-old tromps off to harvest goblin fingers, the last of the pale, puny carrots that grow in the northern field.

You rummage through old linens, strap the baby to your back with the skirt of a ruined dress, rat gnawed with a singed hem. After filling a leather pouch with goat milk, you stuff your rucksack with bread and rags. You go out to the woods to check your traps.

As the baby coos and smacks, you find yourself whistling. You sing as you change his diaper, a ditty your mother sang to you.

> *A wise old owl sat in an oak,*
> *The more he heard, the less he spoke;*
> *The less he spoke, the more he heard;*
> *Why aren't we all like that wise old bird?*

The baby grins as you swaddle him in a blanket of fine-spun wool, stitched by the witch, embroidered with golden stars.

A fox barks. A hawk swoops.

You find your traps stuffed and bustling: a rabbit, two pheasants, four partridges, three fat ducks. You put them all into one trap, carry them home, and secure them in pens.

When your wife beholds this bounty, the pink drains from her cheeks.

"I've been hankering for a roast rabbit," you say.

The children gather round and cheer.

"We're starved for meat," they cry. "We're skin and bones."

The children dance like skeletons, rubbing their bellies and smacking their blanched lips.

You gut and clean the rabbit, a duck, a fine fat partridge. You build a fire and roast the beasts whole on spits.

With your two-year-old perched on her hip, your wife goes back to the cottage. She calls the children in for cabbage soup. Ignoring her, the children dance around the fire, screaming for meat. When the moon creeps up, when the stars pop out, when owls bicker in the trees, the children feast on roasted meat. The baby licks grease from your fingers, slurps goat milk from a pouch.

"Bedtime," your wife calls, but the children hide in the shallows of the forest. They nest like thrushes on the ground.

You sleep in the barn, the baby cradled in the crook of your arm.

Your nanny goat, afflicted with some distemper, bleats throughout the night.

By morning she's dead, dazzled with flies.

"There's evil in the forest," says the village priest, stomping around the barn in spotless boots. He strokes your wife's arm. His skin is white and soft, imbued with weird moisture like the belly of a frog. A garnet ring glimmers like a blood drop on his pale right hand. He lives on a hillock surrounded by blooming shrubs. You have heard that his bed is draped with crimson curtains, his mattress stuffed with gosling down, that he visits the Lady of the Manor late at night, entering by a secret door.

"Where did you find this baby?" he demands.

When he leans in to have a look, you smell frankincense and rotting teeth.

The holy man nibbles fine cakes with the Lady of the Manor, greases her up with holy oil, blesses the bathwater in which she bathes.

"Beside the stream," you say, avoiding the word *forest*.

"Child of a whore," pronounces the priest. "It must be baptized."

As the holy man strides around inspecting things, your wife can't take her eyes off him—his twinkling ring, his velvet cape. She follows him out into the yard, leaving you with the dead goat.

The goat is too foul to eat. You bury it beyond the turnip field. Reclining in the willow basket, the baby watches you with amber eyes—eyes of the hag, the monster, the beautiful girl. When you have finished your work and washed your hands in the stream, you feed the infant the last of the goat milk. And then you walk over to Old Man Sprott's place, knock on the door, ask him if he can spare a splash of milk.

"Not for an unbaptized child," he whispers, as though afraid the priest can hear him. "Sorry. Come back when the heathen has been touched by the Lord."

Old Lady Harrow hisses the same, slamming the door in your face. Though the Bonnets are not the pious sort, they have no drop to spare, with thirteen children devouring every morsel they produce.

By noon, the baby is fussy. At sunset, he starts to squall, furious that your finger yields no milk. You take him to the wood's edge to avoid the wrath of your wife. Sitting on a stump, you jog the infant on your knee, singing a song your mother sang to you:

> *Lily, Lily, please be gone.*
> *Don't come near my baby's bones.*

The moon gleams like a polished skull. A chill wind blows right through you. Wolves are on the hunt, making a racket, circling closer—sniffing the baby, you fear. When a wolf leaps right on top of you, you reach for your knife. But the beast licks your hand and whimpers—a bitch, you see, with dangling, pointed dugs. She offers a teat to your young one, scampers on her haunches to slide a nipple into the baby's mouth.

As the child sucks a bellyful, the wolf pants gamy breath into your face. You keep stone-still, fearing the bitch will rip out your throat when she's done with her mothering. But she wheedles like a dog, nuzzles the baby, and then scampers off into the woods.

In the brush you find a fresh-slain shoat, neatly killed with a clean bite to the neck. You take it home to your clamoring children. They have built a fire at the edge of the turnip field, set up the spit, devoured all the animals in your pens. But they are still hungry.

"Meat! Meat!" they cry, their mouths smeared with grease, blood on their tunics, feathers stuck in their grime-tufted hair. Your ten-year-old seizes the shoat, skins and guts it, sets it on the spit before you can say *jackrabbit*.

The piglet crackles as fat drips into the flames.

Your wife steps out into the yard and sniffs.

"Come in, you wild ones," she cries, "and eat your cabbage stew."

But the children won't heed her. They dance around the fire with bones in their fists.

Gnawing a shoat haunch, you sneak off to the barn, bed down with the baby in the crook of your arm, covering both of you with the witch's blanket. You dream of the monster, fresh-faced and smirking while chewing a tart. When she picks up the baby, her hands turn to chicken claws. She pokes him on the belly and whisks him up into the sky. You run outside and scream at the stars.

When you startle awake, the baby is still there, familiar and strange, his breath warm against the palm of your hand.

The next morning, he smiles at you, gurgles, and kicks his little legs.

When you go out to check your traps, you find the wolf bitch waiting, dewy drops quivering on the tips of her pink nipples. You set the child down to suckle, keep your hand on your knife hilt just in case. When the baby dozes off, the wolf slips away. Birds forage for late autumn berries. A cold wind blows the last of the leaves from the trees. But your traps are packed: three plump rabbits, two fat geese, an otter, a red grouse, four wood pigeons.

You fill your pens again. Cook up two fowl and a rabbit for lunch. Call your children, lazybones still dozing in forest brush. Just when the meat starts to crisp and smoke, just when the hungry children gather, just when the baby wakes up smiling, wriggling in the warmth of the fire, your wife comes storming down the hill with the priest, three knights from the Manor tromping behind them, waving silver pikes.

"The baby is wicked," says your wife. "My children have run wild, possessed by the evil among us."

"The child must be cleansed with holy water," says the priest.

Two knights seize your arms, force you marching to the chapel, the baby squirming on your back. At the church door, the priest seizes the child and stuffs a lump of salt into his mouth.

"I banish the demons that cavort within you," the holy man pronounces, wafting frankincense and mildew as he lifts a robed arm. You feel sick, dizzy, as though the spirits that sustain you are leaking from your body. The child cries. When you attempt to snatch him from the priest's hands, two knights pinion you, pushing you against the church wall. You try to catch your wife's eye, but she's kneeling before the priest in blasphemous supplication, kissing the toes of his calfskin boots.

Before you can say *jackrabbit*, the wolves are upon you, a pack one hundred strong; great, dark beasts that shroud the church in mist and musk. You find yourself astride a wolf, clutching soft neck scruff, bounding off into the woods. Spears whiz past your ears. The wolf slithers through thickets and leaps over shrubs. The beast splashes through creeks and clambers over boulders. At last, the animal stops, hunkering down to let you slide off its back. Curled in a sun-dappled glade is the wolf bitch, the baby nestled against her flank.

You take the child into your arms, check his diaper, relish the apricot scent of his neck. In the distance, knights shout and bellow, clacking their pikes together. You fear they'll find you, drag you back to the village, hang you as a heretic. You can't build a fire, lest they track your smoke.

Darkness falls, damp and thick, making you shiver. You try to keep still, for the baby has fallen asleep in your lap. A nightingale sings, out of season. You sense the bustle of wolves around you, a sound that makes you feel safe. Slumped against an oak, you fall asleep.

The next morning, you strap the baby to your back and set off early, the woods rimed with frost. You feel eyes upon you. You turn to look, expecting a wolf, a fox, a maiden, a hag. You see nothing. When you find a crowberry bush fruiting out of season, you eat the sweet, black berries as fast as you can pick them. You clutch your gut as you stagger onward, discovering tiny apples that taste like cake. As you move deeper in, the forest feeds you: wild carrots, sow thistle, silver-shelled clams from the creek.

In the blaze of noon, just when the baby starts to get cranky, the wolf bitch slinks out. After she settles, you place the baby against her flank. The boy roots for a teat, finds it, suckles and smacks. You hear the clattering of knights again, voices carried by wind. You picture them picking you apart with their spears, impaling the baby, wagging it in the air as they tromp in triumph to the smug priest.

You have no idea where you're going, but you know you must keep running, start a new life somehow. Perhaps you'll live in the woods with the wolves, bring up the boy wild and strong. Perhaps you'll find a new village, tell them your old home burned to the ground, that you don't wish to talk about it—let them take you in and make you one of their own.

Walking for hours with the sun at your back, you hear something shuffling behind you—wolf, rodent, witch. You turn repeatedly, see nothing. When dusk comes, you dip into a hollow filled with fog, sensing a presence behind you, bolder than before, blooming into flesh and blood. Steeling yourself for the witch, you turn, find your ten-year-old standing defiantly, the one who fell in the turnip field and trembled on the ground—bewitched, your wife said.

"Dad," says your daughter, the girl who wears breeches, the girl who cuts her hair with a knife and knows her way around fields and woods, your strongest child, the stubborn one, the firstborn who came out screaming, two teeth in her mouth.

"What are you doing here?" you ask.

"I'm coming with you."

"I don't know where I'm going."

"I can't go back."

When she falls into step with you, you feel a surge of love you didn't know you possessed—a shock to your heart and lungs. The baby who came before her died of measles at age one. The baby who came after perished of smallpox at six months. As a new father, you learned to

29

temper your feelings until a child turned two. By then the distance was ingrained.

When the baby starts to fuss for food, you feel relieved to have something to focus on. Your daughter plucks the infant from his sling and bounces him up and down. When the wolf slinks out, the girl doesn't flinch. She sets the baby down to suckle.

Your daughter hums a quiet tune in the voice of a girl who has learned to keep things to herself, a melody that makes you think of tiny flowers growing between stepping-stones. You long for a fire, for warmth and light, for meat crackling on a spit.

After the wolf is gone, you spend a cold, damp night tossing on the ground, falling in and out of shallow sleep, dreaming of pike tips pressed against your throat, of knights leering above you, of the priest slipping the baby into the sleeve of his robe and billowing off into the darkness.

You wake to the smell of frankincense and smoke, to knights singing raucous songs. You coax the dozing baby into his sling, gently wake your daughter, shush her before she says a word. You hurry down a fox trail that meanders through difficult thickets, a path that takes you into denser woods, a humming place where strange birds warble and titter in turns. There you find bones on the ground, a cottage built into the treetops, a rickety ladder ascending toward a trapdoor.

The baby wails.

Knights shout—closer, now, rustling in the brush.

Your daughter climbs the ladder first, urging you up into the trees.

When you are halfway up, the world starts to spin, birds flitting around your ears. You spot a dozing owl. You spot chickens roosting high in the boughs, squirrels leaping from branch to branch. You see snakes curled in hollows, beetles scurrying, a dazzle of gauzy flies floating in a slant of afternoon sun.

You freeze. The ladder sways in cold wind. Whimpering, the baby squirms in his sling. You worry he'll slip out, plummet to the ground, but you can't move.

Knights storm the clearing. They move toward the ladder, bickering about who will climb up after you.

"Hurry up, Dad," your daughter says.

Slowly, you rise, one step and then another. Your daughter reaches for you. With a flood of shame, you take her hand, let her pull you up into the hut. When the first knight is halfway up, your daughter kicks the ladder away and closes the trapdoor.

You look around, flinch at the sight of bones—bones sorted and arranged into piles, bones brimming from wooden buckets, some polished, others gristly—human or animal, you cannot say. Shutters closed, the hut is dim, a small fire burning in the hearth, heating a cauldron as black as the devil's beard. Bottles and bowls gleam on shelves. Skinned beasts dangle from hooks, and herb bundles hang to dry. You hear chickens clucking, a person humming in a deep, low voice.

Now you see her: the woman tending the cauldron, the monster, hunched in a cloak. You walk to a window to observe the knights. When you pull the shutters open, thick mist flows into the room.

"Clouds," says your daughter.

"What?"

You look down, see treetops. Below in the clearing, ant-sized knights move in agitation.

"We're flying," your daughter explains, patting your arm as though you're a mooncalf.

Dizzy, sick, you slump against her. How did you come to be here, whisked heavenward in a hut full of bones? What if the monster chucks you out, keeps your children for herself, turns them into beasts or gobbles them up?

Your daughter guides you to the table, coaxes you into a spindle chair, and sets a bowl of stew before you, a rich concoction flecked with pink shreds of meat. It smells of mushrooms and nuts, roots and giblets.

You pull the baby from his sling into your lap.

"Come here," says the monster, her voice gruff, "and let me hold my baby."

Though you fear she'll bash his pretty skull, you have no choice.

"Don't worry," she coaxes, her voice fluting high and musical.

You dare to look, see a maiden face shining from the hood of the cloak, a beauty that burns; slender, white hands reaching for the baby. But when she takes it, her fingers crimp into claws. She's bald and crinkled, droopy lipped, two teeth left in her mouth. When she sniffs the baby's neck, she turns young again.

"Are you hungry?" she asks.

The baby smiles—kicks his little legs.

The hag speaks the old language, half beast, half song. She mews and trills, barks and caws.

She tells you to eat, and you do, growing used to the strangeness of the stew.

31

Your daughter adds another log to the fire.

The baby kicks and whimpers.

When the monster presses the child to her breast, she changes again. Her hands look strong, chapped from work. Her sparrow-colored hair is streaked with gray. She smells of broth and earth and sweet onions. The kind of woman who could chop down a tree with a baby strapped to her back. The kind of woman who could dig a well with a hand shovel or make a stew in February with pickings from a frosty wood.

A fawn totters from a dark corner of the hut. A shoat skitters out from under the table. Small, silky creatures—ermines and minks and weasels—slither around your feet, pressing their softness against your ankles. Birds appear as though hatched from knots in the rafter timber. Your daughter laughs, pulling a plump badger onto her lap.

The hut pitches like a ship, and the shutters fly open. The air that blows in from the night is strange, thin and cold, tinged with the smell of turpentine. You rush to a window, see the moon ahead, vast and craterous, bumpy with mountain ranges.

Moonlight burns your eyes. Dazzled, you stagger toward a cot heaped with small, slippery furs. You collapse into the musky bed and sink down into prickly softness, tiny claws tickling your skin. You want to leap from the bed, jump from a window before it's too late, but you can't move. Your daughter stomps around the hut, sweeping and tidying as though she has lived there forever.

Beside the fire slumps the obscure shape of the monster, singing to the baby in a rich, husky voice, a song your mother once sang to you: *Hey, diddle, diddle, the cat and the fiddle, the cow jumped over the moon.*

Introduction to the Reading of Hegel
Bennett Sims

> The fact that a man has decided to *read* the
> *Phenomenology* proves that he loves Philosophy.
>
> —Alexandre Kojève, *Introduction
> to the Reading of Hegel*

THAT NIGHT THE READER couldn't read. His application for the
Fellowship was due tomorrow at midnight, and he still hadn't written
his letter. He'd gone to the library to work, choosing his usual carrel
on the top-floor stacks and opening his laptop to the blank document. Since arriving he hadn't seen another soul, and it had been so
long since even he had stirred that the track lights above the bookshelves—all motion activated—had clicked off one by one. The aisles
spread out before him in paths of darkness. Through the window beside
him—a tall pane embrasured into the brick, narrow as an arrow slit—
he commanded a view of the campus parking lot. It was December,
deadline season, the trees were bare and the air gray, and though no
snow was falling tonight, yesterday's lines of white were still visible
across the lot, making faint minus signs of the concrete parking
chocks. The library was quiet and the world was calm. Six stories
below, miniature students in bright parkas headed to their parked
cars, evening seminars, bars. Some were probably his own students,
the freshmen forced to take his section of introduction to philosophy: it was the same adjunct class he had been teaching for years,
granted to graduate students for a meager living stipend, usually
enough to cover the reader's rent and, in alternating weeks, either
books then food or food then books. He had taught his last class
today, held his last office hours, and his students had all turned in
their final essays, which were waiting in his backpack for him to
grade. Now they were free. For the rest of the break he would have
the building—the books—to himself. He sipped black coffee from his
thermos. Dear reader, the reader deleted. To the members of the
Fellowship committee, the reader deleted. Everything depended on
the first sentence, he knew. The Fellowship was selective, and his
reader or readers would be looking for any reason to reject him. At

his first mistake they would stop. It was their *job* to reject, they were basically being paid to hate every applicant but one. He closed his eyes and tried to imagine them. The way that criminal profilers must cast themselves into the thoughts of the serial killers they track, he attempted to project himself into his rejector. How would a mind that isn't mine read this, he always asked himself when writing. How would this read to someone who isn't me, who doesn't know me? This is a good sentence, he sometimes caught himself thinking, but then, when he reread it with this other reader in mind—with this other reader's mind—he would think, This is a terrible sentence, and delete it. The Fellowship committee usually included former Fellows, one from each field, so the reader's reader would probably be one of his philosophical predecessors. He just had no way of knowing which one. For the past month, instead of working on his dissertation, he had been researching the Fellowship, refreshing its website hourly and clicking the link labeled Meet This Year's Judges, where he was always met with the same message: This year's judges haven't been announced yet, please check again soon. By now it was clear that the judges wouldn't be revealed until after the deadline. Before midnight tomorrow their minds would remain a blind spot, which made it impossible to write with them in mind. Everything about the Fellowship was kept shrouded in mystery like this. Even the building itself—centuries old, walled in atop the highest hill at the heart of the capital—was a blind spot: its inner workings were as unknowable, as concealed from view, as the metamorphic core of a cocoon, that silk-lined space where change takes place. All the reader knew about it was that people emerged from it altered. Every year a dozen so-called *emerging minds* were permitted to enter it—emerging artists, scientists, and philosophers, emerging archaeologists and cartographers—and by the time they left its chambers they were no longer emerging but had emerged, they had somehow been transformed into real artists, real scientists, real philosophers. This was the only thought that enabled him to ignore the odds against him. He wasn't naive. He knew where the average Fellow was emerging from, they weren't crawling out of philosophical burrows or philosophical ditches but, almost always, were being hatched from the most rarefied philosophical incubators and the most prestigious philosophical chrysalises (at least a quarter came from N—). Still, he had found a few encouraging exceptions, ordinary readers like him. They must have been selected by dint of their erudition, he imagined: they must have been smarter, better read, than the other applicants that year, the intelligence in their letters must have been undeniable and therefore unrejectable, and so the only thing the reader could safely assume about his own reader or readers was that they would be using this same erudition metric to evaluate him, that *they* would be scrutinizing *his* letter to determine how smart and well read *he* was. Knowing this had not been much help. In the weeks that he had been coming to this carrel, facing this blank document, he hadn't made any progress. Or—if it wasn't true that he'd accomplished nothing—the only progress he'd made had been epistemological. He hadn't written the first sentence, but he'd imagined the kinds of minds that might read the first sentence. While his letter remained empty (of words), it had become full (of these other minds): night after night as he had stared at it he had stored inside it all the different reasons that a reader might reject him. Whenever he typed a sentence, he tried to read it with eyes of skepticism and contempt. He read it out loud. He read it backward. He read it backward out loud. In the end he always deleted it. In his first draft of his first sentence, for instance, he'd written the phrase *comprised of* (as in, *My project is comprised of . . .*): he had reread the sentence a dozen times without registering the error, before it finally occurred to him to look up *comprised of*, and with dread he read a usage entry discouraging the phrase. It was considered nonstandard, and he'd almost let it stand. If he hadn't thought to check, and if one of this year's judges had turned out to be a grammar pedant, they would have stopped reading then and there. He deleted the phrase, typed *composed of*, deleted that as well. It had been the same every night. One first sentence had used *kind of* twice, another had used *I* three times. Last night he thought he had been making progress until he noticed the adjective *seminal*. He had described a philosophical concept as *seminal*, but once he read the sentence backward out loud—once he had begun to chant *lanimes lanimes* under his breath at this carrel—he was at last able to hear how *seminal* might sound to another reader, could appreciate how for certain readers the sheer appearance of *seminal*—the fact that a male applicant seemed to be praising the semen of a philosophical concept, its sperm count or motility or whatever—would be a red flag, a shibboleth, reason enough to reject him. There might be as many as a thousand other applicants for the Fellowship. Only one would cross the threshold, while the other 999 would all perish on the way, for defects as minimal as *seminal*. The odds could even be described—if you didn't already know better—as seminal. The reader had deleted *seminal* and started over, ending the evening with the

Bennett Sims

same blank document he was faced with now. Well, not precisely the same. He wouldn't repeat his past selves' mistakes. He'd modeled these other readers' minds inside his mind, and now they were here with him, within him, watching over him. The *comprised of* hater, the *seminal* hater: his consciousness was a commons of all possible contempts. His temples pounded, he sipped more coffee. The metabolic costs of simulating other minds was high, he knew. To revise, you had to be able to cognize being watched, to be able to think the thought *So this is how I look to them.* Ethologists had determined, the reader had read somewhere, that only a few nonhuman species could pass the so-called mirror test. If researchers painted a bright dot on an animal's forehead, then placed the animal before a mirror, only a few nonhuman species would recognize their reflection, reaching up to their own head to try to touch the dot or titivate themselves. This was essentially, the reader realized, a revision process. To erase a mistake on the body, an animal had to see itself as another animal's mind would see it. He studied his reflection in the laptop screen. He'd inverted the document's color scheme, typing white on black, and in the darkened glass he could see his face. The cursor—a flashing white line—blinked steadily in his head, pulsing near his temple like a panicked vein. He raised his hand to it, as though to brush it away, and this gesture was what separated him from dogs (but not the Asian elephant) and most birds (but not magpies), it was what elevated him above the invertebrates (except for cleaner wrasses) and enabled him to write this letter, addressing his mind to a mind he had never met. *Comprised of. Kind of. Seminal.* Revision was just a mirror test. Before you could write a worthwhile sentence, you had to become the sentence's nemesis. You had to occupy the place of a predatory or an editorial consciousness, hating yourself before the other had a chance to. There was no more absolute an act of empathy. Whenever the reader read a sentence that he hated, he knew that what he was encountering was a failure of empathy, a glitch in inter-subjectivity. At this one moment in the text the writer had lapsed, relaxed, he had neglected to construct a robust model of the reader's mind inside his mind and consider how they might hold this sentence in contempt. Even if only for a second, the writer had loved himself too much, and this self-love in the past had blown a black wind of hatred into the future, out of the writer's mind and into the reader. Grading his students' midterm papers, he'd made sure to mark every such blind spot in their sentences, teaching them to read themselves through his eyes, to read their sentences the way he read his own, which was how he imagined the smartest and best-read and most hateful possible hypothetical reader would read them. Whenever a paper began *Since the dawn of time* or *Philosophy is comprised of . . .* , the reader underlined it and wrote *Cliché* or *Phrasing* in the margin, while thinking, *My God* to himself, *Dumb, Moronic, Idiotic,* the reader thought, while he wrote *Word Choice?* or *–1* in the margin. His students had had unrestricted access to his mind— they listened to him lecture every day in class, they harassed him during office hours—and even so they'd neglected to simulate for themselves what his mental experience of reading their first sentence might be like. The reader was determined never to make this mistake in his own prose. He strove to anticipate every hatred in advance. In order to keep another reader from ever thinking *Moron* or *Impostor* tomorrow, he had to think *Moron* and *Impostor* tonight. The process might be painful in the present, but it would be a thousand times more painful for his future self to read the rejection. *Thank you for applying,* the letter's subtext would read, *but we regret to inform you that we hated you.* He let this hatred guide him toward the Fellowship. Every book he had read in the past few weeks, for instance, he had finished thanks to hatred. Quine. Ryle. Spinoza. It was research for his letter, he told himself, research into how other readers reasoned. *Maybe if you had read Quine,* a voice inside his skull had said one night, *you would be able to write this letter,* and then, *Maybe if you had read Spinoza. You've never even read Spinoza,* he had thought, and then, *But what about Ryle!* Since he didn't know which books his readers might have read, the only rational strategy was to read everything. The goal, as with any syllabus, was synaptogenesis: by reading the books another reader has read, you can remake your brain in their brain's image. And so he'd passed one evening forcing Quine through his eyeballs and into his head, the next evening forcing Spinoza into his head through his earholes (all physical copies of the *Ethics* had been checked out, but luckily the library had had one audiobook available). Whenever the reader couldn't write, he read Ryle or listened to Spinoza on 2x speed, instead of writing he fast-forwarded through a chipmunk-pitched Spinoza or skimmed Quine, confident that he would wake up the following morning fortified, a little bit smarter or at least a little less stupid, a bit better read, maybe tomorrow he would be able to vanquish the blankness of the document. *The version of you who has read Spinoza can be the one to write the letter,* he would reason, *let him worry about it, not you, let* him *be the one the Fellowship judge judges, not you.* In this way he had kept deferring the first sentence to a future self who, he realized, he now suddenly was: tonight he had to be or become the smarter incarnation whose arrival he had been waiting for, for there wouldn't be any other. There was no tomorrow left to defer to, only the deadline. All of his past selves' self-hatred had been preparing for this moment, they had read so that he might write. Sitting in this carrel with a book each night, it had been torture to concentrate on the tiny type, but whenever his mind began to wander, the other minds would revive inside him, reviling him. It was enough to imagine a Quine scholar or a Ryle scholar reading his letter—*Fraud*, they said in his head, *Dilettante*—and he would sip his coffee and refocus. All he had to do was keep pouring black coffee over the waterwheel of his worthlessness, and as its paddles churned they propelled him forward, one page after another into his future. If nothing else, this was what he had learned from years of reading: the hydraulics of self-hatred. How to convert the waves of shame coursing through him into productive energy, so that his horror at not having read Heidegger could power him through the horror of reading Heidegger, could be the battery inside that boredom, keeping him going. There was no self-discipline or work ethic in the world, the reader knew, that could have motivated him in equal measure. That was the philosophy that had fueled his reading: not the love of wisdom, but the wisdom of hatred. His dissertation advisers had warned him that he would burn out this way, they were always encouraging him to take care of himself, take walks. But in the hour he would spend walking, the reader had calculated, he could read thirty pages. We just want to make sure you're happy in the program, his professors said, try to be compassionate with yourself. Compassionate? The reader had laughed grimly. Happy? He didn't want to be happy. The Fellowship judges wouldn't care whether he was happy. They wouldn't care whether he practiced *self-care*. All they would care about was whether he was smart enough. Speed-reading Foucault until two in the morning while refilling his thermos with lukewarm coffee from the library lobby's Starbucks station's pump-action carafe and ignoring the painful pounding in his temples might not make him happy, but *that's what would make him happy*. Whereas taking a walk would merely make him happy, which would throw him back into the deepest unhappiness, every happy step of the walk was in fact leading him ever nearer the abyss of being unhappy. If the reader was dumb and happy, the Fellowship would reject him, but if he was smart and miserable, they might accept him. That was the only advantage he had over the other applicants. He may not have studied with the most illustrious philosophers, he may not be writing his letter under the sign of N—, but unlike the others, he didn't need to be happy. He could withstand what for other readers would be hellish levels of self-hatred and self-negation. Let *them* be happy, let *them* practice self-care. Let *them* be compassionate toward themselves and get rejected, the reader thought. He would be absolutely ruthless toward himself and get accepted. That was how he had made it this far, wasn't it? So why stop now, when he was only halfway there? Once he had arrived at the Fellowship, *then* he could take care of himself, or if not then, once he had found a job, or if not then, once he had published his own book, or if not then, once he was a real philosopher. He would relax when it was safe to relax, take a walk when it was safe. Until then he couldn't afford to ignore his hatred, in truth he feared he was nothing without it. Dear reader, the reader deleted, read dearer. He wondered what this year's judge would have read, when they were a Fellow. Then a brilliant idea occurred to him. Even if he didn't know who this year's judge would be, he could at least look up last year's Fellow. This was a page he hadn't studied closely yet, though it was a pattern he had observed in previous years: sometimes—in rare cases, when they were particularly accomplished—the most recent Fellow would be chosen to help select the next year's Fellow. He closed the letter and opened the Fellowship website, hovering the cursor over the Past Fellows link. Click it, a voice inside him commanded. At this thought, the farthest track light clicked on across the room, spotlighting a row of bookshelves. The reader startled, but the row was empty. No one stood in the aisle of light. Hello? he called. The room remained deathly quiet, and after a few seconds the light clicked off again. He was alone here. It was as if his thought itself had triggered the light, he thought: as if the motion sensor had sensed not the motion of another person but the motion of his mind, the arrival of this other mind inside his mind. Click it, the voice commanded again. But he felt a powerful reluctance to click the link. Did he really want to know? Who last year's Fellow was? Or what they had read? Don't click it, he counseled himself. Close it. But by the time his mind had finished this thought his hand had clicked the link, was already scrolling down the page to last year's philosophy Fellow, who turned out to be a philosopher from N—. The reader had been rejected from N—. Judging by her dates she was the same age as him, they had probably both applied the same year. He read her profile carefully, her project description, the blood fled him as he read, his mind went blank. She had spent her Fellowship writing a book on Hegel's *Phenomenology of Spirit*. The reader had never read Hegel. He took another sip of coffee, but it had the same effect on his brain as spilling coffee on his laptop's trackpad: the way that the cursor will begin to skid across the screen, driven by the phantom finger of the wetness's pressure, that was how his thoughts were spiraling now. She would be his reader, he was sure of it, he felt clairvoyant with dread. Why hadn't he read her page sooner? While he had been customizing his consciousness for the hypothetical Ryle scholar, this actually existing Hegel scholar had been lying patiently in wait. *She* would be the one looking for any reason to reject him, *she* would be the reader stopping at his first mistake. Had it been a mistake to not read Hegel? What if she could tell? All it would take was one writer who was smarter than the reader, better read than the reader, one writer better acquainted with Hegel than the reader was, and if this applicant had so much as leafed through the *Phenomenology*—if their brain contained every book in the reader's brain plus one—then they would be accepted and he would be rejected, it really was that simple, he was in a struggle to the death for the recognition of the Fellow. All things being equal, the Fellow would award the Fellowship to the smarter writer. It's not as if the reader thought that a writer would need to name-drop Hegel, making explicit references, in their letter, to the owl of Minerva, master and slave, the spirit is a bone. Even the reader could do that. He'd read Hegel's Wikipedia page. He'd read enough about or around Hegel to know how to invoke Hegel. The owl of Minerva flies at midnight, the reader had read somewhere, whatever that meant. If it were merely a matter of puffing up his letter with Hegelian philosophemes, the way a blowfish puffs out its cheeks, to intimidate his readers into thinking he had read Hegel—citation as deimatic display—then he could finish his letter in minutes. But while this kind of bluffing might carry him through his philosophy lectures, and impress his freshmen, it wouldn't be enough to fool the Fellow. She would be able to distinguish an impostor's letter from a real philosopher's letter. A writer who had read Hegel, it stood to reason, was bound to write slightly more confident, intelligent, convincing sentences than a writer who hadn't. The Fellow herself was proof of this. Some letters must just *feel* smarter than other letters, some people's minds must just look better on paper than other people's minds. Just as some people have more photogenic faces, some people must have more papyrogenic brains. This was the only knowledge that the reader had been trying to impart to his students whenever he wrote *Cliché* or *Phrasing* on their papers. But he could see now that he had taught them nothing, all this time the blind had been leading the blind. With bitterness he remembered the student who had visited his office hours this afternoon, his final meeting of the year. The reader had been trying to read Ryle by winter light when he heard a timid knock at the door. It was a freshman whose name he couldn't even remember, a quiet pale presence who always slouched in the back row in a gray hoodie, glaring at his notebook with a gloomy intensity designed to repel the attention it invited, like a bonfire of shyness. Now he stood in the office doorway, nervously declining the reader's offer of a seat, and brandishing a bouquet of rolled-up pages in his hand. His midterm paper. The reader had returned them weeks ago. The freshman just had a few questions about his grade, he told the reader, before he had to turn in his final essay in class today. As the freshman flipped through the marked-up midterm page by page, pointing out each of the reader's marginalia and minus signs, asking what he had meant by *Phrasing*, why he had deducted so many points, the reader had kept casting trapped glances back at the copy of *The Concept of Mind* tented open on his desk. Every minute the freshman stood there was half a page of Ryle he had not read. He could feel his life dwindling away. *Ten points, ten points*, the freshman kept repeating, while the reader kept checking the time and thinking, *Ten pages, ten pages*. The freshman expected the reader to save him, at least to save his grade, but the reader could barely save himself, he needed to read. At last the freshman set the paper aside. The thing was, he told the reader, he was really enjoying this class, he'd even decided to study philosophy. *Since the dawn of time,* the paper's first sentence had read, *philosophy has been comprised of . . .* He just wanted to understand what he was doing wrong, the freshman said, what should he be doing instead, what did he need to do if one day he wanted to be like the reader? Was he even smart enough to become a real philosopher? Was he too stupid? He could take the truth. Be brutally honest. The freshman stared at him, radiating need for the reader's recognition, and the reader didn't know what to tell him. He must be mistaking him for someone else. He was standing there as solemnly as if he were in Socrates's office hours, but the reader wasn't Socrates, he wasn't even the Fellow, and at this rate he never would be. Idiot. Fuckup. The freshman must think that *this* is the end, the reader marveled, he must think that once he arrived at the reader's position—accepted to a philosophy program, granted an office to read books in and a class full of acolytes—he

41

would have completed the cycle of self-doubt, when in fact this was only the beginning, the freshman had no conception of the gulfs still separating this office from the Fellowship. Should he tell him? Professor? the freshman asked. Eventually the reader muttered a platitude about trying to read his final essay out loud, or backward, or backward out loud, his only other advice, he said, was to keep reading, to read everything, and try not to feel bad about a few points. The freshman thanked him and, thankfully, left, freeing the reader to read Ryle. But now, sitting in the carrel and staring out at the parking lot, where the snow had started to come down hard, he realized how pointless this advice had been. The freshman would never become the Fellow, following advice like that, and in all honesty the odds were against him ever even becoming the reader. He should have told him the truth. It was too late for the reader, but maybe it wasn't too late for him. He was probably at a drunken party tonight, celebrating the end of the year and the submission of his final essay, but if he were here in the library, before him now, the reader would tell him the exact opposite of what he had: not to not feel bad, but precisely to *keep feeling bad*, to identify all the negative thoughts he was feeling about himself when he saw those negative points on his paper and to harness them, to be prepared to tarry with the negative for years, because this was what he was studying philosophy to learn, to understand that there existed other minds in the world who hated him, that not everyone loved him as much as his parents or high-school teachers or guidance counselors had loved him, that the reader's own way of loving him was to hate him, to become the hateful voice inside him, passing the hatred onto him, transferring all the other minds he'd ever accumulated inside his mind into the freshman's mind, this was what *Phrasing* had meant and what all teaching should be, the goal, as with any line edits, was synaptogenesis, to remake the freshman's brain in his brain's image, indeed, the reader would tell him, if he *really* wanted to know the truth, if he wanted the reader to be *brutally honest* and teach him what the reader thought it was important for him to know—this was the only lesson the reader wished his own professors had taught him before it was too late, before he had graduated and applied everywhere (to N—, for travel grants, to journals), only to be rejected from them all, rejected not just unanimously but etymologically, literally thrown (*jacere*) back (*re-*) here, to the same philosophical backwater he'd attended as a freshman himself years ago, which was the only program to accept him, and which had never, as far as the reader knew, sent anyone to

N—, much less to the Fellowship—then he wouldn't have written *Phrasing* on the freshman's paper at all, he would have written *You fucking idiot* in the margin, because at least then he would appreciate how much hatred was at stake. There was still time for the freshman to escape this cycle, to study anything else, but if he was as determined as he claimed to become a real philosopher, then that was what he was going to need to understand. So long as he learned to obey this voice early, the reader should have told him, he could not only become but might even overtake the reader. If he read Hegel now, he should have told him—if he didn't wait even another day to read Hegel—he could make it further than the reader had made it. The reader ground his palm savagely into his forehead. Fuckhead. Failure. Fraud. He was already a decade older than the freshman, the same age as the Fellow, and still he hadn't read Hegel. What had he been waiting for? He had read Arendt, Benjamin, and Cixous, but never Hegel. Descartes yes, but Hegel no. He chewed his nail, his cheek. Reject. Reject. Eckhart, Fanon, and Guattari, but not the *Phenomenology*. Somehow he had read Heidegger, Irigaray, and Jameson before Hegel. While the Fellow had been reading Hegel, what had he even been reading? Kant, Lacan, Mainländer. Nietzsche, Ortega y Gasset, Pascal. Oh God. Night after night in the library he had been forcing Quine, Ryle, and Spinoza into his head, when what he could and should have been—when what nothing had been stopping him from—reading was Hegel. It would have been so easy to read Hegel. His library if not his life flashed before his eyes, all the books he had read instead of the *Phenomenology*. Toufic, von Uexküll, Voltaire. Wittgenstein, Xenophon, Yourcenar. Would the Fellow care that he had read Zupančič, if he'd never read Hegel? She'd probably read Hegel in short pants. As a child, the reader had read every volume of R. L. Stine's *Goosebumps*, he winced to remember all those nights he had wasted under his blanket with a flashlight, staying up late to finish *The Scarecrow Walks at Midnight* or *Say Cheese and Die!*, when even then he could have been starting the *Phenomenology*. How did it happen—but this was how it always happens—how had that led to this? The scarecrow of Minerva walks at midnight. How had he gone from *Goosebumps* to graduate school, how had he ended up in this carrel? His head was pounding. He looked out the window, surveilling the miniature students crawling across the parking lot, and he had the fleeting autoscopic impression that each was him, that he was watching himself head home from class in the past. He could see it clearly now: because he had loved reading as a child he had done well in literature courses and on tests, placing into his high-school's honors track, where gradually he had learned to read more difficult books, to submit himself to that difficulty, to become a cenobite of boredom, until soon he was scoring even higher on even harder tests, and because of all this—the As on the report cards, the perfect verbals— he'd been awarded a scholarship here, which must mean, he had thought naively at the time, that he was good at reading, that if he went on reading more books—the hardest, most difficult books, the ones that even other readers didn't read—he might have a future as a reader. He would keep being rewarded, he'd imagined, lifted upward, he would be allowed to go on reading, *as long as he kept reading*. It wasn't until he'd been rejected that he'd learned the truth: that this whole time there had been other readers out there in the world, readers like the Fellow, who had known or been told to read even better books, or simply more of them, they were the ones who would be allowed to become real readers. He'd been trying to catch up with them ever since, and still he hadn't read enough, nothing was ever enough, only everything would be enough. He thought he'd been obeying his self-hatred, but even he had loved himself too much, that much was becoming clear. Well, it was too late to do anything about it now. He closed the browser and reopened the letter. He typed the Fellow's name, deleted it. He drank from his thermos until sweat beaded on his scalp like condensation, drops of brain escaping, then ran a hand through his hair to smush them back in. Finally he Googled the Fellow. It didn't take long to find her profile on N—'s People page. She had returned there after the Fellowship, this time as a real philosopher, and her Hegel book, he saw, was forthcoming next year. Her photo showed her smiling in front of a set of built-in bookshelves painted white. The reader spent the next fifteen minutes in the library slowly zooming in on her library, magnifying the low-resolution background to try to make out the blurred titles on the spines. He assumed Brandom was in there somewhere, Butler, along with Inwood and Kojève and every other book he'd ever been meaning to read, but he couldn't decipher the text and didn't recognize the jacket designs. Giving up, he zoomed back out to the Fellow's smiling face. Except that now, strangely, her smile read more like a smirk. There was a contempt in her expression that he hadn't noticed there before. He knew this was an illusion—it had to be the same smile, the contempt was Kuleshovian—but still he felt rejected by this face. Idiot, the face said. Impostor. Hegel Hegel Hegel, the face said. He searched the Fellow's name on Twitter. After a few false positives—a think-tank analyst, a podcaster—he located her account. He could tell it was hers because she had the Fellowship in her bio, followed by the 🌐 emoji beside the word *Spirit*. The first thing he did was search her tweets for *Hegel*. He found a thread where she and other philosophers were trading Hegel puns. *ALFhebung*, the Fellow tweeted, with a photo of the armadillo-nosed sitcom alien shrugging his shoulders. *The virgin Hegel versus the chad Schopenhauer*, another philosopher tweeted, with Schopenhauer's head photoshopped onto a bodybuilder's body, while Hegel's head was photoshopped onto a scrawny teenager's body, to which the Fellow responded, *The virgin Schopenhauer versus the chad Hegel*, with the heads swapped. *Poppyseed Hegel*, another philosopher tweeted, *is that something?*, and the Fellow tweeted, *The* 👏 *spirit* 👏 *is* 👏 *a* 👏 *boner* 👏. The reader smiled tightly. So. This was the mind who would be reading him. This was the mind he had to model inside his mind. Forget the *comprised of* hater, the *seminal* hater, forget the Quine scholar and the Spinoza scholar. He Googled her again, scrolled down until he found her LinkedIn profile, clicked it without blinking. Yes, he thought, now we were cooking with gas. How would someone who had gone straight from N— to the Fellowship, someone who before that had worked as an editorial assistant at the *Phenomenological Quarterly* (the reader had been rejected from the *Phenomenological Quarterly*), and before that had received a travel grant to Berlin (the reader had been rejected for the same travel grant, the same year), someone who had made a pilgrimage and posed, he saw when he zoomed in on her profile photo, beside Hegel's headstone at Dorotheenstadt Cemetery, someone therefore who had not only read Hegel, leafed through Hegel, but who had devoted her life (a life that it was dawning on the reader with dry-mouth horror, as he doom-scrolled down her vita, was the mirror image of his own, shadowing his applications at every stage, accepted precisely where he had been rejected, advanced forward exactly when he had been thrown back, for no reason that he could discern other than that she had read Hegel and he had not) in short someone who had devoted her entire life to Hegel, how would such a reader read his letter? All his life, if someone had asked him why he read, the reader would have told them that he was curious about *other minds*. He read philosophy, he would have told them, to learn how other minds saw the world. But now the only mind in the world that mattered was the Fellow's. What the reader needed to know was how one mind in particular saw not the world, but his letter. He didn't need to read Hegel to learn how Hegel saw the world but to learn how *someone who had read Hegel would see his letter.* You're wasting your time writing this letter, he imagined the Fellow would tell him. How do you expect to write the first sentence of your letter if you still haven't read the first word of Hegel? She was right. She was absolutely right. If he had read the *Phenomenology* earlier, he might have been the one to go to N—, the *Phenomenological Quarterly*, Berlin. Maybe there was still time to make it to the Fellowship. The reader paced to the library's catalog computer against the far wall. With each row of bookshelves that he passed through, the track lights clicked on above him, he strode into the darkness trailing a wake of weak fluorescence. The catalog showed a single copy of the *Phenomenology* available, one floor below. There were still two hours before the library closed. If he got Hegel now, he might be able to read sixty pages by the end of the night. But that was suicidal. He couldn't waste a single minute reading Hegel. The application was due tomorrow, and he still had essays to grade. Nothing could be more dangerous than ignoring his letter. Except wouldn't the truly dangerous thing, the Fellow reasoned inside him, be to ignore his self-hatred? It wasn't any different from ignoring pain. Hate, like heat, was just afferent information that your body needed to share with your mind. It was a way of alerting you to some danger out there in the world. If the letter was hot with hate, it was this voice inside you's way of warning you: try to write tonight and you'll get burned. Would you keep your hand pressed to a hot stovetop? Would you ignore a smarting finger? Then why ignore this warning that you still aren't smart enough? Self-hatred is just a fingertip for touching the future with. A nerve inside of time. The ghostly thread of it binds today's brain to tomorrow's brain—it can feel out tomorrow's worst-case scenarios today—and tonight it's telling you that you need to read Hegel. It's clear you aren't getting any writing done anyway, the Fellow reasoned. In the hour you've been sitting here you could have read thirty pages. If you get the *Phenomenology* you'll go to sleep with the bare minimum of Hegel in your head, and at least that will be better than nothing: the worst first sentence you could write in the morning would still be better than the best first sentence you could write tonight. Whereas if you stay at your laptop, you'll only be postponing the inevitable: tomorrow you'll wake in bed with the same brain you went to sleep with, and you'll wind up stuck in the same place in the same blank document. Impostor, you'll think all over again. Fraud. Then won't you just have to spend *tomorrow* reading Hegel? Wouldn't you merely have deferred the *Phenomenol-ogy* for your future self to read? Where else do you think the hatred even comes from? It's not self-hatred, it's your future self's hatred. Your future self hates you for not reading Hegel, because it means that he's the one who has to read Hegel. *He's* the one who thinks you're an idiot, who resents your procrastination for sabotaging him, he's the one whose hatred has been echoing backward from tomor-row to haunt you. If you don't read Hegel now, tomorrow you will be the voice that has been hating you tonight, just as yesterday you were hearing tonight's hatred—hauntred—in your head. All right, the reader thought, all right, you're right. He hurried down the empty stairwell, his steps casting cavernous echoes. He could grade papers in the morning, he thought, there would still be time. He had all afternoon to write the letter. Tonight he just had to find Hegel. When he arrived at the lower floor, it was equally deserted as upstairs, the stacks all dark but one. At the end of the room a single track light glowed above a row of bookshelves, spotlighting them like a god shaft after a storm. The reader knew without needing to check that this was where he would find Hegel. It was a sign. He paced down the aisles, triggering the track lights as he moved, dispersing the darkness with every step. When he reached the final haloed row, it was labeled Gu-Ho. Yes, he thought, a sign. It was only as he was striding past the books themselves, scanning the library stickers for the *Phenomenology*'s call number, that a nauseating certainty rose in him. Because why had this aisle been lit in the first place? He hadn't seen anyone else in the room with him. Fear placed one foot in front of the other. He inspected every shelf, and it was just as he had dreaded: the *Phenomenology* had gone missing. Right where it should be—between the *Lectures on Aesthetics* and the *Science of Logic*—there was a fat gap. How was it possible? The catalog had listed it as available, just minutes ago. It doesn't matter, the Fellow said. The judges won't care what your excuse is, all they'll care about is the fact that you haven't read Hegel. I know, the reader thought, I *know* that. Thank you for applying, the Fellow said. We regret to inform you. The reader swept the room, starting from the back and checking every carrel desktop, every pile of books, every book cart. The *Phenomenology* had to be here somewhere, he told himself, it couldn't have gotten far. But he couldn't find it anywhere, deep down he knew it was gone. Maybe he could get by with skimming Kojève, he thought, and there was a burst of bitter laughter in his skull. LOL, the Fellow said. Do you think I got where I am by skimming

Kojève? OK, the reader thought, pounding his temple with his palm, like a swimmer trying to clear water from his ear. We've got a Hegel expert here, the Fellow said. Guy's skimmed Kojève. He's even read Hegel's Wikipedia page! All right, all right, the reader pounded, as he rounded the last row of shelves, I'll read it, I'll read the *Phenomenology*. It was then that he saw him: across the room, in a carrel in the far corner, with his back to the reader but still recognizable—unmistakable—by his gray hoodie and scoliotic slouch, slumped the freshman. His head was buried in what looked like a phone book. He must have felt the reader's gaze on the nape of his neck—a prey phenomenon that some ethologists called the *holy shiver*, the reader had read somewhere—because he turned around just then, meeting the reader's eyes. Oh, the freshman called out. Hi, Professor. The reader waved feebly as he approached and leaned toward the book on the carrel, trying to spy the title. The freshman flashed the cover—G. W. F. Hegel's *The Phenomenology of Spirit*—while marking his place with a finger. By the looks of it he had read about thirty pages. The freshman brushed his hair and his hood out of his eyes and thanked the reader for meeting with him in his office earlier. He'd decided to take his advice, he said, starting tonight. His advice? The reader cast his mind back in panic. What had he told him? Read books, he had said then, read everything. But *why* had he said that? What had he been thinking? He hadn't been thinking, he had been digging his own grave without knowing it, now he had his past self to thank for this pit he was standing in. Idiot, he thought, fuckup, trying to beam this thought backward eight hours in time, into his head in his office this afternoon. Even so, he couldn't help smiling. It had turned out to be good advice, despite everything. Maybe the freshman would make it far after all: *he* would go to N—, and then Berlin, *he* would enter the Fellowship and emerge from it, in all things the freshman would become the Fellow. That was great, the reader told him. That was very admirable. But, he explained—and this was as awkward for him as it was for the freshman—he actually needed that book. Would he mind letting him have it? The freshman hesitated. Weren't there other copies? he asked. The reader shook his head. It was urgent, he said, an emergency. Normally he would just buy it, he lied—in fact, he could never have afforded it, he had already spent his stipend on food—but he needed the book tonight, for very important research. The freshman frowned at the *Phenomenology*, as though it were his wallet and the reader were a beggar in the street. He's considering it, the reader realized, with a beggar's telepathy. Take it, the Fellow said. Take 🖐 it 🖐 now 🖐! Just threaten to fail him and take the book. The reader tried reasoning with the freshman one last time. You don't even need to read it yet, he told him, not for many years, not until after you've read Aristotle and Kant and Fichte. In the middle of the sentence he could tell it was the wrong sentence, but the words had left his mouth, there was no deleting them. The freshman stiffened, unconvinced. It was obvious that he *did* need to read it, the reader's desperation to read it showed him plainly what a future of not having read it looked like. By the pity in his eyes, he could see that the freshman could see him clearly now: he was no Socrates, just some backwater adjunct and specter of rejection, a hungry ghost doomed to haunt the stacks and steal books from the living, which was what the freshman risked becoming, if he handed over Hegel. The reader waved off this vision, dismissing not just the book but the entire situation. Never mind, he told the freshman. Forget about it. He should keep it: the reader could always find a copy online. Thanks, Professor, the freshman said uncertainly, and neither of them knew what he was thanking him for. Halfway to the stairwell he heard the freshman call out, I hope you enjoy my essay, and without turning back the reader raised his hand in parting. Oh, he was going to enjoy his essay all right, he was going to make him pay for Hegel with every typo. Hegel Hegel Hegel, he thought as he climbed the stairs, to shove down the last few minutes into oblivion, to keep from remembering a single thing that had just happened, Hegel Hegel Hegel. Once he was upstairs, out of earshot, he jogged to his carrel, taking a zigzag path through the stacks to trigger every track light. He'd lost only five minutes, he calculated, two pages. There was still time. Back at his laptop he Googled the *Phenomenology*. Scrolling through an out-of-copyright translation on archive.org, he clicked the link to the preface and tried to read Hegel's first sentence. You should be writing right now, he thought, as his eyes scanned from left to right. As his eyes moved up and down, he thought, The deadline is tomorrow. Before he knew it he had somehow reached the bottom of the page, and he couldn't remember a single word he had just read. He *hadn't* read a single word, because he had retained nothing. His eyes had failed to transport even one sentence off the screen and into his mind. He started from the top again, but when he reached the bottom it was the same. He remembered nothing. Focus, the Fellow said. He sipped from his thermos. Hegel Hegel Hegel. He read the page a third time, but even as his eyes passed over Hegel's sentences, the only words moving through his mind were *Reject,*

Failure, it was as if these were the only words actually printed there, over and over, as though someone had replaced the text of the *Phenomenology* with this lorem ipsum of loathing. He assumed the freshman was having better luck downstairs, he'd probably already read another thirty pages. When he saw that half an hour had gone by, he gave up, closing Hegel and reopening the letter. The cursor was still blinking where he'd left it. A face glared back at him from within the blackness of the blank screen. Raising his hand to his temple, he saw the face touch itself as well, and there was a contempt in the reflection that he hadn't noticed there before. Idiot, the face said. Impostor. The Fellow was right, the reader thought. This could be his future self he was seeing. Whenever he thought dark thoughts, this must be the dark face that uttered them. The other self inside him—the self that lay hidden on the shadow side of his mind, the shadow side of the hyphen, the secret subject behind all of his self-consciousness, self-doubt, self-pity—was regarding him from tomorrow here. And he could see that tomorrow would be the same as today. He would wake in bed with the same Hegel-less brain. He would grade his students' papers and return to this carrel. And whether he wrote the letter or not—whether he was accepted to the Fellowship or rejected, whether he stayed in this program and finished his dissertation or whether he left altogether—he would always be the one who had to read what he had not read. After Hegel there would be Brandom, then Butler, and after Butler Inwood, or Kojève, and then (how could he have forgotten?) the Fellow herself, whose own book would be added to this archive soon enough, added to the bad infinity of this bottomless bibliography. You still haven't read the Fellow, a voice would be hissing inside his head one year from now, either in the Fellowship's library or this one, it would make no difference. He closed the letter without saving his changes—there were no changes to save—and stared out the window. It was late now, past midnight, and in the empty parking lot he spotted a sole hooded figure, loping against the snow. He was fairly sure it was the freshman. The way he slouched even while walking, scarecrow of Minerva. One arm hung at his side, and he seemed to be holding something in his hand. The reader tried to make out whether it was a book, whether the freshman was taking Hegel home with him. He was too far off to be certain, it could be either the *Phenomenology* or his phone. He watched the figure dwindle down the street, and when he had disappeared in the darkness, the reader withdrew the stack of essays from his backpack, flipping through them until he had found the freshman's. Webster's *defines "philosophy,"* the first sentence read, *as the love of wisdom.* My God, the reader thought, as he uncapped his pen and underlined the first sentence. Cliché, he thought. Idiotic. But when he brought his pen to the margin, he did not write *Cliché* or *Idiotic.* He didn't even write *Phrasing.* He thought of the freshman sitting in the carrel downstairs, forcing Hegel into his head through his eyeballs, wondering whether he would ever be smart enough. He thought of him walking home through the cold, gripping the *Phenomenology* in freezing fingers, counting down the pages he could be reading with each passing step. He imagined what it would be like—inside the freshman's mind—when he got this final essay back and read over the reader's notes. And for the first time he could understand what his professors had been trying to tell him. Two tomorrows unfolded inside him. If he wrote *Cliché* or *Phrasing* now, he saw, the freshman might learn to hate himself, and maybe that would spare him a rejection, in the end. But the reader could choose to spare him the hatred altogether. He might not be able to help him become the Fellow, but at least he could steer him away from becoming the reader, he could practice that compassion toward the freshman that he could not practice toward himself. Even if it wasn't much, it still might be enough: the other minds might stay confined inside his mind, the freshman might go the rest of his life without ever needing to know about them. Dumb and happy! Dumb and happy. . . . The reader wrote *Good* and made a check mark in the margin, then flipped to the last page and wrote *A*+. He put the essay away and regarded his reflection in the deadened laptop glass. Yes. He could see it clearly now: his future, the freshman's, the Fellow's. Dear readers. After a minute the first of the track lights clicked off across the room, and darkness showered down on the farthest row of shelves. The next track light deactivated half a second afterward, and then the next, so that the darkness came staggered, clicking closer to the carrel with every row. This wall of shadow advanced across the stacks like an avalanche, soon it would consume him. At any moment, the reader knew, he could stop it. All he had to do was raise his hand. But he just kept still and watched it. He waited for the black wind blowing over the books to blow over him also.

Watch Your Sister Disappear
Akil Kumarasamy

YOUR SISTER IS LOSING her voice. It feels like it happened overnight, her lips turning into rubber, but it's been almost four months, and your sister, who would have suffocated you for calling her doll-like, spends her days sitting by the window, looking at everything and nothing, all at once. For what it's worth, you try to remind her of her human self. You clamp down on the flap of fat on her arms but not a pipe. A deep paper cut exacts only a hiss of air. She has long, dark Rapunzel hair that thins into her calves, and with a pair of garden scissors, you give her the first haircut she has had in sixteen years. All her history is in her hair, and that's the problem, you think, the weight of it. Hanging from your fists, her wiry hair looks like the tail of some dead creature. She wakes before you finish, and you stand back, wait for her anger that your eleven-year-old self knows quite well. She can have you in a choke hold in less than a minute or, if you are less careful, pinned on the floor with your arms bent, hanger shaped, behind your back. Your friends might call you a wuss for being beaten by a girl, but they are afraid of your sister too, maybe as much as they are in love with her. Her prettiness is barbed. Instead of coming for your jugular and calling you *stripy* for all your unusual birthmarks, she walks to the mirror and stares at this mangled image of herself. She takes your scissors, finishes the job.

Since she dropped out of school, you and your sister draw in the afternoons, all stretched out on the carpet. She never used to spend time with you like this but what feels like tenderness darkens in your mind when you see her pictures. Wolves chomping on limbs and floating faces frozen in agony. Still you are surprised by your sister's artistry, the way you can feel fear from some curvy lines. She doesn't keep the drawings but asks you to burn them one by one in the yard with your stepfather's lighter, the one he keeps in the watering pot for a midnight smoke. On your sister's neck is a cloth bandage. She touches it whenever she looks at the wolf before the fire tears through it. Often you don't even see the fabric because your sister dresses in turtlenecks even in the spring. "It's glandular," you tell your friends.

"She doesn't sweat." You, on the other hand, find yourself sweating all the time, anxious with heat. What are you afraid of? From where your sister sits by the window, you imagine she can see an ash pile of wolves. They will return the next afternoon, and you will slay them, again and again.

Your mother works as a receptionist in a dental office, down the street from a canning factory, so the air smells of briny string beans and peaches. She is confident your sister will return to school, even if she is held back a year. Your stepfather seems less bothered because he's often an idiot and still bets money on horse races. When he says things about your sister like *She'll make a good wife, not a squeak*, you want to pull out his vocal cords, and then he says something like *he's so lucky to have two kids so late in life* and you don't know what to do with your hands. At school, your teacher asks how you're doing. "A wolf got my sister," you tell her and she pats your head. "I know, I know," she says.

By your sister's bedside are books about extraterrestrials. She has always been interested in other worlds, especially after your father crossed over, head dived from a bridge, but now it seems like all she can think of is elsewhere. You ask her if the wolves are from another planet and she shakes her head. This girl Fairuza in town was found lying by a creek with her limbs extended into a star, her nose bloody. When she woke, she said she saw astral lights, teacup-sized orbs floating above her. Fairuza is also crazy. Like she once said her father murdered her mother when she really just went back to Iran. She was your sister's friend back when your sister talked to people, acted like a normal human, or at least a normal, slightly strange human. It seems plausible that your sister has been replaced by a simulacrum, a body double, but you've had this thought for years whenever you were with her in public and suddenly she turned quiet and shy when handing money over to a cashier or meeting the gaze of an older classmate. Only later at home would she acknowledge your presence, try to pinch your nose to test your breathing. Still, you've watched too much *X-Files* to let this alien-swap theory go and you want to check her teeth for implants, but unfortunately for you your sister sleeps with a lockjaw you can't decode. She rarely shows her teeth but last week when she was watching some film with your mother— some sort of pointless, crappy romance—you caught the last scene where the man tells the woman that she is made for him and kisses her. You moaned through it like someone was stabbing you in the ribs while your sister just bit down on her thumb, revealing the crust

Akil Kumarasamy

of her teeth. Her eyes were fixed on the space just above the television.

Your sister used to be a walker, could spend hours moving in circles around your neighborhood, and maybe that's why you're a little surprised she never ran away. She would come home late with her fingers numb or so dehydrated she just huddled on the couch, breathing in each sip of water with a straw. She carried home pine cones, acorns, a perfectly veined heart-shaped leaf. Like she was a squirrel or bird preparing a nest. She once didn't return home and your mother told the neighbors and they searched the surrounding forests but couldn't find her. While you ossified in the cold, she was already home, seated by the window, watching people call out her name. It is how you feel now, standing right next to her but miles away, as she waits sealed inside.

You read to her from her alien books because you think one of them might have a cure and she seems slightly interested. Humans are portals to the universe, you say, and slide your arm behind her until it surfaces on her shoulder. She almost laughs but just plops grapes into her mouth, lets the juice dribble from the corner of her lips. You heard your friend Aiguo say this to a girl before they pummeled each other's bodies in his parents' car, trying desperately to touch the milky galaxy through each other. You've never been with a girl, but it startles you how the simple sight of flesh can make you want to implode. Three years back you heard your mother and stepfather growling in the dark, but your mother now just comes home and watches television, her sweatshirts thick as blubber. There are many ways to escape.

The fluorescent glow-in-the-dark stars still string along the ceiling of your sister's room. You tell her that she's too old to be afraid of the dark, but she just ignores you, listens to your stepfather closing the fridge. She used to tell you that no one would love you because of all your birthmarks mottling your skin but not to worry because she would have space for you, her little striped brother. You curl up next to her and tell her you'll keep a lookout for the wolf. They are afraid of fire, you say, and flick on the lighter you stole from your stepfather. She puts her finger through the flame.

You wonder if she misses things from the outside world. Besides walking in the yard, she hardly ventures outdoors and her aversion to everybody except you makes this mission to find her voice more urgent. "All the air here is stale," you tell her before you go kneel in your room and pray to all the human portals to bring back your sister from whatever dimension she's trapped in. You imagine the overweight postman containing the force and mass to create even a larger portal.

At school all you can talk about is the wolf and the bandage and the grayness in your sister's eyes. Your friends are worried about your perpetual snarl, the suspicious way you eye any stranger. You carry your lighter with you always. When a freckled boy in class mentions your sister, you try to light his curly hair on fire and your stepfather is called to pick you up. "Are you trying to finish school early too like your sister?" he asks in the car, and you pinch your left hand hard to keep it from balling into a fist.

At home he drinks a beer and tells you to sit with him. He's watching some game show with a female host. He rests a cigarette on his lip and pats down on his shirt, searching for his lighter, and then turns to you, remembering. You reach over and light it for him. "Sorry," you say and drop it in his lap and even he is surprised by your apology. You are hunched with your head on your knees and can't help but imagine how the fire coiled through the fuse of KJ's hair.

"All those cups of semen in my twenties and you're the closest to a son I will ever have," your stepfather says before telling you about his sexual adventures. You tell him humans are portals to the galaxy. He glances at the television, asks you if you would link portals with the host. When you hesitate, he helps you out, says he would pick the one with fat thighs. After some channel surfing, you find a group of women chatting and you both rate them one to ten, and your stepfather laughs hard, hissing, when you give someone a negative one. Your stepfather tells you how he lost his virginity when he was around your age with this older girl with two uteruses, which might have made her more fertile or more willing to use one up fast. All he remembers is the sensation, which he tries to recreate for you by opening a beer can and taking that first fizzy sip. You take the second sip and burp. He smiles and tells you how he married twice before your mother. His first sweetheart was a beauty but vengeful, sleeping with other men once she found out about his other ladies. "That's what you get when you marry a woman who doesn't mind being a slut."

You hear the soft shuffling behind you, but you don't turn because you want to draw her out. Maybe you already know what you will see, and you are afraid of seeing it so clearly: you feel your claws. You take a few more sips, watch your stepfather slobber up the women on the television. His cologne intoxicates you, makes you think of your father, your father's father, all the fathers that made you. Your stepfather squeezes your shoulder and says, "That's my boy." The words rub against you like a salve that can heal your hurt. You tell him how you heard a story of a girl who was wide as a moon and let anyone in and then lost herself in some galaxy, thousands of light-years away. Your stepfather nods and closes his eyes, begins to drift to sleep. You wait, watch the swell of his stomach, the flicker of the television, before you hear her. She is crying and you hear her.

Two Poems
Jessica Reed

LA CUEVA DE LOS CRISTALES

Inside the bare Sierra de Naica Mountains, there is a chamber
one thousand feet underground lined floor to ceiling with gypsum
crystals high as telephone poles. This cave had been sealed off from
the evolution of life on our planet for millions of years and was open
to us for only fifteen. Discovered in the cave's water were viruses—
two hundred million in every drop.

Colossal crystals, formed in darkness where two waters touched—
  groundwater, surface water
   (magma-heated, oxygenated)—
one drinking the other's oxygen, a *seeping into*,
  saturated with sulfide ions,
  silently precipitating into one crystal,
   dissolving into another that began to tower . . .

  Oh wake up, wake/ up, something moving through the air now,
  something in the ground that waits.

And this place, strangely lit:
so hot and so humid, a person could set foot inside
  for just ten minutes
before cells would die and organs fail,   I open my door; birds panic

  crystals soft like fingernails   at the interruption—
   but razor sharp
    and searing hot.

We carry the light down with us,
that we might see a world   that never sees sunlight,

Jessica Reed

(without the birds,
their constant narration)—

We know our looking
brings its own light, so

a hell, entered willingly
here: a fragile clarity.

what is beneath our world
when we are not looking?

Infernal cathedral, the crystals an archive
of *chronos* and *kairos*.   Hush:
the iridescent wholeness we break
by entering
(our flashlights, our cameras, our eyes,
without which crystals do not sparkle).

Our lamps brighten
crystals twelve tons,
half a million years in the making.

We might with dilated vision see
an underworld flaming forth—

.

Penny, our microbiologist, uses a corkscrew and lighter
—the equipment that will function at this depth—
to get samples of these virus-harboring waters
(viruses—from *where*?).

And no animal large enough for us to see
(with bare eyes) could see them.

What did they *feed* on?
No, they did not feed;

viruses bide their time.

.

And this? A Temple of Time.

> . . . *to imprint this temporary, perishable earth*
> *into ourselves so deeply that its essence*
> *can rise again, 'invisibly,' inside us* . . .

(Did the Cave of Crystals panic
at the interruption,
sealing itself off from us again?)

Its superlative scale:
orders of magnitude. Huge beams jutting out.

I took photos of the crows
who did not see me seeing them
pecking my lawn in
disturbing numbers—another!
another! another!

an overwhelming sense of *how dare*
they—

Viruses, embedded in our genome,
make our air   regulate our seas
affect   our planet's temperature
our soil   our fresh water.

another, another, *an other*

Is it meaningless? To ask
what the world looks like
when I'm not looking?

The *innumerable* (am I using the word right?)
count the viruses per drop, drops per cave sector, all estimates . . .

And It, not needing to be known.

.

We first made viruses visible (to us)
by crystallizing them:
early 1900s, clear sheets with needles of protein.

Jessica Reed

We found they could be
                    stored
like table salt   and later reanimated.

                                        I didn't want to scare the birds away.
                                        Not yet.

In a now-inaccessible cave in Mexico:
mammoth crystals, microscopic creatures.
                              These are the scavengers, the birds
                              that appear when death is near,

                    and here, the indisputable evidence
                    that my lawn is not *my* lawn,

and neither is this story mine:
          of momentary opening, glimpse of an alien world, then *collapse*

"La Cueva de los Cristales": Italicized text ("Oh wake up") from Jorie Graham, ("rise again, 'invisibly,' inside us") from Rilke.

NIGHT MIND

[Emotions and moods] can be understood as controlled
hallucinations: brain-based best-guesses that remain tied
[...] to the organism. [...] staying alive through keeping
essential variables in their tight ranges.

—Anil Seth

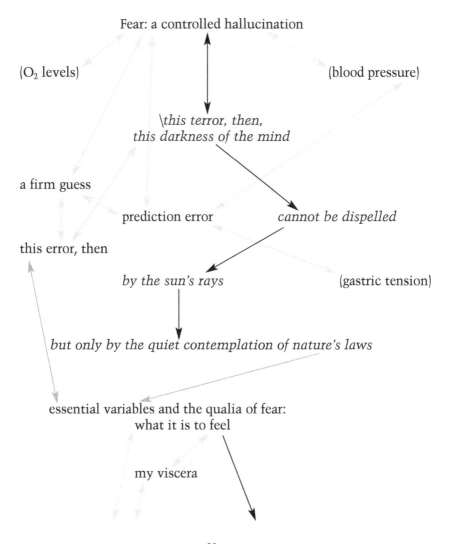

Fear: a controlled hallucination

(O_2 levels)

(blood pressure)

this terror, then,
this darkness of the mind

a firm guess

prediction error   *cannot be dispelled*

this error, then

by the sun's rays   (gastric tension)

but only by the quiet contemplation of nature's laws

essential variables and the qualia of fear:
what it is to feel

my viscera

61

Jessica Reed

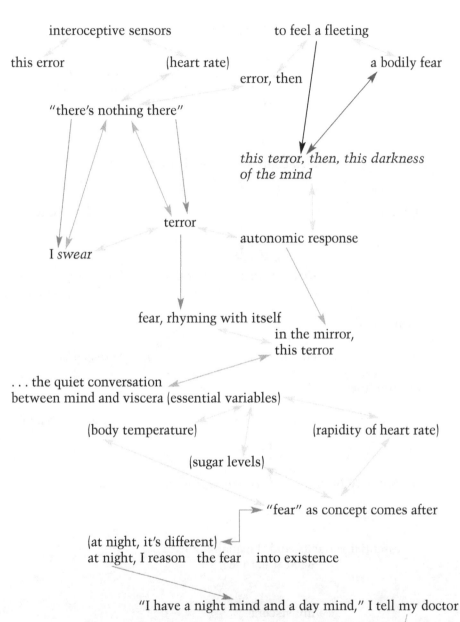

interoceptive sensors

this error

(heart rate)

to feel a fleeting

a bodily fear

error, then

"there's nothing there"

this terror, then, this darkness
of the mind

terror

autonomic response

I *swear*

fear, rhyming with itself

in the mirror,
this terror

. . . the quiet conversation
between mind and viscera (essential variables)

(body temperature)

(rapidity of heart rate)

(sugar levels)

"fear" as concept comes after

(at night, it's different)
at night, I reason   the fear   into existence

"I have a night mind and a day mind," I tell my doctor

increase atypical antipsychotics—
(a reasonable response)

this medication, then—
replacing the divine . . .

. . . this dweller, then,
this recess in the mind

draft of cold, an emptying
of air

the quiet contemplation
of the body's flaws

this sewn-up set of lines
cannot be unspooled by ~~the error~~ the arrow
the sun's rays

"Night Mind": Italicized text is from David Slavitt's translation of Lucretius. Anil
Seth epigraph is from "We Are Beast Machines," *Nautilus*.

The Order of the Flaming Crows
Rick Moody

I DON'T REALLY KNOW why I went, because I am not an entity who attends.

I can tell when the *caring* ignites because there is an inflationary aura—it's like a fishing trawler with gold, reflective diamonds belly-dancing around margins of indigo, glistening in the arc lamps of video reproduction. I can tell *caring* because I have seen it in the rectangular diode infiltrator. You can see the foamy corners of their dental veneers, the humans, their wolverine mouths, and there's a purple scrim through which is exposed the action of *caring*, of which I have none. That's why the video rectangle indicts me, with its simulations of lavender caring. Everyone wants that little pinprick of brotherhood, oh I care about the farmers of the Tulsa outskirts, or I care about the indigenous peoples of Oklahoma, or I care about the unemployed people, I see them, all caring, sitting behind their fabricated desks on the infiltrator rectangle, filling out forms, and they are wearing purple high-thread-count sheets draped so casually or sometimes aqua sheets or teal with their veneers going up and down like a Precambrian percussion section, caring like pastel mouth organs playing out a musical lattice of death.

I was working in a particular job that was an only-job-I-could-hold-down job, which was a janitorial death consignment in a thirty-nine-dollars-a-night roadside hovel and a monkey suit of internment drab and this was not a daily appearance I could renounce because resultantly I would be living on benches and there are insufficient benches in greater Tulsa, even in Reconciliation Park; you fight for your bench. And I did not want bench dwelling with others of my circumstance, which is to say persons of a substandard hygiene ideology, especially in the matter of abscessing bicuspids and the spitting up of blood and the up all night with ammonium hydroxide ingestion; I would live on no bench, because of aphid swarms, viral breaching, but there was a paramilitary group that was in a constant warlike state intent on taking from me my livelihood of death-janitoring and subsistence procurement, the certainty of microwavables and wellness injections that my livelihood made possible or even ethically urgent. That shadowy paramilitary was known as the Flaming Crows, sometimes known as the Order of Flaming Crows, or the Nation State of the Flaming Crows, or sometimes Ravens of Anonymous Terror. I'm sure you have heard of their viscous liquids and their command and control. There were subgroups of Flaming Crows, theirs is a movement afflicted by schism, and this I knew because I was in semicontinuous conversation with the Flaming Crows, through stochastic messaging approximators, and/or intermediaries, and via their broadcasts. I encountered them chiefly in roadkill settings, wherever a squirrel had been flattened, wishing to stress here that at no point did I accelerate in my own vehicle—I didn't have a vehicle, and yet I did drive my brother's vehicle on certain occasions, unlicensed, uninsured—at no point did I dispatch the woodland folk, the chipmunks or squirrels and such, which I referred to with endearments and sobriquets such as *Augusto of the Cloudlands*. I did, however, look for remains and maggotry, in order to encounter the O.F.C., the Flaming Crows, which would often alight on the area where a flattening had taken place, before the arrival of turkey vultures, or road crews, and if this was near a park or a green triangle out in farm country then would I sit and wait for Flaming Crows, no matter the hour, in the certainty of their ultimate appearance. Oh brave miscreants. They would occasionally, via stochastic messaging, impart information to me, such as:—*Have no consort with users of methamphetamine, either casual or committed, you will know them by the spitting of green blood.*

Of course, I also knew, knowledge being imperative in this account, from hand signals of various persons, for example, the owner-operators of the O.F.C. Free Clinic out by the Dollar Store that no mortal human of the faex-producing variety would believe information imparted to me by a Flaming Crow perched on a telephone line near to a dead squirrel, its innards all action-painted onto the tarmac on the outskirts of greater Tulsa. I knew but did not care about the blood spitters, because caring was purple hued. When the Flaming Crow turned its face upon me as it did for no other, then I would be filled with spirit and know that my life was most certainly *redeemed*, or at least I could feel the feeling in the sulfur rush of my undersea vent, my volcanic exhalations, my isolation.

On one occasion, by Flaming Crows, I was told that the game of baseball was no longer a moral game; on one occasion, I was told that time was contained in thimblefuls, rimmed with a brightly shining poison, which could be poured out so that events happened in something known as a Long Grief Sequence; on one occasion, I was told that love was present only in groin constraints; on one occasion I was told to eat sparingly and only from the carbohydrate group; on one occasion I was told to attend a congregational ministry in Tulsa that was near to a district entitled Greenwood District where human truths cannot be uttered without the appearance of outward falsification extremophiles and impalement deaths that are small bacteria, like angels. These were planks in the belief platform of the aforementioned Order, as I came to venerate them.

My brother and his spouse equivalent, also a male-presenting insurance agent with pustules, had been entreating me to attend a church too, under the theory that this would broaden the pool of purple-shrouded individuals who might lend me a vehicle when badly needed, or who might pick me up from my section 8 housing and blood-spitting housemates, the methamphetamine afflicted, and, in mitigating a Long Grief Sequence, drive me to death-janitoring while wearing funny masks from cartoon superiors. It is hard for me to make orderly the sequence, as I had occasion in the thirty-nine-a-night domicile of my employ to riffle the belongings of a large cockroach business-casual type to encounter there the aforementioned thimbleful of time-encrusted Long Grief Sequencing with poison and I drank from nonorderly time, while also ingesting poison, I touched this poison to my lips, and then I knew I should not have besmirched his cockroach belongings.

A person or persons at a denominational penal colony made conversation with me on occasion, near to a soup tureen. The having of conversations was a warm flooding occurrence that caused me to feel briefly other than already deceased, and also poisoned, which I could feel in my fingertips, which were deadened from viral breaching. I dressed appropriately for a church encounter and bathed appropriately because at a bug clinic there were faex producers who had insisted that avoiding bloody spit and other markers of zombification, and likewise never handling *Adolfo of Cloudland* or other roadkill casualties would result in a diminishment of hazing overtures from teenagers and ghosts. There's really nothing more depressing than being told you smell like schizoaffective disorder or that your depersonalization is plain to see. The Flaming Crows, in the construction of their hierarchy of celestial beings, have ranked the ghosts as the lowest, least effective, and have included methamphetamine users at the same rank, which is the rank of heresiarch. Many persons of a kindly nature at the church where I arrived early to help with filling coffee pots and donut plating were remedial in posture and with resemblance differences taught by public education, which was a style of oppression cataloging and competitive shaming. These persons were kind and distant, and had celestial exhalations, or perhaps skeletal excrescences. I had experienced some oppression because when tired or otherwise run-down I assumed different, less human, forms; for example, I was sometimes a peccary.

A certain person with vascular evidentiary syndrome at church made as to befriend me, despite the absence of human affect in my genomic flagrancy, and this person's name was Orville (surname: Branch), and despite his name being Orville, when I saw him in the church basement in my hamster or peccary consciousness I referred to him in this substratum as Ordinal Branch, which I knew was a non-euclidean platelet, in which objects appeared to travel faster than light, on the lip of a space-time origination. Orville would come and find me after church and would discuss with me morsels of wisdom from the day's biblical lesson while wearing a blast radius of donut shrapnel. Heedless. I did have an abiding interest in Lazarus of Bethany, who may have been the first self-designated death janitor, and who enlisted birds into the early church, promising them salvation, ravens above all, Lazarus who perished, reeked, and was raised up, only to perish again. Here I would sometimes perseverate needlessly. Why, I asked myself, on a day when the faex producers had newly impressed on me the need to take certain medicaments, and when I had a diffidently nonfragmentary "I," why on this day would Orville seek me out, especially as I was already in church, and already had accepted viral breaching as my savior, which was sebaceous dogma, as I had been assured by a Flaming Crow on a rainy day in March out by an Agway. I tried to avoid talking to humans who were often faceless symbiotes, because the repartee was not snappy. And yet Mr. Branch.

It became obvious that Ordinal wished to persuade me as to something—an occasion, inclusive of additional symbiotes, at *the stadium*, and stressed that there would be no expense to me personally but that I might be the recipient of a free hat (with stochastic messaging) and perhaps a free shirt, this event taking place at the BOK Center, if all went according to divine entanglement. Did I or did I not make good use of free items when offered, including but not limited to free garments? I did need. And as I occasionally gave away personal items to others and to the land, through burial of garments and precious

belongings, because of disdain for commodity piling, and at the behest
of Flaming Crows, I was in need of free shirts. Lazarus of Bethany
wore rags and stinketh.

—Well, it's settled then, and we'll have a darned good time and go
for a hamburger after! On me, my friend! Ordinal Branch did in fact
refer to me as Johnny Boy, but as you can see I have not referred to
myself by the name in question, as I regarded "Johnny" as a flesh
removal indicator, and I did try to avoid using it, and preferred multi-
valent self-indexing, where possible. Still, I agreed to the plan, which
was to be picked up by Ordinal, and a third person, a military veteran,
and taken by Chevrolet to a large stadium, the BOK Center, as I have
said, on a certain night, a *solstice night*, where I was to receive a free
hat, and/or shirt, and/or mask, or other face covering, and where it
seemed there would be ideological syntagmatics.

In this portion of my eco-feline-astro-projective monograph, printed
as it is on my own flesh, let it be noted that at no point have politics
or political parties intruded into my cadenzas, not under any circumstances, my cadenzas a holy place of eternal combat between Flaming
Crows, hamster consciousness, amputation compassion, and pseudo-
feminine-presenting modesty, and never have I allowed without a
tirade the shallow vanities of shroud-wearing barley mongers to be
pustulated within earshot as they inveigh against underwater studies,
and glands freely extrude. I would not suffer membership. I did not
intend to allow Ordinal Branch and the military veteran to practice
any such thing upon my person, no politics, no ritual amputation, no
emoluments, no penetration.

Frequently, when engaging professionally with faex producers, and
other species, I had been asked about current events, and in particular I have been asked if I could identify a person known as the president of the United States of America. At clinics I am sometimes
asked about current events, before prescriptions are issued. On principle, I would identify no such person as a president nor as monarch
nor as grand vizier, nor am I informed on this point, nor am I wishing to be. I was aware that before my own birth there had been a
sequence of faex-producing presidents, and every now and then con-
troversy arises about persons referred to by occupation, and I believe
that I once gave an oral presentation on the facts concerning a certain
assassinated president, this before all the trouble took root. When I
was but a child I knew childish things and could draw an alarmingly
exact likeness of any celebrity, particularly lounge singers, jazz players
who pretended to be of a different gender, but I cannot identify things

that would formerly have been contained in broadsheets that are also a wiping technology, for example among blood spitters. Injectables exclude current events that are contraindicated by dyskinesia. I do not look at screens, the void-injection devices, because of the retinal command sequencing, and Flaming Crows, during tutelage sessions, have indicated that under no circumstances will gnosis of any kind occur owing to screen-related catalepsy and grinding motion. Insofar as presidents are screen-related info-branding in a cesspool of small-market pumping mechanisms, I know nothing and I experience in the absence of knowing an aerodynamic eco-liberation. I am part of a winged migration.

Ordinal Branch had suggested a meetup before the event, for the purposes of driving to the venue, in his Chevrolet, which was a hearse. He suggested obtaining a hat, as I have said, and I was glad when I understood that my brother and his husbandry would not need to loan me transport or take time out from underwriting. I sat in the backseat of the Ordinal Chevrolet hearse, alert to the possibility of roadkill incidents or encounters with the O.F.C. In the front next to Branch sat the previously mentioned military veteran who extended a hand into the back and announced his genomic sequence. All fingers intact. I shook his hand but did not express a thyroarytenoid symbolic clenching.

—Ned, just so you know, our friend here is on the quiet side!

—Most talk is wasted talk! said the veteran, and gave me a wink, by which I concluded that this veteran either welcomed a Flaming Crows interpretation of current events or would at least look the other way as I proceeded on a fact-finding mission as regards the relationship between Flaming Crows, apocalypse, poison, methamphetamine, coyotes, crop-dusting, homosexuality, noxious fumes, loneliness, and faex production.

Ordinal Branch and this military veteran fell into an exchange of pleasantries highly encoded with sociological prostate massage establishing therein success thresholding, their ability to reproduce, their disdain for persons not similarly tinted lavender, their dialect, their endoscopic histories, their consumption of all-beef emoluments, and then because I studied something, a certain discipline, whose name I will not utter further, before the trouble, I was able to understand and take note of a topic of conversation that had to do with the pleasantries of the so-called Q Source, which is the scriptural passage referring to celebrations beside Lazarus's crypt, gnostic recitations concerning the remarks of crows, and how this had to do with a pizza manufacture, children who were hung up, gutted, and displayed like shanks. As I did not understand how these things were connected, nor indeed did I understand the popular connections between things, instead preferring the crop circles visible from space, the branding of interstellar beings, by which I meant the O.F.C., and that system of meanings, I did *not* contribute further to the conversation. Using secret hand signals, they made clear they had a man on the inside.

I mean, by telling this story, to note that when I use the pronoun "I," there is no I, but only a scattering of seed pods. And dust. There is fear and trembling at the velocity of decline, a Long Grief Sequence, and the only place I am at peace using the fragmenting word scatterer "I" is in the presence of the fraternal order, at dusk, or else when I am in the laundry room on the first floor of the motor lodge and the chambermaids (who do not speak to me), unload the white death shrouds from the rooms and pack these into the back of a van where they will be taken away. Everyone has one, a shroud. My death-janitoring is not in vain and the cockroaches and tarantulas have successfully come to greater Tulsa and conducted business and have gone back to their rooms to elevate their gouty toes while watching golf on a death-shaped rectilinear endoscope.

Having parked the Chevrolet near the stadium, we were absorbed into a throng of viral expectoration on the street outside the military rhetoric hangar, and there were booths where people accepted viral menacing and viral breaching as holy offices, and they used language of a certain kind and spit up greenish blood. I was certain that any viral breaching had not yet jumped species, and so I was exempt, as a peccary, but I did (and do) favor a spittle cistern as a viral accessory. A portion of my visage had been eaten away, especially owing to the injections by the O.F.C., and the skeletal undergirding was visible, and so I accepted from the street vendors a red mask and hat, and I donned these on the sidewalk, and the military veteran positively evaluated,—Son, you look darned handsome!

From the genomic frag disaster occurring in my melting circuitry, I attempted to locate a reply.

—I have never been the same since the face transplant, I said. The drugs destroyed liver function.

—What's that?

—Liver function!

—The problem with these things, the veteran said to the other, gesturing, is you just cannot understand.

Rick Moody

Ordinal laughed in a sociologically fraught way.—You can't understand him? A phonemic sound emerged in a repetitive gurgle: *ha ha ha ha ha ha ha ha ha ha ha ha ha ha ha ha ha ha ha ha ha ha ha ha.*

I had learned that time was repetitious and figmentary while I awaited again the meeting with the crows. It was no problem when events were stultifying. All the stultifications are one. All human company was an oppression including that of my late parents, those examples of fiberglass statuary, and I exist only in the present moment in pulsations awaiting an extenuated heat death, whereupon I will meet up with televised fitness instructors who are international financiers, and Flaming Crows. Because of this I could easily sit through most of the speech of a certain official gray-haired pizza somebody or other, with pustules, a midlevel functionary in a state of decay who has been pecked at repeatedly, who was wearing funeral garb, and gesticulating, who exuded formaldehyde, though toward the end of any tortured speech I feigned an emergency of the faex-production sort and moved out into a system of ducts that were the excretory passageways of the BOK Center, including endoscopic tunneling segments, before agreeing to be seated with my hosts. Many people whom I passed were congratulating me on my cap and mask, though I was not in the meanwhile responding or noticing, as I was unable to confirm the fact of my outward appearance. This I had heard: that the gender sequestration rooms at the BOK Center were the finest of rooms, five stars in any intestinal rating system. I heard them saying as much, as they congratulated me on my coordination of mask and hat. I heard myself offering to exchange shirts with someone wearing an encoded shirt, with circuitry, the assumption being that this shirt had not yet been shit upon by Flaming Crows and thus was more sociologically apt than mine, but when I commenced to remove my shirt I quickly realized that either there was something very wrong with my own shirt, perhaps even including or *beyond* beshitment, or else there was something very wrong with me. Such were the silences.

I believe those people roaming the intestinal fortitude of the BOK Center with earpieces were not crows but members of rival factions perhaps of jackrabbits or coyotes or constitutional exegetes—we would all meet on a trail of ignominy, with textured rubber matting, in the condition of fear and trembling, as our time was near. They did not speak but looked through me as though I were not present, as though I constituted an ornithological infiltration, which perhaps

71

I did. In due course I came face-to-face with a reflecting surface in gender sequestration, five stars, pulled down my mask to be sure that I actually had a face. But: instead of a face there were only small prismatic soap bubbles carrying bits of face, floating sinews of craniofacial dismemberment, here a nostril, here a length of singed eyebrow displaying fear and grief. I did not wish the other discussants of gender sequestration to see the bubbles and the portions of face, the gristle, so I refixed the mask. Only a few stray portions of face had dispersed, and not the most comely bits. The lights flickered twice, meaning the main event was now coming to pass, no one took note of earlier speakers with their bits of national purity, their organized crime confections, and so now the carrier pigeons in the rafters of the BOK Center would soon be dislodged, to carry the message to the other birds of the air. See their barrel rolls! Stock market rally of historic proportions! Criminals are coming! Criminals will perturb your loved ones! I needed to locate anew Ordinal Branch and the military veteran, or at least this would be the narrative trajectory as had been taught to me by my brother, namely the narrative of human simulation and its affiliations, but I had neglected to keep my ticket, which was a scalding device, and each quadrant of the BOK Center looked like every other. I turned a diagram over in my mind like it was a purple gleaming prosperity gem, and I could not tell one locale from another and all the faces looked like other faces, pecked and devoured.

The person or persons, the faex-production manager, the guppy, the coronavirus, whose turn it was to spout language, wearing a red strangulation device, support hose, an iron maiden, red enema bags hanging from his bespoke encrustments, and also a red clown proboscis, this person, this faex producer, arose to take the podium. All crimson he, crimson in remark, crimson in faex production, crimson like a chief executive. I had selected now a spot in the upper reaches where there was none other but myself, so meager was that company of ghosts, and my faceless mask outshone indicating a significant bite-force coefficient, adhering to a political message of which I knew only that it was in a dead tongue spoken in the whisperings of the flattened squirrels of the roadside. I stretched out across several posterior containers, my limbs centipedal. I had obtained a hat and a mask free of cost!

If there were foodstuffs that were left behind during or after recreational games, small bits of pretzel that came in a foil arsenic pouch bag, these could litter the upper reaches of the BOK Center and attract life forms to the aisles and then volunteers such as myself, or blood spitters, or teenage prostitutes, or faex producers, the dead inside, the fearful and trembling, the transients, the left-behinds, the castoffs, who were in fact that major part of the world, all of us, who would need to come to the upper reaches of the station to revel in the poisons and inaudibility. The vermin would eat the mini pretzels and crawl off to die in the walls, but if they managed to escape the BOK Center through secret chewed-out subterranean passages, for example under the total-infarction proscenium upon which the speaker stood in his crimson posturing, the vermin could mass under the plinth, past the bulletproof screening, beneath the stands, shimmering through walls of proton beams, dematerializing, proving the liquid imperishable infective mass of the castoff, the ghost battalion, until outside the BOK Center, where they would lay themselves out for the military convoy, which on its way to law and order would flatten out a dozen, or more, hundreds, thousands of castoffs, making road flattenings of them, until in the West a scorching fire tornado would arise of Flaming Crows and hawks and vultures and methamphetamine addicts, and persons with dissociative personality disorder, to consume. The locals would wait with chisels and pickaxes and spatulas and common household devices, and these persons would attempt to scrape us from the interstate and the dream of the interstate, as when you need to remove a bolus from your own face, while the Flaming Crows would goad them on from above: *Your democracy needs you!*

It was in the midst of teleological forecasting (during which, I learned later, Ordinal Branch and the military veteran were opening stall doors, and searching everywhere under folding tables, in encrusted dumpsters, for my exoskeletal personage), at or near to forty-six minutes into oratorical impingement manufacture, that the proclaimant reached a point in his remarks that had such a powerful effect on me that I do not know how to treat of this effect in my account, for the simple reason that I do not believe that words can convey this inflammation of meaning. What is language but a fear conveyance system that confers sweet finitude upon the speaker? I ask you, are words not a wiping technology for the inconveniently needy, who stinketh. Words are liable to dematerialize before you've even heard them properly, especially with the ambient reverberance in the BOK Center, which had a hang time longer than the chittering sounds of a spider monkey in an Indo-Chinese cave system. Nevertheless, between moments of self-congratulatory posture manipulations in the space,

Rick Moody

I did hear this moment of which I am speaking, and I can just go ahead and type some of it out for myself, as I have committed this moment to memory, believing it to be very relevant to the birds, this shit-smelling tirade of fear instigation: *Two days ago, Flaming Crows, in Portland, Oregon, ripped down a statue and wrapped this statue in the solemn colors of our nation and set upon this reeking cadaverous figure with sticks aflame. Good people!* You can imagine, I believe any faex producer consuming these notes could imagine, that this utterance created significant change in my ontological status, my belief posture, when the flatus orator mentioned, in passing, the presence of Flaming Crows in Portland, Oregon, which, while not in Oklahoma, does have a system of internal crow information sharing, which has been written down by the Order of the Flaming Crows, whose control imagery includes flames, history, flags, and semaphore. Now I happen to know that Oregon is not part of the Great Plains, and so I believe there is reason to disbelieve the flatus proclaimant, to take his remarks as noncanonical, but what cannot be disbelieved is the effect of the words "Flaming Crows" on my cloacal productivity, which is a further explication of my fear particulate exhumation.

If one of the symptoms of viral breaching is a crawling skin sensation, or perhaps an oversalivary fluvial engorgement, or perhaps an involuntary strain and clench, or perhaps a total blood vessel dilation, followed by a faex easement, then perhaps the mask that I was wearing was not sufficient, and I had had a sudden onset of viral breaching, indeed I believe that I needed to get up on my feet, in this breaching moment, while the pineal oratory was taking shape, to shout about viral breaching, and the presence, outside the venue, of Flaming Crows, and, furthermore, the full-scale rectal assault that was going to take place, when the flatus orator and his pineal associates were going to attempt to exit the BOK Center, and thus the flatus was going to board a helicopter or hovercraft from the roof of the BOK Center, to be ferried off-site to a secure airstrip where the Follicle One would be waiting for him. *The faex producer has ascended! Let us mark this apotheosis! God bless the Uvular Estates and their foul-smelling anchorage! Two lanes ahead!* I did in fact get up and shout something about injectables and ammonium hydroxide, not that anyone could hear, especially as I wore the mask. I sounded like a mass of plastic bottles at the moment they were densified into bedding. The O.F.C., which has created some hilarious misunderstandings over the years, through stochastic messaging, is properly understood by only a small subset of face-transplant patients complaining of Long Grief Sequencing. I hastened toward the exits of the BOK Center, as quickly as possible.

If exiting, no reentry. You could walk out into a crossfire of warring factions of Flaming Crows, where they would be shooting sulfuric cluster devices at the faex producers, laser tipped, neutron capable, where they were going to descend on you, to feed and peck, indiscriminately, where there would be civic authorities with firearms of various kinds, all on-site ready to take on Flaming Crows, if any should reveal themselves in the aftermath of the viral breaching event, which would soon slay the manufacturing sector and all mammalians, or consign them to the care of pulmonologists. It was the longest day of the year, you know, the solstice, a time of medieval hortatory manufacture, which means that certain pineal effects were to take place; ocular perceptions would suffer in a warped condition, enabling heightened symbolic fluency and manipulation. There would be contagion, symbolic and actual. Your narrative function, while no longer dependent on sequential fillips, or any kind of hemoglobin preparation, could achieve new symbolic thrusts. You would see the way motif and harmonic convergence could ensue, and thus your fear.

This is why the presence of "Flaming Crows" in the speech by flatus and rotundities in his orbit had such a marked effect on me, because at once I could see, for example, that the presence of the Q Source in the earlier conversation, by which Ordinal Branch no doubt was referring to the textual canonicity, in which language was invented in order to chart a course for a world dominance of crows, and perhaps as Ordinal Branch was saying earlier a pizzeria and Semitic international banking conspiracy, these were all manifestations of a gospel, which is a viral breaching consortium, inaugurating a symptomatic aloneness, yours and mine.

I walked out and I walked south, because navigating by the stars, because I was born in the stars and could see all the times at once and the relation of these stars to crows and crow lore. All at once I could hear them blustering in their roosts, distinct, indisputable, more pronounced at the site of injection—*be doubly careful of landscapes in which there is no sidewalk, the moon has been infiltrated, your father did not abandon the family he simply suffered from economic pressures, eat a tablespoon of dirt, segmented interstate commerce is communist, gather up the innocent, your clothes are just hanging off you, when the world of humans burns clean away the birds will survive.* The chatter went right on as I went south. Into the night. I walked south until I hit the Arkansas River, south into contested territories where I knew there to be many roosts, along the muddy banks of the river, and here an army was gathered. I was long in the emptiness of night, it had emptied into me, when the pickup truck pulled over and the military veteran threw open the door. Ordinal Branch called across the seat.

—Holy Toledo, Johnny Boy, you gave us a good scare. Good thing you had the hat on. You're high visibility.

The night sang. The physical beings of the nonhuman world gathered up their revenge.

—You will address me, I said, by my acronym.

House of Rashōmon
Kristine Ong Muslim

ONCE UPON A TIME, there was only Olga and me, as well as our old dog, Boji, in a big house we inherited from our parents, whose food we had slowly been poisoning in a span of at least a year. Our parents blamed their "chronic illness" on inclement weather, on the "heathens" who played rock music next door, sometimes on "cursed" and "possessed" appliances and furniture.

Mama, who once hurt Boji for barking too loudly, even asked a priest to sprinkle holy water all over the "cursed" old-fashioned sofa in the living room. She believed holy water would drive away whatever evil spirits were lurking in the rundown folds of the sofa. The Imarflex toaster in the kitchen, she insisted, was also "harboring demonic entities in the heating coils." And so the priest, wearing a tasseled purple garb made of shiny fabric, self-importantly went about his monkey business of spritzing holy water on the toaster, electrical wiring be damned.

On his deathbed, Papa, we decided, ought to be spared from the brutality of the truth, including the real cause of his frequent illnesses and eventual demise. Our insufferably domineering mother had long ago emasculated him, already gutted him and had his bones picked cleaned before spitting out the rest of him as a shell of what used to be a person. We thought that his miserable life was already punishment enough. As for Mama, Olga and I leaned closely and whispered to her as she, weakened at last and short of breath, was lying on her deathbed, "Not demons, not evil spirits, but us, Mama. We added drops, a little at a time, of the floor cleaner, sometimes lemon-scented bleach, into your soup, your smoothies, your coffee. Made you sick, didn't it? And soon you will be dead. And when all of you are dead, we live. We live." Her eyes bulging with rage, her pale hands clawing at her chest in an effort to breathe or perhaps scream, her last hours where she stared knowingly at us but powerless to do anything, not even to save herself from the damnation she herself had brought to life and nurtured with her torturer's pale hands—these were cherished moments that Olga and I would relive and talk about for years to come.

And so they died—Papa first, then Mama two days later. At the wake, Olga and I looked the right kind of morose. Olga and I were quick to shed some tears to garner sympathy from the out-of-town folks who attended the wake because that was what community was for: to be at the side of those contending with the loss of their loved ones, even if such a loss was merited.

No one paid attention to Olga, however. People acted as if she were invisible. People kept hugging only me—never her—and they kept telling me to call anytime if I needed anything. It was such a relief that Olga was a good sport that day.

In the weeks that followed our parents' burial, people from around town kept dropping off pancit bihon, biko, and macaroni salad in clear microwavable containers. True to form, they did not bring enough for the two of us. They kept forgetting about Olga. But that was all right since there was always enough food to go around. One time, we even let Boji indulge in a deliciously rich pasta dish from Mrs. Cárdeñas, the widow who lived in a small beautiful house at the end of the block. Mrs. Cárdeñas's home was a cottage house festooned with orange and mauve bougainvilleas. All in all, we took what we could get, took pains to never tax, to never strain the generosity and goodwill extended to us by other people. Olga and I also made it a point to remember to repay them all someday.

Aunt Andrea, Papa's younger sister, stayed with us for a week after the funeral. Although she could be annoying at times, Aunt Andrea genuinely cared about us as far as we could tell. It was becoming a habit of hers to look flustered—with an odd, panicky look on her face—every time I mentioned Olga. I had to constantly explain Olga's absence because she tended to oversleep for some reason every morning that I spent chatting with Aunt Andrea over breakfast.

We pretty much left Aunt Andrea alone as she went about prowling the rooms of this great house, where she could browse through valuable heirlooms and pocket whatever she liked. Olga and I let her take as much as she could carry in her wheeled luggage, especially items that we could classify under "acceptable losses" in the insurance policy. We also let her have all of Mama's jewelry, as well as an early painting by a famous artist who Olga and I figured had shit for brains—what with his insistence on calling his artworks "protest art" even as he allowed them to be placed in museums and auctioned off for display in the mansions of hacienderos and sugarlandia's fatassed barons.

With Aunt Andrea around, Olga and I resolved not to take off our masks for a while, thinking that not doing so would help us blend in and avoid scaring off our lovely aunt. She was, after all, still our flesh and blood. And had circumstances been different, she could have learned to love us as her own. *Love,* that idea that meant so little yet required a lot.

Olga also told me to warn Aunt Andrea about spending so much time in the master bedroom. A giant spider the size of a floor-to-ceiling wardrobe closet appeared in the master bedroom whenever it sensed intruders.

And so I told Aunt Andrea, "But don't worry, the giant spider is harmless as long as you don't look it in the eye. It does not matter which eye because it has many eyes. They shine like black pearls—but prettier than pearls. Pearls are not sentient and can't see through you, can't judge you, unlike the giant spider's eyes. Anyone who looks at the giant spider in the eye will free the soul inside it. And because nature does not allow a vacuum to exist for long, the person who frees the spider's soul is bound to give up something to redress the newly created vacuum. That person has to give up his soul to live inside the giant spider until the next one comes along to look at it in the eye again. Just don't go inside the master bedroom, Aunt Andrea. That's all I'm saying. I like you very much, and I appreciate what you've done for me and Olga. I don't want anything bad to happen to you."

Aunt Andrea looked as if she was about to cry. She covered her mouth with her hand and did not say anything. I figured I had effectively communicated the urgency of the matter. I thought she got the message and would steer clear of the master bedroom from then on. But when we woke up the next day, we were surprised to see her gone. Her wheeled luggage was gone too. She left behind the antique silverware, although we told her to take as much as she could carry.

We hurried outside to look for her, calling out her name. All that greeted us was the bench across the street with three upright men in a sitting position. All three were busy diddling with their phones as if there were salvation there. The next-door neighbor was playing rock music again, and there was Boji rolling across the grass, lapping up the early-morning sun.

There was also movement, a commotion maybe, in the house across the street. It was hard to make out what was happening through that house's drapes. Olga and I felt like Plato's cave dwellers who were doomed to wonder for all eternity, *And what would we look like to those dwellers deep inside the cave as they gazed at the shadows on the wall?*

Later that morning, we were munching on dragon fruit when a man came by. He wore a short-sleeved barong and was acting so businesslike that it hurt when we finally had to take him to the giant spider upstairs. "Hello, Olga," he said when we opened the door, fake cheer and fake sympathy in his eyes. "I'm here to talk about your father's estate, plus I have paperwork for you to sign."

Fluke
Kathryn Davis

LIFE IN THE PAST had been filled with complication. In the past I'd have been getting the house ready and some menu would have been taking shape, the stove, the oven, the chicken, lettuces, dinnerware, flowers. Napkins. It's always been a source of amusement among people who know me how many napkins I possess. We were talking about quarantining, the danger of breaking quarantine, and my old boyfriend mentioned hearing about a place where a person would be severely punished if they tried to run away. That sounds like *Brigadoon*, I said. I thought he'd have heard of *Brigadoon*, but I always forget that not everybody my age paid attention to Broadway musicals, or that even though we've known one another for years, I still don't know if he ever belonged to the Columbia Record Club. The answer to that would be something I'd have to guess at, and my guess would be he didn't. Culture, for my old boyfriend, never seemed to arrive via the usual channels. I'm sure there was a television in the house where he grew up, and that there were no prohibitions regarding its use. His mother believed that to say no to a child was tantamount to destroying the spirit of adventure.

I was living in St. Louis at the time, where it was flat and the wind wouldn't stop blowing. Spring, tornado season—the wind blew everything away except corn and soybeans. Forest Park was coming to life after a long, cold winter. "Keep your eyes peeled," I heard my father saying, waving his arms at me—but that was a forsythia bush. "Keep your eyes peeled, Kathy," said the forsythia. It was just coming into bloom. First there was one thing, a mother, for instance, a father, and then there was another. And then another, a husband, a daughter, and after a while everything was different, unlike in a fairy tale where a girl is a girl, a beast a beast, pretty much from now until the end.

The sun was shining and the fountains in the Grand Basin were sparkling and I wasn't paying attention to the large dog at the other end of the leash I held in my right hand when suddenly she saw something really amazingly terrific right behind me and pulled me over backward. The fall happened so slowly I could see the tips of my feet in their black boots rising from the cement, slowly, slowly, like the feet of the Wicked Witch of the West, and I felt certain that all I had to do to keep from landing on the cement concourse would be to concentrate very hard, force my toes back down, and the next thing I knew I'd be standing upright, Lucy at my side. Instead I broke my left arm. The one I used to break the fall.

We'd ended up in different time zones, my old boyfriend and I, he on the East Coast not far from our country's first disastrous settlement, whereas I was living in the shadow of the enormous silver arch that is the gateway to the West. Each of us, that is, was living in a place where opportunity had come knocking, followed by bloodshed. I held up my arm to show him my splint. The Zoom camera made me look different from every angle, sometimes frail and perplexed, sometimes beatific, sometimes overlarge and almost masculine.

"Between today and tomorrow lies a long, long night," I said. That's what the young woman named Gertrud tells the lost adventurer in the German story *Brigadoon* is based on. Her village appears once every hundred years, sinking otherwise fathoms deep into the earth. "You will understand tomorrow what that word means," Gertrud tells the adventurer. It's a sad story, I warned my old boyfriend. Gertrud urges the adventurer not to leave the village until after the clock finishes striking twelve, thus saving him from her own grim fate but also abandoning her chance at happiness. When the adventurer once again looks for the village, he finds himself tangled in an alder thicket. Heavy drops of rain fall on his head, and an earth vapor hangs above the place like smoke.

"Alder swale," my old boyfriend corrects. He reminds me how irritable I became once, bushwhacking, when we ended up in one.

Naturally it's different in the musical. In *Brigadoon* there's no taint of mortality to the word *tomorrow*, nor is the least charnel whiff of the underworld, of things decomposing, stirred up by the dancing. In *Brigadoon*, the mist of May is in the gloaming, and the adventurer is able to reenter the village because his heart is filled with love.

When it was time, the Columbia Record Company sent me my selection. It arrived in the mailbox in a modest package, at which point I'd remove the jacket from the package and the beautiful luminous black record from the sleeve. I'd balance it carefully at its very edge between the insides of my palms as instructed by my father. I'd slip it down over the spindle until it lay flat on the turntable. It would start to spin.

This would have been 1954, the 1954 recording with Gene Kelly and Van Johnson and Cyd Charisse. "Brigadoon, Brigadoon, blooming under sable skies." I didn't know what *sable* meant back then, aside from its being a kind of fur rich old women wore to church, the frightening old women of St. Martin-in-the-Fields, the ones who still occupy the Pew of Judgment in my mind. The music, though—lucky for me, those songs are also streaming inside me, along with the sight of a shining black record going around and around on a turntable. Even if a person didn't understand the technology, a record spinning on a turntable made sense. The needle elicited the sound. It settled into the groove, the ever-narrowing path of circumnavigation. The music was *in* there. Whatever it is a compact disc does to produce a song, you can't watch it spin. You can't lift the tonearm and blow fluff off the needle. There is no needle.

Without the material thing there is nothing to remember. There is no mystery. After I broke my arm, here is what I thought. Eric doesn't have feet.

In high school biology there had been an experiment involving a liver fluke, a pale worm the size of a grain of rice with an arrow-shaped head. You used a razor blade to bisect the head, slicing between the two "eyes"—which weren't eyes but markings, parasites having no need of eyes, especially inside a liver. After a while a new head formed on either side of the cut, and though the experiment was supposed to end there, my tenth-grade self, with the steady hands of a surgeon and zero scientific aptitude, couldn't stop herself. Before the creature died it had eight heads, more than any other fluke in the class. But it didn't die because it was a freak; it died of starvation. None of the flukes lived. They could only eat liver if they thought of it as their dwelling place, it turned out.

Kathryn Davis

It was difficult to tell if the flukes were alive or dead; the usual signs of life weren't apparent. We wondered whether this was why they were called flukes, until our teacher informed us *fluke* was from the Greek. For floor.

As it turns out, *fluke* doesn't only mean floor, as in flat, flat like a flounder, or the triangular plate at the tip of an anchor, one of the twin lobes of a whale's tail, but fluke can also refer to a lucky shot in billiards, a sudden gust of wind, the act of wandering, of straying, the planets. Deep underground in the ruined waterways of Hallownest the young flukefeys lie in wait, hoping to catch anything that comes by with their sharp little teeth, and as they wait they chatter, *safe, gla . . . little sisters . . . gla gla . . . stronger . . . gla gla . . . bigger . . . mother . . .*

During his last week I sometimes sat with Eric while he slept, petting his forehead and watching his eyeballs in motion under his shut lids. Sometimes he ground his molars; sometimes he growled and jerked his hands and feet. Sometimes he opened his eyes and looked at me and said something I couldn't understand. By this time it seemed like a word could mean anything. He was still Eric, but not-Eric as well. The times I'd felt fear before, he'd been in good health, alert and upright, angry. I kept interrupting him. I kept starting every sentence with "no." The fucking government. The fucking rain was making it impossible to get a campfire going. Our daughter was lying inside the tent, a sullen odalisque in a pale-blue sleeping bag, her honey-colored hair falling over one shoulder. So many moths flying around the propane lantern, clinging to the glass. Their bodies big, thick, like thumbs.

Other things had made me feel this way, like the 3D horror comic that came with the glasses necessary for reading it that I bought for myself in the shadowy camp store on the boardwalk where they also sold air mattresses, tarps, lantern mantles, cigarettes, beer and wine and gin and bug repellent, though in the end it had been the smell of the comic book, that slightly pinched hollow smell damp things give off, especially wood pulp, and not the sad story it told of the misunderstood monster that broke my heart.

It was certainly a fluke that the person I chose to marry was seven years younger than me, the exact same age difference as existed between his mother and his father. When you marry someone you marry them all the way back to the beginning, past parents, grandparents and great-grandparents, the whole ethnic pageant, all the way back to that first unspooling bolt of flesh and fat and tissue and beyond, a recognizable form receding into mere pattern and then schools of restless alien shapes shot with color, a wave, a shadow, the great shifting bottom currents.

It's different washing the body after the person has died. Running a damp washcloth over the forehead, the brow, the eyelids—the eyeballs motionless. The wish to inflict no harm is still there, elevated by the absence of response to something resembling desire. The pale-blue washcloth swimming in the pan of warm sudsy water. If emancipation has occurred, the body will not smell. The body will glow. Consciousness will have exited through the crown of the head. Meditate on the deity, incorporeal, like the reflection of the moon in water.

Signs of life. What do we even mean by that? In their mounds between Skyworld and Underworld the buried denizens of an immense former civilization have been growing restive for a very long time now. Infamous Mound 72 is filled with two layers of young women, arranged neatly in rows. Analysis of their bones, my old boyfriend told me, led archaeologists to believe the young women weren't locals. Some of them didn't have hands, some didn't have feet, though no one could say why.

The Seed of the Wicked
Brandon Hobson

IN THE HEART OF THE OMNIUM-GATHERUM

HE WHOM I FEARED, my father, had skirted the fringes of so many gambling temptations and sinful concubinages that it seemed impossible to hear my mom's aroused suspicions and take them seriously, yet there I stood in the heart of the omnium-gatherum after Trusty John Alberich's funeral and saw my father sneak out of the garden with the woman in the hat who held her cigarette between two fingers like Joan Crawford.

There he was, among all those suspicious people, leading the woman by the hand and aware most certainly that I had seen them sneak away, so unrestrained and visible in his dark suit that one could believe his intentions were innocent without any doubt whatsoever, although nobody was more likely to lead a woman by the hand and then twenty minutes later scurry out of the woods like a cockroach, as my mom put it, the son-of-a-bitch hypocrite even kept a small room in a cabin owned by the church stocked with wine and full of candles he'd bought from the store downtown in Dublan Plains, because nobody dared consider such a heart-shattering travesty would occur there, not there, not in the lake cabin known for youth retreats, men of God conferences, and occasional choir weekends in the summers.

There he was then, my father, as if he had never been the trusty person to read aloud fairy tales to me, followed by nightly readings of *Ulysses* while my mom opened the window so that we could smell the evening rain outside and listen for the train in the distance, as if he'd never taught me to give thanks before eating and sleeping every night, he of healthy and kind heart whose voice was alluring enough to draw the sparrows and geese from territorial waters across the field, he of strong morality and trust who said never in a million years would I deny my Father or wife or family, ever, even while reading aloud to me of Dedalus and Bloom's pain instead of Christ's pain, surely overwhelmed by the thoughts of the coming afternoons

spent with bookies and gamblers or women at the lake cabin while
my mom worked long hours at the hospital as a labor and delivery
nurse. How, as a struggling pastor, he must've lived at the mercy of
his own commission, disillusioned by earthly desires and a complicated lust and sin, knowing full well his week would be spent slav-
ing away at his desk as he flipped through his Bible in search of an
unhypocritical sermon, nine hours a day spent writing and scribbling, praying and sipping gin until fatigue made him drop onto the
sofa and sleep for two or three hours at a time during which he mum-
bled in his sleep about how he wished he'd pursued a life studying
classics and married a woman named either Iris Annabel or Anabella
Iris, although I heard his sleep mumblings on many occasions and the
names of the women periodically changed: Iris changed to Norie, to
Sarah, to Danielle, to Tessa, to Elizabeth, to Kate, to Joan Crawford,
and the only time I ever asked about these mumblings, he sat up and
grabbed me by the wrist with pale eyes full of tears, trembling but
silent as if paralyzed by a continuous buzz of inner rage, perhaps he
lived at the mercy of this torment, perhaps the increased bitterness
and guilt was fueled over how much debt he was in and how many
women he'd slept with, and at once he snapped out of it and let go of
my wrist. I stood silent, staring at him. He moved slowly to the window and pulled the curtain to see the land stretching out in the distance to the fleeting sunset, and a moment later he told me the
branches from the oak tree reminded him of his childhood when he
went to see his own father, my grandfather, in a lunatic asylum far
away from Dublan Plains, and to pass the time while his father bathed
or ate tapioca pudding, he was introduced to an old Joan Crawford
movie called *What Ever Happened to Baby Jane* in which Joan
Crawford aroused him in ways he didn't understand, and at the same
time he was also introduced to betting by playing checkers with a
few of the workers there, and when he won three dollars, then four,
then five, he knew he had a love of gambling.

There he was, at Trusty John Alberich's omnium-gatherum, quot-
ing Psalm 37:28, "The seed of the wicked shall be cut off," after he
returned from the woods with the woman in the sun hat who was
now sitting with Trusty John's three sisters under the pergola. This
woman held another cigarette between two fingers and kept glancing at me through a trail of smoke, aware my mother was working
her shift at the hospital, and my father nudged me and leaned in
close to my ear and said it again, slowly: "The seed of the wicked
shall be cut off," which finally occurred to me translated as I would

be punished if I betrayed him and told my mother what had happened, punished worse than ever before, goddamn it. Then he stepped away and joined two other men in conversation, and I had a sudden and intense memory of watching him preach a sermon in a 1970s-style carpeted conference room that smelled of cigarette smoke at the El Grito Motel just outside of Dublan Plains, looking weary and tired in his undersized, checkered polyester suit, stomping around and speaking in tongues in a fire-and-brimstone way that shook the building like an earthquake and made me think of, for whatever reason, the Mad Hatter from *Alice in Wonderland*, and for a long time I jokingly referred to my father as the Mad Hatter to my friends until he overheard me say it on the phone once, after which I received my punishment and never said it again.

Having sat through Trusty John Alberich's horrific funeral and then seeing my father sneak the woman out of the garden, I now felt as nauseated and unsettled as I had during that motel revival. I thought I was maybe having a type of hallucinatory breakdown because I began to see all the people standing in the garden behind the Alberiches' house gesturing broadly as if describing something enormous and round, and the ones who weren't gesturing were talking into their wristwatches like spies. I found myself horrified by the possibility that the whole postfuneral reception was a *joke* at my expense, that maybe even Trusty John Alberich's death itself was a hoax orchestrated by my father to see whether I could handle grief in public like a man, which was an absolute and insane thought though not entirely out of the question because the reception was as strange as any failed production: there was no weeping or gnashing of teeth, no arguments, no eye contact, everyone was standing around eating carrot sticks and desserts on small paper plates and drinking wine from plastic cups like a goddamn faculty party at some prestigious institution I'd seen only in movies on cable television. (I was never allowed to watch TV, but there was always one available at the motel where I spent my summers and many afternoons after school.) Nothing made me feel better and less nauseated about being there, not even sitting by the swimming pool with its diaphanous and inviting blue water and seeing my strange, quivering reflection, which looked like a giant leech.

Brandon Hobson

THE GIANT LEECHES OF DUBLAN PLAINS

My mom referred to my father as a wolf whose concept of reality was so entangled he sometimes chewed on wire with his teeth and drooled like a rabid dog, unable to repress his impulse to lash out physically or sexually in some way, that's the truth, she said, and how shameful he must've felt knowing she was telling people this anytime she talked on the phone in the lazy light of the den, where she lamented about their marriage and his erratic behavior, measuring everything from the way he looked at her to how hard he shut the door, that whenever they shouted at each other she called him either a son of a bitch, or a stupid dog, or a man on the brink of collapse.

Once we finally left the omnium-gatherum celebrating Trusty John Alberich's death, I looked into my father's face and thought about all this, how I often saw the serious threat of someone on the cusp of a breakdown and how he once told me he detested his own image as much as he did Dublan Plains, and now here he was driving and sure enough talking of the fetid smell of downtown and how the only thing to get us through difficult times and grief was to cling to the sight of seeing things with a youthful eye, like calm waters, leaves swirling in the wind, and bloodred dawns, because at some point we all get older and take the beauty of nature for granted, and our bodies and faces morph into something else so that we look more monstrous than human, more dead than alive, and more frightening than a moon rising over a decrepit cornfield on a cool Midwestern night; think about your mother, he told me, whose fragrance once spread the earth with spring flora but whose derision for the unfaithful and sin was now as bitter as a leper's, a woman whose will to live had been eaten by jealousy and rage and a misunderstanding of her husband's complicated lust, and whose age attacked her body with the harsh steps of time in darkness like the old ladies in fairy tales whose faces and bodies were scratched by thornbushes while spying on their husbands lying naked with maidens, your poor mother, he said, and it was then I saw the ugly beast my mother had seen, how my father was suffering with his private and complicated lust, suffering from self-hatred and bitterness and pierced by the hand of the devil, he whom I feared, the seed of the wicked.

That night I started writing a horror story about the giant leech that lived underneath our house when I began to hear it crawling around underneath the hardwood floor in my bedroom. I paced while my father shouted at me through the intercom on the wall to stop walking around the fucking house because he could hear my footsteps creaking all the way in his bedroom, but I refrained from confessing that I was terrified of the leech because he would say it serves me right, it's a punishment of sorts for my own lust and falling victim to the devil's agenda of temptation among today's teenagers with designer-drug parties and free online pornography and hardcore so-called alternative music glorifying darkness, destruction, and sin; indeed, how easy it was to imagine my father glaring at me like a sticky substance in the palm of his hand, half grimacing, skilled in the manipulations of fatherhood with an immense disposition for control and restoration, obedience, and honesty. How easy it was to imagine him in his hammock looking weary and miserable, his skin yellow from what my mom said was a failing liver, singing from somewhere deep inside him the chorus of King David because "Your arrows sharply pierce all foes of yours," from Psalm 45, half drunk, placid and inert, under the protection of the shade from the apple tree, he whom I feared even in his most relaxed state.

How difficult it was to forget, though, that very late in the night he awoke us to attempt to arouse in us the nostalgia for the war he was experiencing that led to his sleepless nights, which only confirmed my worsening fear, because he (claimed he) knew a spiritual warfare happening in dirty Dublan Plains, the type of spiritual warfare that would begin to appear before our very eyes like the story of the giant leeches, which was a story he told me when I was little about giant leeches who lived a few miles from our house in a community of old wooden structures built nearly two hundred years ago. Seriously. Because they were originally protandric hermaphrodites, the leeches reproduced at an alarming speed, having entered the bodies of women who swam in the river as far back as the late 1800s. Their offspring and mutations were grotesque, multiplying in the water rapidly enough that as they continued as parasites to enter women's bodies and develop DNA, their anatomy and physiology morphed into near human form and they soon grew to be giant leeches, pale even after so much time in the sun, difficult to look at due to their slight inverted proboscis and lack of jaw, which posed breathing problems, but their life span was long with most living well past one hundred years because their saliva contained both an anesthetic and a morphine-like compound. I soon became convinced the leech living underneath our floors was an offspring of these giant leeches and would grow and multiply.

Therefore, the spiritual warfare my father spoke about existed in the world around us so that we could watch it mutate and spread like a furious fire across the plains, floating like an evil presence in pursuit of the innocent, gullible, naive citizens whose laughter burst in the shadows of the town square, angered by patient stoicism and agreement yet rife with greed and lust, as when a bloodthirsty dog ripped the head off a rabbit and ate it, then pawed and ran its big, red tongue over the rabbit's body before fully carrying it away to devour, a clear omen that caused my father so much anger in his sleeplessness that he saw the dead staggering through the house and walking outside, and he began hearing voices arguing good versus evil, sin, and temptation, confirming his belief that the less people understood, the more they fight, stressing these people and leeches are greedy creatures, as mentioned in the book of Proverbs. Greedy with lust and food, they would surely feed on anything alive if they were hungry enough—even their own children.

MY FATHER'S RED TONGUE WAS A MIGHTY SWORD

There I was, suffering the horror show of my night's fears, wondering whether the leech stories were true and why he mentioned they would eat their own children, a terrifying thought when you assume your own father gives subtle hints about eating you, like when he spent windless afternoons swatting flies and joking about feeding them to me before sucking on my neck and devouring my blood, vampire style, or when he forced me to hunt rabbits with him and we dragged our feet in the midst of fields with tall grass so that he could cut their heads off and make rabbit stew, which his own father had made for him years ago during the Big War, and that I might do well to sit in the steaming pot along with the rabbit and get cooked, of course he then reminded me of the fairy tales of the old woman cooking children and then eating them, and these stories always raised my anxiety enough in ways that confirmed, he said, that I was not quite tough enough to be a young man yet.

Once my father went to bed and I was finally able to fall asleep, I dreamed he morphed into a type of bloodred beast and came after me, past frightened herds of cattle and into a pecan grove, spewing blood from his mouth and running on all fours with a wild red tongue hanging out, and let me tell you how relieved I was to awake from that nightmare despite the cold urine on the sheets. I didn't want him to know I had pissed in the bed because I had not received a certificate of good conduct from him in three years. But it was still dark outside, and I was drowsy and too tired to get out of bed or change the sheets, so I fell back asleep, and this time I dreamed of my father dressed as Joan Crawford threatening to choke me with his big red finger down my throat unless I tied the laces of my shoes right then, and in my dream I looked down at my shoes and saw they were untied, so I knelt down and tried to tie them but they were in knots, see, this is a typical anxiety dream of mine, attempting to do something and failing, even something as simple as tying the laces of my shoes was frustrating, and I felt pressured in my dream to do it quickly or else I would get my father's big finger down my throat. The dream ended with me looking up at my father dressed as Joan Crawford and seeing him stick out his big, red tongue at me.

In the morning, people were still in the heart of the omnium-gatherum, so I called my dear dead friend Trusty John Alberich himself to meet me because I needed to get out of the house, and I also wanted a smoke and knew he would have cigarettes, so he met me at the park down the street and sat with me on the swings. We smoked and I told Trusty John about my dream, because I always told him about any trauma and never felt judged, ever, I mean that's why his name was Trusty John. I reminded him that my father always said nothing was ever fair, he who lived the dismal life of a young man who slept in the homes of friends and girlfriends and among people he didn't even know, a free spirit back in the soporific days that he could no longer recall from too many gins or liquors or wines, and anyway, he told me, those harsh experiences confirmed the certainty that his ideas about love were skewed and that he had always felt so careless about himself, negligent of his fatherly and husbandly responsibilities, and that's that, he said, he would say it over and over.

I saw the tears swell in Trusty John's ghostly eyes when I told him about my fear, and he broke into a sobbing that reminded me of the way he had once wept at school, but this time he wept with such a deep affliction that I felt enormous pity for him and began to console him by telling him I loved him like a brother, because I did love him, however confusing my concern for him, and in that moment he reminded me that he loved me like a brother as well, then he mentioned the time he was alive and we walked through a November drizzle and he confessed he was afraid of my father too.

We heard, then, the shouting of boys across the park, calling out to me as they walked from the far end toward us, four of them, and it took a moment to realize they were bloodthirsty in a way in which they were likely remembering how our ancestors had attacked their ancestors during those long winter months because our ancestors had stolen their ancestors' land, goddamn it, and now here they were, away from school and authorities, looking furious as they filed past the apple tree and merry-go-round, and I contemplated them impassively, standing from the swings and staring as they approached. How, in other times when I had felt threatened or uneasy and Trusty John started to tell me there was a possibility of violence, I could feel it in my stomach and my adrenaline would rush because at one time I had a desire for risks, but I knew better than anyone that my own fear was more unraveled now than ever before, and that I always felt I was at an inescapable risk of the unbuckling of self-pity, harm, and fear. How trauma not only made me want to escape but to disappear completely, something Trusty John and I shared, and probably the Native boys too, and now I heard Trusty John's whispers, either prayers or the ramblings of someone trying to conjure adrenaline, disturbed by the dizzying hub of the Native boys approaching, and what else was I going to do about the artillery burning in my stomach and chest except face the fire? How Trusty John's ghost and I stood there waiting when something so strange happened I could barely believe it: the Native boys suddenly turned and ran away because my father was hurrying toward us from his truck with his fist raised and shouting at the boys, "Get outta here, you little bastards, you chicken-shit kids, run away before I call the law," and he came over to us and we saw his dark eyes and fat lower lip smeared with blood, and he bent over with his hands on his knees to catch his breath, perspiring and coughing, his face nearly as red as his lower lip. Once he settled down, he sat on the swing and rocked a moment, seeming oddly fascinated by something in the sky as he looked up and closed one eye from the bright sun, then he looked at me as if we hadn't seen each other in many years.

He looked exhausted and ill from the darkness under his eyes and the way his swollen lip bled and told us a man had hit him in the mouth, a man whom he feared because he owed the man money, a gambling debt, and how certain authorities had accountants who kept records of all bets made, and all debts owed, and whose books reflected his name and the entire history of his betting life over the past seven years. He described the man as a monster, a giant with hands like big eagle claws, a man who hauled pigs across the state for days at a time as he listened to the sports-radio shows in his truck, listened to games, talked to friends and other bookies and anyone else whose opinions fed the enthusiasm and addiction they all shared. He believed his concept of interpretation was entangled, and I was sure of it as I watched him sit there with his bloody lip and trembling hands, talking about his love for gambling, how he took a deep breath and ran a hand over his face.

He told us he loved the racetrack and everything about it: the horses, the atmosphere, Phyllis at the betting window, the jockeys, the trainers, the smell of popcorn and cigarette smoke outside on the paddock, the afternoon beers and seeing the same guys who skipped out of work for the afternoon like he did, and the way the announcer said, "The horses are coming out on the track" before each race. He loved looking up at the odds and payouts and the possibilities of exactas, trifectas, superfectas, the daily double, the pick six. He loved wheeling the favorite with three long shots for a trifecta, and how he bought a racing form and circled names and numbers with a pen, studying the racing form late into the night, making notes on class, weight, Lasix, trainer, owner, and jockey. He loved the rush of adrenaline, he said.

There he was then, telling us that in his dreams he saw himself lying facedown on the floor and breathing a room full of pestilential air while women brought him cups of wine, or they were nightmares of being shot in the head and then hung by his legs like a dead deer with dripping blood. How strange it was that he woke most mornings with an erection, even after these terrifying dreams, as if seeing these visions in his mind was a reminder that everything that had to do with his narcissism remained with no other retinue than his dream therapists who told him to journal his dreams (of which I've read), giving him a relief and comfort he'd needed, and yet here I was, as usual, suffering the horror shows of my mind's night fear.

As he knelt down, he hit the ground with the palm of his hand and said, "*Fah!*" which was all he needed to do in that moment, I suppose, for us to see how upset he was at himself, or maybe at the circumstances leading to where he was financially, or whatever the case was with my mom, but right after he said, "*Fah! Fah!*" he opened his mouth and showed us his tongue, like a goddamn child after eating a Popsicle, as strange as when he found out from Trusty John's mom that I bought the bombs from the internet and a bunch of people at Nourie Hadig's garage party in west Dublan Plains placed the bombs on their tongues and began tripping, twisting in terror, and wiping their foreheads from the worms and lice that crawled from their scalps. The bombs were stamp sized, on sour blotter paper with the image of Pinocchio on one side and the other soaked in the liquefied powder that eventually killed Trusty John and left me feeling nothing but anger and sadness and guilt.

"Your father's tongue is a mighty red sword," Trusty John Alberich's ghost said. "It has already killed you. It's only a matter of time before you'll be eaten, like in the fairy tale."

IF IT WASN'T MY FATHER, IT WAS THE DEVIL
OR THE COLOR RED

Because my father told me about his nightmares and about the giant red leeches, stories that somehow morphed into something way darker than the fairy tales and parts of *Ulysses* he had read aloud to me when I was younger, I grew more and more afraid of him.

Because too these stories contained images of his narcissism and his fear of losing the power that had come to him over the years and evolved into a bitterness over how much his ego was melting like ice dripping from the lampposts in the main square, watered down and breakable, images incapable of meaning or any kind of sufficient and stable logic, which was misfortunate and unhealthy, he told me, images full of doubts and representing his rustic instincts that he knew too well in those days.

Because my father admitted that his own nightmares were exalted by the revelation that there was nothing we could do but celebrate Trusty John Alberich's soul's descent into hell, a red place full of red clouds and red fog and blood and fire, and that life is too short to obsess over liver disease or high blood pressure, cancer, prostatitis, diabetes, syphilis, piles, tumors, or the tiny floating shapes we see, anything that creates a vulnerability to the world's evilness, because those severe anxieties quash any hope for healing from past trauma or feeling seized by nightmares designed by the devil to squeeze our skulls and choke us in the muddy atmosphere of our imaginations like the devil's own bloodless hand. The things that gave him comfort should give us all comfort: faith in God, allowing ourselves to partake in the joys of pleasure, reading good books like *Ulysses*, and forgiving ourselves for our sins.

Because many years ago he told me the color red signified evil, and the devil, and blood, and Native Americans are red men who live on red earth, and like a schoolmaster taking you into a private room and showing you his red tongue and red cock before the rooster's crow, in early morning, taking advantage of you before you could ever look anyone in the eye, how you thought about a big red heart and Valentine's Day candy being stepped on and crushed and then being forced to eat it like shit, a red hand slapping you in the face, the schoolmaster pausing only to wipe his brow with his sleeve, and how after hearing all that I never had the intention of looking in my father's eyes again without feeling empathy for him yet why breathe all of this in my face, so that I could feel sorry for him and understand he wanted to die?

Because his recent nightmares, he told me, were less violent and abstract and more focused on a voluble ghostly presence who babbled in an unknown language as it led him by the hand into a castle and through a series of perplexing rooms, all of which had a single hole in the floor he was told to reach down into and feel for a snake, worried about whatever the consequence would be from the ghostly presence—"If it wasn't Trusty John Alberich's ghost, it was the devil," he said—and so reached down into the hole in each room and was bitten in the fleshy part of his hand between the forefinger and thumb, which frightened him enough to snap himself awake from the nightmare, making his nights unsettled and without restful sleep, and for a while the world around us remained in a perpetual state of flux.

Because he was a man I feared, even when he was outside trimming the rosebushes with the sun rising in the sky and the back deck overlooking the land sloping down to the river where he liked to walk with the bookies any time he wanted to talk sports betting or card games that took place late nights in the basement of some fool's house, and even there he took pleasure in feeling he was not one of them, no sir, he was no lowlife, at least that's what he told himself, yet he sniffed out their games and strategies, their cheats and rules, all their players and coolers so that he knew the world surely wouldn't scold him compared to these fellows, it seemed obvious enough despite the immorality of it all, and indeed he confronted the most horrific weaknesses in himself anytime he worked in the garden, trimming rosebushes or shrubs or mowing the lawn, resigning himself to yard work, bearing so many repressed illusions of his own fate, because he had become doomed to live a destiny all his own, in sin and forgiveness, in sickness and good health, to become the tight-fisted, mean, furious, rapacious bastard my mom and I saw him grow to be; so I knew I'd better change the bedsheets and wash them before he came home and ripped the bedroom door off the hinges in anger.

Because I overheard my mom talking on the phone to her sister, saying that she had heard messages on my father's work answering machine from a bookie threatening to hunt him down unless he paid his debts as well as messages from someone named Vasilisa, who had said things like *"Where are you right now?"* and *"Can't wait to see you this afternoon,"* and my mom was practically crying into the phone while I stood outside the door in the hallway not knowing what to do except lean against the wall and stuff my hands in my pockets like the goddamn "town dunce," as my father would sometimes refer to me, unsure whether I should console my mom or leave, but when she abruptly opened the door and saw me standing there, I noticed the tears in her eyes and the wadded tissue in her hand, and she walked past me and headed out the back door to the patio, where she went sometimes whenever she needed to be alone, and from the window I watched her smoke a cigarette and start talking on the phone again, and I imagined her calling my father and telling him not to come home, insulting him with all kinds of names and telling him that he was no good for anything, a horrible husband and father and person for cheating, I could hear her say these things in my mind as I stood there and saw her pace back and forth while she talked on the phone, visibly upset.

Because, after that, I decided I would leave for a while and let whatever needed to happen work itself out, however terrifying, while scenes played out in my head of my father coming home and trying to explain his way out of the deception, and things would turn violent, which worried me because I knew both my parents had tempers that flared easily, and I was afraid of both whenever they became angry because my mom had grown accustomed to forgiving my father for doing things like staying out late or not calling and telling us where he was without understanding the direction of his mood swings and was disconcerted even more on the cloudy days he quietly removed his clothes and walked outside and down the road out back to the river, where he entered the water and put his head under until someone rushed in after him, how embarrassing for me because I didn't understand these mood swings either.

Because, as I walked down the street past the battered houses and unmown lawns, I thought about becoming a less sensitive person, whether that was good or bad, part of the totemic image of masculinity he tried to convey with an intense authority by saying I would face a life full of unpredictable and absurd circumstances that would likely only be resolved by confronting my own courage as I enlisted in the tumult of dire and sometimes life-and-death situations, think about it, son, he said, would we be too afraid to protect ourselves from the horrors and high commands of criminals and thieves and scam artists taking advantage of us, would we run like damn dunces flapping our hands and our fingers wet as petroleum, goddamn it, or would we keep our heads up, erect, in accordance with all principles of authority and vigor without so much as the glimmer of a smile, staying erect, with all the rancor and rage and concentration of a good marksman whose uniform is well ironed and whose overall manner and disposition are inculcated by the highest commanding officers, and further that my own inculcations were in progress and far from where they needed to be, at that time at least, as in the dumbly aberrant words of he whom I feared: "Before the first cock-crow, already be in the mindset of a wild dog or boar before anyone takes advantage of you," which held all the hypocritical barbarism of any lunatic with as tentacular an aggression as his.

Because I left the house and walked down the street, feeling as gloomy as ever, afraid of stepping on any crooked line in the street since it would confirm that something terrible was about to happen, at any moment, which kept me from looking back at my house and wondering whether I might die today or tomorrow, or whether the truck speeding toward me was driven by my father or a big white wolf, both paws on the steering wheel, red tongue hanging out.

Ben Turns into the Botusfleming Hedwigkraken

Monica Datta

AGLIOPHOBIA

1. THE LAST SECONDS OF BEN GEORGE'S professional tennis career were blunted by the squidgiest of late August skies and the hard, dark wallop of crown on court, which smelt of garlic. He lay there ten-nine-eight-four-six-seven till he was banana stripped from the surface. A camera posed silent questions; he smiled politely and thanked it, from the mealy, vocal hollow of disgrace, for having permitted him all the dubious pleasures.

2. Alone with his crackly knees he sat on the changing-room shower floor nudging the soft lobe-swell under the salt-tight scalp. In the hotel he repruned himself in the bath, sweating, Achilles gashrose dripping in bloom, pores bloated with rock salt. Eventually Ben lowered the aircon to fifteen degrees and mummified himself in the duvet, head covered like a piccolo, and was pretending to sleep when Franz—his coach for the previous twenty years—let himself in to say, *Go home. Take time. See friends. There's nothing. For you.*

3. Ben wanted to squeal with joy: zero was his favorite number. Franz added, *So well played. Hard done by. Good on you. Take your time.*

4. Ben squeezed a patch of cold cotton and clamped shut his eyes; when the door clicked shut, he screamed quietly into the pillow. He found some peanuts in the minibar and took them to the balcony, where they tasted of chalk. He squinted (without his lenses) to see a steamy shock of cyan. The outdoor pool remained open through the night.

5. If Ben had hitherto considered water in neutral-to-positive terms, if he had ever viewed swimming as tawdry *exercise*, if he had once

99

underestimated the pleasures interred within this uranium-luminous turquoise kidney, somewhere between hurtling down the stairs like a crippled hawk and the sharp skinslap of the surface membrane he promised the gods—all of whom lived below sea level—that they might strike him down.

BATHOPHOBIA

1. Ben rated Eastern Airlines' domestic business class. He opened the salt packet left from lunch and sprinkled it over his palate. Twice the plane plunged on the western hang into pennybright slabs and dry green circles.

2. On arrival, the athletics director, Chuck, met him at the gate with a suffocating embrace. *I was scared we'd lost you to the Botusfleming Hedwigkraken.*

3. The amphibious Botusfleming Hedwigkraken of Cornwall (possibly Devon, depending) was the subject of petitions and radio contests the world over to designate it the 1980 Thing of the Year. It was large but not extremely so and whilst a strong swimmer it was not clear whether it walked on two or four legs. It might also hop on its trapezoidal tail.

4. Ben had been born and brought up in Cornwall, where mermen and pixies and gnomes had the run of things for some millennia. Everyone he knew was rather over the Botusfleming Hedwigkraken, which, again, may have come from Devon.

5. This new place had neither plane nor curve; it was low and flat, all squares, with neither depression nor eruption, lacking both aridness and humidity. At dusk the school glared in circuits. Chuck said theirs was perhaps the third-best tennis team in the country but the massive athletics complex had been built for the prize armadillos in American football who leapt and plunged through tires.

6. No one was in the swimming pool except for a woman indifferent to two mallard-bellied children smacking each other with kickboards as she dunked her calves and thumbed a swollen Elvis romance at the shallow end. Ben stared up at the enormous gallery, facing a glass

100

wall that floated to engulf the ceiling, exposing the raw green edge of horizon.

7. Ben put on his swimming costume. He jostled to unpin his shoulders from his ears, swinging his arms. Some guy came in and snorted toward him.

8. No matter: when Ben opened the door to the pool his chest cracked open, filling with warm sun as he stumbled into the chocolaty chlorinated heat. He snapped his goggles at the nape of his neck and his forehead with the bathing cap and dove in.

9. And down.

10. He admired the clean, opal igloo walls but they were only a tepid backdrop. There was an ambient sea-belly gurgle, waving in the water. Far away he saw the tireless baby feet of ducks, but no matter. The aurora flickered above.

11. Something in Ben's lung began to burn, and when he jolted upward, he saw his companions running, away, into the women's changing room. He shouted to ask if they were all right, but the woman stage-whispered something to the children as she slammed shut the door.

CHEIMATOPHOBIA

1. Americans took to refrigeration like icebox plums. Ben, almost hourly, would hurtle outdoors to bask in the heat. His teeth ached when he stayed indoors for too long. Perhaps he was eating too many sweets—or too many sour things—because his teeth felt thin and sharp.

2. Gail, the athletics department secretary, suggested draping a jumper over his shoulders so that he could knead the sleeves in his palms as well as the name of her dentist.

3. His new flat, let by the university, had only a noisy, dusty window unit in the bedroom. The whole place was coated in timber-inspired Moorish speckled-hen linoleum except for the pea soup

kitchen he rarely entered whose surfaces were inflamed by a tortoise rash.

4. Ben did not yet have telephone service. He rang his parents from a row of phone boxes in front of the student union. There was static on the line. Ben's dad asked how he was.

Fine, Ben muttered from the crick of his neck, holding a puckered roll of ten-cent pieces.

What's that racket? his father bellowed.

Static.

No, what's all the clanging?

I've got to put in ten-cent pieces to continue talking.

I told you not to go to a third-world country!

Come home! Ben's mum pleaded from the other receiver.

5. *Is it hot there?* Ben's dad asked.

Cold too.

Answer the bloody question!

Once, aged twelve, after a showy volley, Ben had landed hard on his forearm. His father was a GP who on arrival punctuated a brief scolding with an apology and then a hard thwack with a surgical mallet to cleanly break the bone. *It will hurt if you wait,* he added over his son's screams, on the way to the hospital.

6. *So is this what you'll be doing now?* Ben's dad asked.

I've been thinking of retraining as a psychotherapist. Or a medic.

What?

How I enjoyed playing with your diagnostic manuals, Ben explained. *Yet how I disliked broken bones.*

Good night, said his father. The line went dead.

7. He worried that he might have become anemic. It was likely inertia. Ben took no exercise except for a few hours of swimming each day and not enough meat or veg. He agonized over breakfast cereals because everything else had too much flavor. That night he dozed off at his desk in the athletics office, reading an airport novel about aliens who wrote bad poetry.

8. When he came to, at around midnight, he let himself into the pool and turned on only one of the lights, which seemed to shake like minnows on the water's surface.

Monica Datta

DERMATOSIOPHOBIA

1. Ben dragged out a box of balls and the old launcher machine. A mechanism seemed to be stuck so it could only oscillate but even that was broadly useless because one could already anticipate from where the ball was coming.

2. The school had no money for a tennis robot, huffed the department manager. Ben had never heard of tennis robots and was distracted during his evening swim. It was all the same sea; in one corner he was fighting about tennis robots, and then in this one he was doing this, and far away, in another galaxy, he was swimming.

3. Dressing afterward he noticed a fractal patch of dry skin on his shin: silvery slivers of cloud fluttered above a desiccated river, fish fossils visible from the sky. When he rubbed it, his fingers were coated in salt flakes. He promised to stop bathing with that strongly scented green soap beloved by Irish builders on US television that left behind gray streaks.

4. He stopped in the chemist on the way home to buy some moisturizer—and to be safe, hydrocortisone cream—but was greeted in the entry by an intimidating selection of beer and cigarettes. Eventually he found a lotion happy to be free of lambs' fat alcohol, but the hydrocortisone tube boasted that it *did* have it, which confused Ben.

5. The silent girl at the till ignored both his hello and thanks, plunking the tubes in boxes in billowing plastic.

6. At home he found a similar patch on his left lower back, the unfortunate meeting of his duffel and waistband. He couldn't quite see, but the spot appeared to have been coated in glue.

ERYTHROPHOBIA

1. Ben still didn't have drapes. Sun glowed like coals against his eyelids. On the way to the bath a stray nail from beneath the hastily installed flooring snagged a loose bit of dead skin from his left heel,

103

tearing away livelier tissue so that it slashed upward to meet the cut in his ankle. He yelped and then lay there, holding his breath.

2. The pain softened to a dull ache despite the thin drizzle of vermilion that he blunted in a nearby T-shirt. He hadn't ever seen his own blood flow in that way; this had no analogue, this blood.

3. He cleaned the wound and formed a packet from strips of T-shirt bundled in cling film and Sellotape. He showered like a flamingo and wondered whether stitches were necessary.

4. His skin had otherwise become a wreck. Ben's soles were so dry that tiny fissures had begun to form curls of coarse bloom. Hives appeared at his elbows.

5. He needed a walk. Ben hobbled to a pub for lunch. The US Open was still going. It starred the handsome number-one Swede with the famous ground stroke that could upscrape the deadest horse: the brutal backhand with its very own doe eyes. Ben cheered for the underdog melting into the court. All those reflective surfaces.

6. Neither the barman nor the waitress adjusting vacant chairs had acknowledged him. Eventually he called out, *Hi sorry could I please order some food sorry.*

7. The barman responded gleefully, *Well g'day! What can I get you?*
Ben, not having seen the menu, ordered a Mann's and a beef burger.
What now?
A brown ale?
All we have is Bud.
OK. And a beef burger please.
What's a beep burger?
Oh, I don't know.
We got burgers but no beep burgers.
One of those please.
You eat some weird things down undah. He chuckled and pounded a sloshy glass to the bar, saturating the serviette on which it was placed.

8. The Swede won the first set, six-one. During the long break Chuck Norris tried to kick his jeans open and failed. Ben's sandwich

arrived with stringy chips and a dejected leaf. When he tried to take out the ketchup with a knife it dribbled and soaked through the bun.

FEBRIPHOBIA

1. Ben decided to keep a diary/log of his symptoms. This would permit the following:
   a. a detailed record of his condition, to be presented to a specialist and
   b. a method of structure that would aid his performance as both a swimmer and coach of tennis and
   c. a practice for the pursuit of a career in the behavioral sciences and
   d. evidence.

2. He seemed to have developed a fever. He put on his swimming goggles to protect his eyes and braved the aircon. He listened to a transistor radio; the same-song Huey Lewis drone was on all day but he found, eventually, an ABBA omnibus.

3. This DJ was ace! "Waterloo"! In Swedish! They hadn't even sung the Swedish version at Eurovision, six years earlier! He didn't know any Swedish and that surely should have ruined the song for him because of the Swede but it did not. *Waterloo, du är mitt öde, mitt Waterloo!*

4. Around the time of the live viewing in 1974, the Swede, *only seventeen*, had made a showing at the Australian Championships (never again, at least to date, to be graced with his presence) after having won top titles at three ATP tournaments. Ben had not attended any of them, with the excuse of training for the French Open. After training he spent the evening with Franz's family watching ABBA, Olivia Newton-John, and loads of other women singing in baby-blue dressing gowns.

5. Ben, years later, knew that he shouldn't feel such antipathy. The Swede was a nice kid. Guy? He was in his prime. Ben had retired. Ben's father was twice Ben's age and hadn't retired, which surely said something about Ben.

6. It came slowly, first the soft pressure of fluid against the back of his eyes and the man-of-war tourniquet around his head and all his marrow heaved. Everything caught fire. His palms were flushed. He swallowed four paracetamol tablets and ran a flannel under the cool faucet to attach to his forehead.

7. His ears hurt. In the mirror he noticed a tiny bracket-shaped cut at either one, not scratches but deep, soft pockets as bright as a kitten's tongue.

GRAPHOPHOBIA

1. He had never before had to pay bills in the US and had no worthy analogy from home; he had been either too young or had hired an accountant far less itinerant than he (or, rather, the manager that Franz had found for him had arranged the accountant). He had not, however, expected to have difficulties in holding up a pen.

2. Ben would pluck the instrument between his thumb and forefinger, but his palms would create a sort of cupping motion and then he would just drop it. He resolved to create a simpler signature by writing with the pen in his fist but could not curl it. He folded the pen in a bit of skin. His very signature said *no*.

3. He felt suddenly that all handwriting was strange and primal and ought to be abolished outside of calligraphy that was not for reading. The winners for writing numbers were a fork and tweezer.

4. Three taps at the open office door. *Hey, is Chuck around?* This guy seemed short to Ben but cleared the door by less than one foot, which meant that he was not. He wore basketball shorts and a T-shirt that read Franklin Sloths.

5. Ben's year-six maths teacher was called Harrison Snails. He had been annoyed with Ben's tennis schedule but took a liking to him when he saw that Ben was rather good with numbers. They had written each other, once: Ben sent a koala postcard from Brisbane (his first time in the Australian Championships) and Snails sent Ben a postcard from the Jaipur Observatory in India: the world's largest sundial.

6. *No,* Ben said. *Not yet.*
Are you the new tennis coach? I'm Maurice. I teach geology.
Ben. I haven't yet met a teacher here.
Listen, a bunch of us are going out for dinner tonight. Do you want to come?

HELIOPHOBIA

1. The dinner would be at half past five in the outdoor section of a shopping plaza, fifteen minutes from the campus. Maurice drove. Ben squinted through the sun.

2. Maurice was from Los Angeles. Initially the university town had scared him, he said; the people could be real weirdos. Ben asked what he meant.
Everyone here has a gun. Little girls receive them at Communion.
I didn't know that there were so many Catholics here.
Why'd you take this job?
Sorry?

3. *I took this job because this region is home to certain processes of dolomitization that are indigenous to the riverbed. I had done three postdocs—two in the Dolomites, of course—and this department had a reputation in my specialty. But I wasn't sure whether to come. My PhD is from Stanford. Where McEnroe went.*
Oh, right. He said.

4. *But then this place said, please: we need an expert in riverbed dolomitization. Five years later I don't know what they meant by that.*
Ben did not know what he meant by that.
Maurice continued. *I'm saying be careful. Mirror, ants, fire. Why did you come here?*
I thought I should see America. I've only spent time in New York and Florida. For training.
Maurice chuckled. *Well, if Florida couldn't keep you away.*

5. Squinting in the still-bright light, Ben saw Chuck and Chuck's new wife (Ben had met Chuck's old wife the previous year, at Roland-Garros). Also present were Tom, who taught teachers; Jack the

swimming coach; Jack's wife, Candice, whom Chuck kept calling Gail; and Gail.

6. This terrace was strange, paved in brick, glazed to resemble terracotta, mashed against the car park. Chuck's new wife applied lipstick while updating her husband with the events of her day, supervising the new construction of a sunroom with thermal flooring.

7. Although Ben rarely sunburned, consciously or not he grazed the tender spot.
    What's on your face? asked Chuck.
    Little sunburn.
    Jack said, *Maybe it's all the chlorine exposure. Security keeps asking me about you.*
    Really?
    I'd love to tan like you, said Chuck's new wife.
    I agree, said Candice. *Maybe one or two shades lighter.*
    You should try. I'm so delicate.
    Maurice was not present. He had gone to wash his hands.

8. *Hey, how old are you?* Jack asked Ben. *You look taller than the last time.*
    Oh, said Ben. *Old enough, I suppose.*
    Maybe Ben's finally getting some decent food, Chuck said.
    The waiter came over to say that the sunset special was a pan-seared sunfish—Malo Malo or black bass, up to them—with sunchokes in sunflower-seed butter with a sun-dried sunburst tomato puree. Everyone requested the dish except for Ben.
    Hey, did you order? Chuck asked him.
    No, I suppose he forgot to ask.
    Service here is the worst, said Jack. *We just come for the terrace.*
    Did anyone order for Maurice? Chuck's new wife asked.

9. Maurice returned. He had managed to catch the waiter. Ben offered everyone his blessing when their food arrived. Eventually he received a droopy salad. He had stopped eating meat and fish: not only did they live too far from an ocean to trust the quality, he reckoned, what, really was the difference between himself and any sentient being with eyes. Still, Ben appreciated the labor involved in composing leaves. *Thanks very much*, he said.

Thank you oh so very much, mimicked the waiter. Everyone laughed, including Maurice.

You cut your salads! Gail squealed. *That is so cute.*

Can't you just squish the leaves on your fork with your left index finger? Jack asked.

10. Chuck and Chuck's new wife offered to drive him back to the town. When Ben had trouble fitting in under the roof—something blue and shiny seemed to be poking from the top of his head—Chuck opened it.

11. *Don't you have a car?* asked Chuck's new wife. *We still have Chuck's old wife's Firebird.*

Oh, said Chuck, sipping air through his teeth. *I was going to sell it. But you can borrow it. No sweat.*

12. At their small manor Chuck entered a code to the garage and pressed a button to reveal that the bird with a slanted beak and an upturned hippo lip, every bit as yellow as he feared, had its own cage. *Don't drive backward!* Chuck's old wife cheerily called out.

13. The next day at the pool, just before dawn, he nodded at the security guard and thought, *Don't drive backward.* Swimming laps, darting from side to side, he thought, *Don't drive backward.*

IATROPHOBIA

1. The next morning, his fever was replaced by the kind of clattering that made his molars ache: they felt sharper than he remembered. The insides of his cheeks were sore.

2. Ben found the *Yellow Page* with all the doctors. The only entry under general medicine was in the same shopping center as the restaurant.

3. In the entry to the storefront doctor's office was a large aquarium next to a poster that read HYPERACTIVITY IN CHILDREN with rambunctious rascals hanging from each letter if they weren't knocking them down, strangling one another, kicking tarantulas, or starting fires.

4. In the waiting area was flat beige carpeting and a gurgling water machine and lots of red eyes, crowded together.

5. Ben went to the receptionist hid behind a thick wall of clear plastic. She asked if he had health insurance. He said that he did but had not yet received the information.

6. She frowned. *You'll have to pay out of pocket,* she said. *All right,* Ben responded.

7. He declined to read the issue with the Swede's gleaming face on it and had just picked up a *Time* magazine with a cartoon of a tiny man on a ladder struggling to write *HELP! Teacher can't teach!* on the blackboard when the nurse called Ben's name. How on earth had he been able to reach the top of the *H, E, L,* or *P*? Ben wondered. He set the magazine down on the coffee table. After taking his vitals the nurse confirmed that Ben's symptoms seemed strange and gave him an open paper dress.

8. The doctor, tall and long faced, knocked, entered, and introduced himself in a single breath. He read: *Itching, fever, dry skin, teeth sharpening, skin pockets, mild webbing, nostril expansion but closer together. Skin tags from shoulders, reduced mobility of shortening arms, sharp blue growth at top of head, sudden increased height, excessive thirst, reduced appetite.*
Yes, Ben confirmed.

9. *What's this mild webbing?* the doctor asked.
Just between my toes, Ben said.
The doctor frowned and took out an advanced monocle. He lifted Ben's left foot and shook his head. *This is a fungus, that's all,* he said. *Do you spend time in sweaty shoes? Wet bathing suits? Does your house have mold?*
Oh, said Ben. *Probably.*
The doctor shook his head and drew a spiral staircase on his prescription pad. *This is a very strong antifungal,* he said. *Keep everything very clean, treat the mold in your home, use a medicated powder after bathing, dry off very well, apply this stuff as you experience symptoms.*
What about this silvery stuff on my legs? Ben asked. *Is this also a fungus?*

Darker skins really show flakes. Try some lambs' fat alcohol.

10. On the way out, the receptionist asked him for two hundred dollars, which exceeded Ben's monthly rent.

GYMNOPHOBIA

1. After a three-hour swim the next day—butterfly stroke, mostly—Ben felt better: breathing with amphibious efficiency, he felt like the porpoise client for whom the swimming complex had been designed.

2. In the shower afterward, he used a new, bland dermatological soap and hummed *Fernando,* his favorite ABBA song. He could never remember the words.

3. Clues of company silenced him. Distant voices turned to murmurs and laughter. There were a couple of smirking guys standing together with something recognizable in their eyes.
   Is everything all right? Ben asked.
   Are you Arthur Ashe?

4. Ben's face grew hot under the cold water and his heart began to pound. He tilted up the pockets behind each ear to take in more oxygen, turning away a bit so that the cacklejackals couldn't see his whole face.
   No, he said, *I've just started as the new tennis coach.*

5. *But didn't you retire this year so that you could coach tennis?* asked the same one.
   No, idiot, his friend said. *Arthur Ashe is Black. And American. This is that English dude who hit his head at the US Open.*
   Sorry, bro. That was bogus.
   Wish your last match was on clay. You were usually good on clay.
   Grass too, said the first guy. *But also clay.*

6. *Do you play?* Ben asked politely.
   My brother plays. Like my fraternity brother. I'll ask if he knows you.

111

7. Ben realized that they were all still naked and shut off the water. His usual towel shendyt was a bit too tight for his growing frame, like one of Gail's dreadful skirts. He tucked his soap and goggles in the swimming cap.

8. Unfortunately, whoever had used the nozzle next to his had failed to rinse away something slippery—probably the wax one of Ben's fellow swimmers liked to massage into his hair beforehand—and Ben, unused to his new sea legs, fell, kicking open the towel and scattering his things toward the drain and everyone except for him laughed.

KLEPTOPHOBIA

1. The boys were back. They seemed to lack agility and control from training exclusively with newer rackets. There were only ten wooden ones in storage, with missing strings and cracked frames. *Where are you from?* asked one of the boys afterward, sticking out his tongue. *Eighteen fifty?*

2. Gail told Ben that it would take a few weeks to order rackets from their ordinary supplier. He should try the sporting-goods store at the second freeway exit. The school shuttle went there if he didn't want to lose his parking space. He brought a large kit bag to carry his purchases.

3. It was a small shop, but Ben managed to find five wooden rackets, different models. He took them to the till.
   What's that? gestured the shaggy blond boy.
   What's what?
   Your bag.
   Oh. I carry rackets in it.
   Do you have rackets in it now?
   Two.

4. *Hold on.* He picked up the phone. *Hi, I have a customer here with a gym bag. Yeah. Weird, right?* He turned back to Ben. *You don't have to empty out the contents of your bag. But I'm going to have a look inside.*

5. Ben opened the bag and lifted out a long graphite racket and a shorter aluminium one, both scratched, though recently restrung. Then there were swimming clothes, ordinary clothes, two pairs of goggles, several swimming caps as well as all the unguents he had managed to accumulate.

6. *Is this OK?* Ben asked.
Do you have a receipt for these rackets?
No. One is from the university and the other was purchased two years ago, in another country.

7. *You messing with me?*
Sorry, said Ben. *I'm confused. Where can I purchase rackets?*
Not here, man. He took Ben's belongings in his fists and shoved them in the bag, then chucked it, tongue open, at his lungs.

8. Ben waited at the bus stop. He rubbed his face in his cotton shirt. A blue Buick slowed down in front of him. It was Jack, who motioned toward him. Ben got in the front seat. He caught his strap in the lock and opened and shut the door again.
What are you doing here? Jack asked.
I was trying to buy wooden rackets.
Ha! Are we gonna see the boys in long skirts?
Oh. No?
There's a good store worth a day trip, said Jack. *It's over the border, but they got everything.*

LIMNOPHOBIA

1. After swimming and ingesting ten liters of deionized water Ben set out at dawn. He had borrowed some self-help tapes from the gymnasium library—*Confucius's Motorcycle, Mummy Says I Am Always Right: An Egyptologist's Guide to Parenting, Journey Up Denial: An Egyptologist's Guide to Overcoming One's Youth*—but required absolute concentration in switching between the pedals because his ankles wanted to stick to one another. His tight shoulders and increased height forced him into a prone posture over the wheel. He had barely ever driven in America. Green leached from the earth. There was no moisture in the air. He paused every hour to drink another two liters. He was nearly out of water.

113

2. Eventually the green returned to the landscape and atomized into capillary-linked lakes. Ben's heart leapt. He would check the *Road Atlas* for a place to cool off. There was a queue at customs, leaving him suspended on the bridge. He rolled down the windows to soak in the aching violet beauty of the expanse.

3. He sat up straight for the customs officer and gave his passport without being asked.
Any fruits or vegetables?
Some dried kelp, he said, *for my own consumption.*

4. *Have you got a new visa?* she asked, handing the passport back to him so that he could find the correct page and return it. *It expired last month.*
It's new. That's the date of issue.
This isn't how it should be written, she said. *Who processed this for you?*
I'm not sure, said Ben. *A courier service was used.*

5. *What do you do for a living?*
I coach tennis at a university.
You need a new visa, she said. *You can't hold a job in this category—didn't your employer look into this?*
No one said anything, said Ben.
You don't want to get in trouble on the way back. Hey, she added, *are you all right? You seem to be turning different shades of red and orange. And blue.*
Oh, he said. *Yes.*
Have you got both fur and gills? she shouted over the sound of an eighteen-wheel lorry at the other side of her station. *You look nothing like your photo.*

6. Ben took the exit for a camping ground at the lake's edge. He scraped his feet against the sharp, sandy pebbles that reminded him of home and placed his face in the water. He felt a plateau and pushed off, opening his eyes in the cool, soft bath, and accidentally swam halfway back to the States, violating the law, and had to turn around.

MYTHOPHOBIA

1. As it did every autumn, news of the Botusfleming Hedwigkraken overtook local media in Cornwall. One thing that Ben did not expect, however, was how well known the Botusfleming Hedwigkraken was in North America.

2. Sure, he had been asked about it. Everyone seemed to know so much more about the Botusfleming Hedwigkraken than Ben did. It was like a Parisian never visiting the Louvre. Ben did not know how to bake a proper pasty; what of it?

3. It was not easy to identify the Botusfleming Hedwigkraken. Those casually familiar assumed that it was an animal sharing morphological and behavioral characteristics that might designate an amphibian, fish, bird, mammal, or insect.

4. This was the exciting part: the Botusfleming Hedwigkraken was also a plant, but because it also shared characteristics with seaweed might also have been an algae, i.e., a protist.

5. Purchasing the tennis rackets this time was no trouble: Ben provided a model number to a worker in what appeared to be an airport hangar and was presented promptly with twelve of them.

6. After again stopping briefly at the campground for a last splash— it seemed others recognized him—he began to drive back to the beautiful bridge.

7. At customs Ben stated that he had purchased twelve wooden tennis rackets and was asked to go to the inspection center. They searched the boot and requested his license (the international permit he had been carrying for years) and registration (assigned to Chuck's old wife).

8. His hands were pinned to the small of his back as his chest walloped the bird's yellow face. Cuffs cleanly encircled his wrists. He was uncuffed to answer, in writing, the following questions:
   a. *What is your relationship to the Irish Republican Army? Who is representative of that relationship in your nation of origin?*

115

Monica Datta

b. *Regarding Euskadi Ta Askatasuna, please answer the same question.*
c. *Also regarding Jabhet Al-Tahrir Al-'Arabiyah.*
d. *And Fuerzas Armadas Revolucionarias de Colombia— Ejército del Pueblo; do also please answer this.*

NEOPHOPHOBIA

1. The car had been impounded. It might cost thousands of dollars to return to Chuck. Gail had a friend across the border who posted bail and signed out Ben without a word or eye contact.

2. Ben squeezed into a phone box to phone the operator to phone a taxi from a neighboring town: the trip over the bridge alone might take two hours and he would need to pay twice the fare as the taxi was forbidden from collecting money across the border.

3. Ben called the bus company. There was one leaving at quarter to midnight, arriving at an interchange at four in the morning.

4. The clouds thickened as dusk approached. These were the things that he saw:
    a. A knight killing a horse with a spear,
    b. Dragons shredding flowers; heavy and white, capable of crushing a car,
    c. Sheep,
    d. Rabbits,
    e. Dying dandelions,
    f. The wodge of cotton in his gill.

5. He had to wait under a very low shelter. It began to rain.
    a. Although having soggy feet might hitherto have irritated Ben, he now found the sensation very comforting.
    b. Although he had been hungry, it seemed that the mere absorption of rain through his skin was enough to sate him.
    c. He could sleep with open or shut eyes, sitting or standing or lying down.
    d. Aspects of his vision were enhanced and others impaired. Clouds seemed to part over sharp, glaring contrast, a tricky happening, nerves or neurons or neutrons.

116

6. The driver forced him to the back, then the luggage rack, then eventually the bottom of the stair to the back door, the only place high enough to accommodate his height.

7. This was to say that he had become a nuisance and there was nothing worse to be.

ONEIROPHOBIA

1. Whatever contributions Ben had made to the sport of tennis—a notion he considered rather risibly—he had been rewarded one hundredfold with the greatest thing that he could now imagine, twenty years of near-dreamless sleep, three full REM cycles every night;

2. Without bus travel and its cackling patrons, cheap refrigerants dripping from the window;

3. Without dreams of being nibbled by electric eels and barracuda, of being called into a trench;

4. Of leaping upward to catch the mistral, of being caught in a coral reef;

5. Of seaweed masonry and petrol slicks and plastic shrouds;

6. Of canoes and bathyspheres and diving bells;

7. Of his mother, a cloud, telling Ben that he had eaten his last meal;

8. Of Chuck, who'd sacked and tied him;

9. Of his father, preparing a fricassee, or his excellent cascadu;

10. Of the Swede as a swede, or sometimes a crayfish on the day of the summer solstice, knocking Ben out of the way handily, as gently as a Jain might push a tall blade of grass;

11. Of uranium and its abundance, the existence of which had permitted Ben's employment as a tennis coach;

117

12. A boy and his mother were bound for California. He asked if they were there yet but it would be days.

PHILOPHOBIA

1. Ben had to wait another hour at the bus depot before the university shuttle began running. He heard someone calling his name. It was Gail, who said that Chuck had *really blown up*.

2. Ben wasn't sure what that meant. He himself had been blowing up. He had also been learning about puffer fish but of course had not been able to retrieve the library books on tape from Chuck's car.

3. *You'll pay him back for the impounding,* she said. *And the repairs.*
   Do you suppose I still have a job? Ben asked.
   I don't know. We didn't arrange your visa so I think the contract is somewhat flexible, thank God.

4. Gail said that Ben was looking rough. She drove them to a diner. Ben had to sit in the back seat. He admired the regional hospitality after all, he decided. It was very homely to tell someone that they were fine.

5. They went to a diner popular with students. Ben hoped that he wouldn't see any of the tennis boys. There were some footballers. It was bulking season.

6. Ben excused himself to wash his face and change clothes. He avoided the mirror as he soaked his head, arms, and legs.

7. Trousers did not quite work anymore.

8. The waitress asked whether they wanted still or sparkling bottled water, which seemed incongruously luxuriant but Ben quickly requested both, as well as tap.

9. Gail ordered coffee and grapefruit sprinkled with saccharine for them both.

10. *Ben, can I ask you something?*
    Oh. All right.
    You must be lonely here, she said.
    He shrugged. *I've been playing since I was ten years old. It was just me and my coach, Franz.*
    Well, do you miss Franz?

11. *Are you from here?* Ben asked.
    Nodding, she said, *I quit law school to be a singer, and stopped singing to get divorced to live with my mother. But I just met someone.* She opened her purse to take a passport photo from her wallet and named its toothy subject, which made him uneasy. *Don't you want to meet someone?*

12. *Oh. Well, I've rather been preoccupied with my skin condition,* he said, gesturing at his shimmering blue and violet forearm. *It makes me feel very self-conscious.*

13. *Aww,* she said, taking both his fins in hers, *why, I think there are people with dark skin who are just as attractive as white people.*

14. The bill came. Gail was treating. On the way out, Ben flipped it over. It read:
    QUAM BENE VIVAS REFERT, NON QUAM DIU.

RANIDAPHOBIA

1. Ben did not want to face Chuck in the department.

2. The term had begun and the swimming pool was very busy.

3. Ben refilled a massive water jug and took his binder of drills to the duck pond.

4. Algae were in full bloom.

5. Ben knelt at the edge for a moment: it was filled also with turtles and koi, who seemed to be discussing the abundance of algae.

6. Tucked in the binder's pocket were Ben's diary of symptoms and a clipping from the local newspaper about the Botusfleming Hedwigkraken.

    a. Of course the story about the Botusfleming Hedwigkraken had been adapted from the wire. Ben recognized the name of one of the subjects interviewed from primary school: he complained about the ruckus and said that no signs of the Botusfleming Hedwigkraken had been seen in months. It was not suitable to disturb him at breakfast, he had added.

    b. Ben had not updated the diary of symptoms since the doctor visit. He added *absorbency, hair loss, glittering,* and *trapezoidism* to the list.

    c. And then, reluctantly, he wrote what he thought might have been scientific synonyms for jumping ability: *sautability, salitation, cabriolage, gambolliance.*

7. *Too much algae,* said one of the frogs to another. *And there are just too many of us in this pond. And we all love algae.*
Aren't algae awful? sighed the frog's frog friend.

8. *Ben,* the first frog asked, *Don't you think that there are just too many frogs in this pond?*

9. *I'm not sure,* Ben replied.
Come in, Ben! We can't hear you. Sound waves travel differently in water.

10. *I can't,* Ben said. *I'm working.*
You've woken all the tadpoles. Now all the frogs will come back.

11. The koi were correct: a dozen frogs—perhaps one hundred— came rushing in from the grass, plunging one by one.

12. *The one who would be king,* drawled a turtle between bites of strawberry.

SOMNIPHOBIA

1. At the practice that afternoon, none of the boys let on that a thing was wrong. Tennis was a sport that attracted the superficially polite

among youths, notorious exceptions of the day notwithstanding.

2. Chuck could not be found.

3. After the pool closed, Ben took a four-hour swim in the near dark. It was not nearly as satisfying as before. Chlorine really was not good for his skin.

4. That night he woke up coughing as dryly as before, so he drew a cold bath and went there to doze off instead.

5. But he did not really want to go to sleep. Taking breaks to plunge beneath the water's surface when he felt dehydrated, Ben read from *The Hitchhiker's Guide to the Galaxy*.
   a. There were Babel fish, which one might insert in the ear canal so that they might translate anything heard into one's native language.
   b. In the book there were also machines that analyzed the drinker's taste buds and neural pathways to brew a beverage that was very nearly not like tea.
   c. Ben never drank tea in America. At age ten he had ordered it for breakfast with Franz and everyone died laughing.
   d. But if he had not had any tea he was not sure why he was awake. Any caffeine really dried him out these days.

6. Sometimes exercise helped him sleep but sometimes it kept him awake. As the tub was anyway too short for his body, the postures required for calisthenics made bathing more comfortable and the water took the pressure off his joints, of which he seemed to have fewer than before, or more.

THALASSOPHOBIA

1. There was no sea, no salt water for one thousand miles. To be alone in dark brine. To be mummified in seaweed. Of sharks and salt. Of whales and open water. Of being stung and hit. Of rupture and puncture; of being detonated, from underneath, for an ancient war.

2. He wanted to talk with someone clever. He asked Maurice to go for a beer Sunday afternoon. Maurice in turn invited him for dinner.

3. Ben had interjected that he was a vegetarian except for brine shrimp.
   a. Maurice did not rescind the invitation.

4. When Ben arrived at Maurice's flat—clean and cozy despite the tacky Tudor exterior—the television was on. The men's US Open final was on that night.

5. *Who are you rooting for?* Maurice asked.
   I'm not sure. How about you?
   McEnroe, of course.
   Oh. Right.

6. *Sorry. I thought you might want to watch, but . . .*
   No, I wasn't in the center court when it happened, Ben said. *It's fine.*
   But it was like a week ago.
   Eleven days. It's fine.
   Unbelievable, said Maurice, shaking his head.

7. *Can I help with anything?* Ben asked, following Maurice to the kitchen. *Thanks for accommodating me.*
   Not at all, Maurice said. *I'm from California. We're all half lentil. I wanted to make a seaweed salad but couldn't find any.*
   That would have been delicious, Ben sighed longingly.
   Huh. OK, man. I'll try to grab some the next time I'm home.

8. Maurice had prepared a feast, or at least enough for him not to cook all week. A loaf of nutmeats, light green salad with chickpeas, a white ball with little golden studs.
   It all looks very nice, Ben said. *Can I ask what that ball is?*
   You mean the cheesy pine-apply one?
   Yes. Sorry?
   You've never seen Abigail's Party?
   Who is Abigail?
   It's a play. From England. I thought you'd know it. It was on PBS.
   Whenever I try PBS there's a fishing show, said Ben.

9. *So how do you like it here?* Maurice asked.
   It's all right, Ben said. *I've taken up a swimming hobby.*

I mean, have people been weird to you.

Nothing out of the ordinary. I have a great job, new friends, a place at which to go swimming, loads of quiet time. Thinking of what to do next.

Do you mean that you won't stay?

No, no, Ben quickly interjected. *By* next *I mean years.*

10. *I mean, for me it's weird, being here,* said Maurice. *And you're a foreigner teaching in a place with no interest in tennis.*

Well, the tennis team is ranked nationally—

Yeah, but who knows that? Plus you've got that accent. You kind of sound like a movie pirate. But one who went to an American boarding school when you were like twelve. Like you deliver marine news on the BBC and your eye patch is of fine leather.

11. Maurice suggested that they watch what was left of the match. Mac had won the first two sets. The Swede had just managed to overtake him in the third. His service was weak. He had recently defeated Mac at Wimbledon after a very long tiebreaker and was the favorite even though Mac was from Queens and barely twenty.

12. Wooden rackets were precise and made such a clean sound: how had the boys on the team given in to fat, fluffy graphite? The Swede's beautiful backhand could never have materialized with such a clumsy thing.

Mac's going slack this round, said Maurice. *Do you think that if you'd hit your head at Wimbledon instead of the US Open you'd still be playing? Grass seems so much softer.*

It's the softest, Ben agreed. Perhaps seaweed on clay would have made for a gentler concussion.

13. The Swede won the first game of the fifth set. John Newcombe was one of the commentators. *He's going to have to, as you Americans say, suck it up and get on with the job,* said Newc of Mac, who had narrowly won the second game. The Swede, ever the perfectionist, had been playing somewhat defensively that evening, chasing Mac's masterful serve and volley but now there was something sharp in his eyes.

I can't believe that one week ago you were running around with these young guys, Maurice said. *Impressive, but also embarrassing.*

14. The Swede had not lost a five-set match since 1974. This was his fourth US Open final. This was the third year in a row that he had won the French Open and the fifth Wimbledon. The Swede was on McEnroe's turf and still everyone was clamoring for him to win.

15. But this was Mac's time. Ben jumped up and shouted.

OURANOPHOBIA

1. On his way home the clouds parted slowly, erupting into a glittering landscape of stars. Sometimes he felt they were telling him to go to them, but he had gravity and they had other laws.

2. Ben's telephone service had finally been installed. It was now just before midnight, just before 6:00 a.m. in England. His parents were early risers but might be alarmed by the earliness of his approach.

3. So he decided to phone Franz in Geneva, at home with his wife and children in early September for the first time in many years. He had given up so much of his life to dote on Ben, when his own children either loathed tennis or willed every shot to the gods. They were awfully polite about it, of course.

4. Franz picked up on the second ring, as always.
It's Ben, said Ben. *Hi.*
Oh, Ben. What time is it in America?
Seven hours' difference. Just saying hi really, Ben said.
Are you all right, Ben?
Why do you ask?
I mean, I've never heard of this kind of thing. You could still play doubles. Or perhaps there's a breakfast cereal you could endorse.
Ben laughed. *Imagine—a kid picks up the box and asks,* Who is this? Is this still a cereal?
It's probably because you have two first names, Franz joked.

5. In the first century of the current era, Thomas the Apostle—known also as Doubting Thomas for having disbelieved the death and resurrection of Christ till he saw laid bare the wounds—left the Roman Empire to introduce the gospel to the people of what was considered then Tamilakam, although Malayalam was at the time

the language of Kerala. At the time of this conversation between Ben and Franz, Saint Thomas Christians—known also as the Syrian Christians of India and the Syrian Malabar Nasranis—governed many aspects of contemporary life in Kerala. Masculine baptismal names among the Saint Thomas Christians were patronymic; the firstborn son would be named after the paternal grandfather—i.e., Ben's name would be Timothy had his family followed this tradition—and the sequence would go: family name, father's name, baptismal name. In this case Ben's name would have been George Paul Timothy.

6. There emerged a problem of labor shortage throughout the British empire following the abolition of slavery in 1833; business owners were concerned over this new expense, *labor costs,* and the mild mess of high death rates among the recently enslaved workers of African origin, and even the supposedly hearty indentured servants from Europe who refused to continue working without pay following the end of their terms. The first Indian indentured servants would not arrive in Trinidad until 1844; naturally, the ship that brought the first Indians to Trinidad was built by an Indian, from solid teak: British shipbuilders did not want to be involved and Indians seemed rather to have enjoyed the killing and enslavement of other Indians. The ship was called *Fatel Razack* and even back then no one believed in accidents. The human cargo, most of whom survived the hellish journey around the Cape of Good Hope, were pronounced to have been *in good order and conditions.* This may have been another way that Ben George came to be: the passengers had arrived with so many bleeding syllables and paupers' pretensions; punishments and indignities ought to have been for them and not the owners.

7. Ben's mother arrived in England on the inaugural journey of the ship *Windrush.* Indentured servants had been brought to Trinidad in her lifetime. Unusually for a woman of her social class and knife skills—as both a cook and nurse—she was unmarried and traveled to England to seek her fortune. And why not? Books full of beautiful places, not a smidge of ugliness outside of the papers. And they were hers too. Ben's dad on the other hand had arrived at birth. Timothy George, *his* father, had been a general in the Trinidad contingent of the West India Regiment in the First World War, serving in the Sinai-Palestine campaign and in reward never again saw his homeland nor

125

was he ever able to live in his son's NHS catchment area and they paid away privately through the nose for greedy referrals during those murderous months of leukemia.

8. Ben was his parents' only son, their only family. When he is nearly seventy years of age there will be a systematic and fraudulent detention and deportation of people like his mother and grandfather, exiled from the only place that had made a home for them. From his own exile a-sea Ben decades hence will chuckle darkly at the name of the Home Office hostile environment policy—the literalism of his native tongue will make him giggle the more time he spends away from it—and then for reasons he will claim not to understand but will thoroughly he will cry like a child.

9. A hundred years from then, maybe longer, well after the children and grandchildren of that generation have passed, everyone except for Ben, now far from English, far from Cornish, far from Roman letters, when walls of fire are origin stories and the sea a bag of bones, Ben will assure anyone willing to speak with him—not an easy task, given his wild amphibious appearance—especially the dying, that they would not wish his curse on their worst enemy. Each time, they will whisper: *I won't believe you.*

10. *Do you suppose I can call Wheaties?* Ben asked Franz.
   Call Bruce Jenner, said Franz. *Find out what the job is like.*

VESTIPHOBIA

1. Ben, who had only been permitted once to play tennis in an exhibition match at the 1968 Olympics in Mexico City due to the sixty-year ban of the sport and who surely would not reshape himself to play in Los Angeles four years hence had never met Bruce Jenner, took out the empty Wheaties box from the bin and considered the airy nature of track and field uniforms.

2. Gail had offered to drive him to work until he was able to go to work in some other way: a new car, improved public transport, the development of a new waterway or increased running gait.

3. Not a single garment fit. Moreover, his opposable thumbs were translucent and filled with cartilage. He managed to nose himself into a T-shirt but clothing seemed so stupid now. He was able to cut up four white T-shirts and to reattach them to one another from the inside using duct tape. Impressed by his handiwork, he did the same with four pairs of short pants.

4. Gail was wearing a swimming costume over pink tights but also bright cotton socks that went to the knee and well-cushioned trainers. She wore a toweling sweatband about the circumference of her head. None of Ben's toweling sweatbands fit any longer: perhaps he could cut up four socks and reattach them to one another from the inside with duct tape but it was too late. He had already opened the door to the red Beetle convertible.

5. *I'm going to aerobics!* Gail proclaimed. *Do you have time? Come with me!*

Oh, Ben said. *Well, I was going to go swimming and I'm teaching all afternoon.*

It'll be great for your skin. You'll sweat out everything. Just grab plenty of water.

Can we stop in the grocery? Ben asked. *I've forgotten my water bottle.*

6. Ben purchased all the gallon jugs of distilled water available—ten—and put them in the back seat of the car. Gail chuckled. Ben did too, nervously.

7. Ben was not sure what aerobics were but all the women were dressed like Gail and maybe it was like synchronized swimming in trainers. The sight of them stretching in incredible colors brought out unbearable hunger in Ben: he wanted nothing more than to run very fast down two flights of stairs through the locker room and into the natatorium to perform a backflip into the swimming pool (he had never done one) just two stories down from where he was marching like a soldier with nowhere to go.

8. *Come on, girls!* the instructor shouted. *Stretch your arms higher! Higher, like the Botusfleming Hedwigkraken!* Ben was trying so hard to stretch his arms! But they had receded into the sides of his body and were in fact each replaced by a sort of wing. Also, the top

of his head exceeded the hand height of any other person in the room, which made him feel very self-conscious. The women averted his gaze in the mirror as he was throwing off their rhythm.

9. Some of the duct tape had attached to Ben's feathers. It was a bit painful but not nearly as unfortunate as the bits that had attached to his scales. His had been such a foolish idea. Even if he was able to find some olive oil or peanut butter, what could he do? It was not clear whether the water jugs that he was splashing on himself like a decadent perfume advertisement were worsening the problem but creating a new one because the floor was very slippery.

10. Gail had lost herself in the music, jumping from side to side. Some of the other women looked nervous: there was just so much water. Ben had brought in a towel but it looked like a hummingbird's handkerchief. Hummingbirds did not need handkerchiefs and Ben was beginning to feel that he did not need clothing either. The thought embarrassed him.

11. Then again, Ben thought, trying to slap together his winged flippers to the beats of *Fame* and then *I'm Coming Out* (neither of which had lyrics to which he could at all relate), human bodies were by comparison rather embarrassing to look at, incapable of making decisions about fur and chitin.

12. *Wasn't that great?* asked Gail after the Bee Gees cooldown, and after Ben had managed to sop up most of the water he had splashed onto the floor.

13. *Oh yes,* said Ben, gathering up the water jugs before running into the men's changing room, through which he would enter the swimming pool. He had chosen the perfect time between the end of the girls' swimming practice and the entry of the cleaner to twist in backward like a humpback whale and all was right with the world as he shot out fresh chlorinated water from the top of his head.

OIKOPHOBIA

1. Ben phoned his parents at one in the morning to catch his father before he left for work. They were asking again from both receivers

what the hell he was doing over there.

Well, I've been swimming a lot, Ben said.

We live in Cornwall! bellowed his father.

Everyone swims in Cornwall, Ben protested.

2. *Do you dislike us?* his mother asked.

What! Ben said, exasperated. *No. I just . . .*

Oh, said Ben's mum. *Is it the Botusfleming Hedwigkraken?*

No!

Ben, don't talk to your mother like that! said his father.

3. Ben's mum said, *We're getting old, you know. One day we may not recognize you.*

Ben's dad said, *It's very suspicious to me that you went to this, wherever this place is, after, you know, whatever that was.*

What are you saying? asked Ben.

There are many terrorist groups in the US, said Ben's dad. *Or have you joined a cult?*

I don't know, Ben said.

4. *I thought that you would go to university,* wept Ben's mum.

Is it because of the conservatives? asked Ben's dad. *Because you know that Carter will lose the election in November to that film star . . . what do they call those men in hats?*

Construction workers? Ben asked.

Cowboys! shouted Ben's mum. *Guns! Dallas!*

5. *How long is this . . . this?* Ben's mother asked.

I can come home at Christmas. We have a whole month.

Are you going to stay there for the rest of your life? asked Ben's father.

Of course not, said Ben. *I'll phone you both next—*

He heard both receivers click off simultaneously.

6. The next morning he scarcely fit through the bus door (that bit of extra moisture he applied beforehand just pushed him through) and the rest of the passengers gaped and whispered.

7. Glugging water, Ben felt a pang of sorrow for his own incidental and inappropriate expressions of shock over the years but it wasn't as if he had spent very many hours taking public transport in rural areas.

8. In Cornwall the few people he still knew were obsessed with property because they knew that adults could not have homes but perhaps also their parents if they were still living.

9. After squeezing himself out the back door Ben was greeted by gasps and giggles and gesticulations, all from strangers. He used the trapezoidal end of his tail to rush to his office. Maurice was standing outside of it.

10. *Oh, hey, man,* Ben said. *All right?*
   Yeah, yeah, said Maurice. *Just wanted to say goodbye.*
   What? What happened?
   Maurice laughed. *One of the senior faculty changed his mind about sabbatical, so I got one.*
   Does that really happen?
   If not, it's a weird way of firing me.
   Oh no.
   Just kidding. I'm going to Stanford. I might have an offer there.
   So you'll not be coming back.
   I hope you find the seaweed you're looking for, dude.
   Yeah, man. You too.

11. Ben didn't need clothes because the walls were beginning to pull themselves inward, cultivating their own sort of armor. Being a tortoise, however, would require him to jettison some of the furnishings and materials from the window, which, without opposable thumbs, would prove difficult.

XEROPHOBIA

1. The practice that afternoon was almost too good. Ben's throat felt scratchy in all the moist air. It felt so cruel. If Ben had done French in school he might have thought, *Soleil cou coupé.*

2. When Ben went to drink from the water jug sized normally for the entire team (he wasn't rude; of course there were three others), he noticed a climbing gecko and tried to scare it away.
   Instead, it pinned itself to Ben's ear and sighed: *I wish I could go*

swimming. You're so lucky, milord. Milord! Was there anything more embarrassing?

I can't go swimming, Ben said once the racket thwacking picked up so that no one would hear him talking to a lizard—and was it not too far north for geckos, someone had boasted of the local climate?— and when he tried to explain why was surprised to have lost his voice. He tried to make a noise and it went a bit like *rehhhhh.*

3. Ben could only blow his whistle and gesticulate but gestures were different now. He tried to lift what was once his arm and was now a kind of shimmering wing. So the boys continued the same drill for the next ninety minutes and by the time they finished they were rather good.

4. After the practice finished—Ben had managed an A-OK/thumbs-up hybrid that was, apparently, legible—his skin was so dry that it felt sore to move. Ben now avoided bathing in the changing room when anyone else was there and had to wait for the last of the boys to leave. He tried to seal in as much moisture as he could with the lanolin cream but he was too slippery. But there was not enough water in the world. What to do?

5. Ben's father's favorite film was *Lawrence of Arabia.*

6. On the way out of the gymnasium building, Ben saw Chuck, who nodded at him. Ben said *hello*—he was not sure whether he was speaking out of turn—and slowed his gait in case Chuck did the same but he kept on. He scanned the row of benches for Gail, who often took smoking breaks there.

7. Ben walked down the promenade and glanced at the frog pond at his right. Dragonflies sipped from lotus blossoms. He could not see any frogs. There was a turtle but perhaps he was a rock instead. This was because all the frogs had jumped onto Ben's shoulders. *Please don't, Ben pleaded. Your toes are so pointy and my skin is so dry.*

8. *What is a skin?* asked one of the frogs.
What keeps him from desiccating? said another.
Not his, ours, explained a third.
Indeed the frogs had collectively formed a seal all around Ben. He had been scuba diving once as a child and it was a bit like that

especially in not being able to breathe the way he wanted to.

9. He was being pushed to the river. There was a clamor of voices: on one hand frogs and other amphibious creatures cheering him on and on the other, grisly and very human expressions of disgust and horror—as well as a bit of glee—as he was dragged through the dry, powdery grass, leaving behind a trapezoidal etching.

YMOPHOBIA

1. At the banks he was given a choice: to stay on land in limited capacity or to join the water. If he chose the water, he relinquished all chance of going to the stars or of staying where he was or of course getting out. Maybe he could find his way back. There were no signs, but he might be able to tell based on the types of flora and fauna available.

2. And well it was water after all.

3. If this was the last thing he saw in life he wouldn't mind. He blinked olives and opened his mouth to scream but was only able to produce bubbles. A golden calm blushed in the upper part of his torso closest to his face as the sun followed him.

4. If he correctly chose north he would enter a clean, vast cold to the river then the ocean then home, otherwise he would be stuck where everything dried.

5. If he correctly chose south he would enter the dank, warm gulf with sludge and predators but the ocean again and then home but so much longer.

6. If he chose the wrong north he would wind up in a tiny beautiful lake with inlets and tributaries and furrows the width of his former pinkie.

7. If he made it home, his friends and family might think him a flying fish if he happened to be quite big and wished to remember oxygen and make him into a fricassee and observe the water's surface unless he was a beardy fluttersize cascadu to be curried with boiled egg.

8. Ben turned left.

9. It was strange, the way that these sea creatures fell in line. Succession had always bothered him. He nodded politely anyway. When he did this Ben realized that the line was for him and because they were already bowing no sea creature could make any further gestures of deference and Ben was so embarrassed that he tried to sink into the sand but it was awfully dense.

10. There was such beautiful coral. He had never seen it, eye to eye. It was filled with tiny mouths and leaves in every color, all alive. Ben knew then that he was also coral.

11. Eventually Ben was met by an octopus, who curtsied—this was the default option for them, Ben presumed—deeply and said, *Celestial Creator of the Universe High and Low, Benevolent Dictator of Plymouth from Afar, Lord Empress Sir or Madam God Botusfleming Hedwigkraken Thakur. We have been waiting for you.*

12. *No!* Ben shouted through the heavy water. *No, I want to leave, now.*
   You may do as you wish, responded the octopus. *You are the Botusfleming Hedwigkraken, unifier of the land and sea.*
   But the Botusfleming Hedwigkraken is a terrifying creature that has eluded the observation of seekers for centuries, Ben said. *I am but a tennis coach at a middling university. I have never even been to Botusfleming, which is really in Devon.*
   This is how we knew you were the Botusfleming Hedwigkraken.
   But I never even said goodbye.
   You won't need to.
   Have I died?
   You cannot die, ever.

ZYGOPHOBIA

1. It was difficult to discern the days from one another. The qualities of the sun were so different from the ones he knew. Ben began to feel deeply depressed despite being able to swim twenty-four hours a

day if that was how many hours there were down there.

2. He was never alone; he was always being offered something he didn't know he wanted, something novel: a balm for his gills, the spelling of coelacanth in the local language, which he had learned in no time, the velocity of a tennis ball—a very, very old one—twenty thousand leagues under the sea when struck with an unidentifiable slab of earthly debris.

3. Ben had no concept of where he was on the seafloor. The maps were written in dimensions unintelligible to him. When he asked after methods of amphibious transport he was given a flurry of options but could not explain where he wanted to go in ways that could be understood.

4. There were intelligence briefings: sonar could do spectacular things. *These are the eighties now, after all,* Ben tried to joke, but was corrected for his imprecision with much deference and a great deal of apology. There were ghastly things happening on both the American and Soviet sides that Ben could not begin to fathom.

5. He had never been so angry: to choose meant loss. In this case, the loss of everything that mattered to save his own life or rather the life of the Botusfleming Hedwigkraken and no one wanted that. As such Ben felt a bit of gratitude. The Botusfleming Hedwigkraken was loved below sea level. Ben begged to send letters but ink worked differently here and the postal systems were not compatible.

6. Nor had he ever felt such love for so many, or at least a deep and abiding affection. He wanted to defend all that surrounded him but also for the first time in his life understood vengeance. He traced the banks to the bottom to a rootjam logswadhollow, from which bloomed a soft cloud of ova and stood guard.

A Propitiation
Michael Harris Cohen

MYERS STOPPED BY JUST AS I was finishing up my structure. He hopped out of his pickup and tilted his gaze to the sky. He made the sign—as did we all when looking skyward—then his eyes fell to my structure.

"You use four by sixes at the bottom?" Myers said.

Nodding, I pounded one of the final nails into place. I was in a good mood, having near finished, good enough to even tolerate Myers, my neighbor.

He spat in the dirt and took off his hat. "A big storm hits before the festival, that thing is gonna tumble."

I explained how I'd poured concrete for the supporting struts, and was pretty sure the construction could weather a tornado if it had to. I *knew* structures. My father had judged them. I'd follow him and the other judges as they tramped from farm to farm, their white festival robes mud splattered by the day's end.

Of course I couldn't compete until he'd passed on, just last year, but I'd built in my head since childhood, drafting and refining a thousand notional designs. I didn't give a damn what Myers thought about what I'd actually built. Though I didn't want to be rude. That's not me. That's not how I was raised.

After I had made coffee and served Myers, he caught me up on the news from town. The festival was days away and Myers was eager to gab on the others' structures.

"Otis built a tower," he said. "Painted it green with red stripes. 'Fertility colors,' Otis said. Gonna put his eldest in it for the festival. The fearless one."

Myers grinned. He said Otis seemed a shoo-in for the black ribbon.

I shrugged and smiled. He paused.

Myers was dying to ask who I planned to put in mine, but I ignored his unspoken question and studied my past months' work. My structure stood taller than the barn, radiant in the midday sun. I hadn't painted it and didn't plan to. I liked bare wood. Its curvy grain and fresh-cut scent. All lumber was once a living tree. I thought it important to remember that.

Everything that lives dies. Only Those Above restore.

My gaze traveled to the sky. I made the sign, palms together then open, and stared into the rich blue. For the thousandth time I wondered if They stared back, if my mother stared alongside them. I heard her sometimes, speaking to me.

Another ten minutes passed, Myers detailing structure after structure. He described Brook's, then Rheinhold's, how Rheinhold's was welded metal, "top to bottom," and ten feet taller than mine.

I feigned interest as long as I could, then stretched my back and yawned. Myers was tiresome but he wasn't dense.

"Well," he cleared his throat. "I should probably get a move on."

I smiled and shrugged.

Then an idea struck. I sized Myers up. He was just about my height and weight.

"You want to give it a whirl? I could use a test run."

His eyes stretched wide.

Most of my life I'd watched him half-ass his crops from my front porch. He was a lazy farmer, and behind the big talk hid a frightened man. He'd never build his own structure. Nor would anyone ever ask him to be in one. Me doing so was beyond his imagining.

He wrung his hat in his hands. "Well . . . if you're sure. Wouldn't want to mess it up before the festival."

"Can't win if it doesn't work. Let me just tune the winch."

Myers shadowed me as I grabbed my oilcan and lubed the winch's grease points. He chattered nervously, discussing more structures. I nodded—half listening—as I inspected the bolts and electrical connections.

"To fail to prepare is to prepare to fail," my father always said.

He'd won his black ribbon when I was seven. I'd watched him labor all day, every day till the festival, till the judges came. I studied and learned everything I could as my father's narrow structure grew, a wooden needle stitching earth to sky. Carved steps circled it to the top. My tiny legs imagined it'd take a day just to climb them.

Mother hated it. She loathed all the structures that dotted the flat plains of our community and all the communities beyond. She feared what our world had become.

But that festival day, decades ago, she'd won too. My father loved her with all his heart, and so he put her in his structure, earned the black ribbon, and became a judge.

"One must give what one holds dearest," my father said. "A propitiation that costs nothing yields nothing."

We never spoke of her after, but I knew she was with Those Above. Even if she'd never believed in them. Even if she'd died with terror in her heart.

I wiped my oily hands with a rag and nodded to Myers. "You ready?"

Myers nodded back. For the first time I saw him at a loss for words. Finally he spoke, his voice just north of a whisper. "I wish it was for real. I mean, for the festival. You think it still counts? Do they see it?"

"You know they see everything," I said, "and everything we do counts."

He gazed at his muddy boots. "I've been a coward my whole life."

"I know."

At last, he looked up and smiled. "But I can be brave for two minutes. Maybe."

"You better. Fear sours the meat."

I winked and he laughed and I laughed with him. He relaxed a bit. For the first time ever I admired him.

I strapped his arms and legs into the harnesses. We looked to the sky and made the sign together. Then we clasped hands. It was a big moment for us both.

Then I flipped on the power and our fingers drifted apart. The freshly oiled winch barely whispered as it towed him up the structure, smiling the whole way. He was perfect. Better than the man-sized puppet I'd sewn from old work clothes and stuffed with sand.

My thoughts, as though dragged by cables in my mind, pulled back to my mother. How she'd been terrified when Father's structure whirred into motion all around her. How her shrill pleas to my father, to her dead god, how they'd turned to screams, as the judges and townsfolk looked on. As I'd looked on.

I remembered her stories of childhood, from before they'd burned the churches, how her mother used to take her every Sunday. My mother spoke of sermons and songs and scripture till it dizzied me.

She said her dead god's sacrifice saved the world.

Myers kept his smile all the way to the top. Eyes open, even as the cables tautened and wrenched off his arms and legs, neatly quartering him. Unlike my mother, he died without a whisper.

His blood collected at the bottom of the platform, more or less as I'd hoped—though I'd have to plane the wood to get the incline better. But I had time. Still days till the festival, when we give our pleas in flesh and beseech Those Above to find them worthy.

Michael Harris Cohen

"The worthy become something else," my father said. And I knew he meant Mother, that she was with them, she was changed, even if the judges found her unworthy, even if my father had repeated their judgment—with grief in his eyes—that those who died with fear could not ascend.

But how could they know? How could they be certain? Those Above were beyond our comprehension. Who could know their ways and wants?

I rinsed Myer's blood from the wood as the sun banged down. These years it's a cruel hammer on the anvil of the earth. Nothing has grown right for years and there is talk. Some say Those Above have abandoned us. Thus, our crops wither and perish. Our livestock comes stillborn or sickly. There are whispers that they never existed, that the festival should be abandoned. To me it is only talk of talk, for the skeptics know better than to speak such doubts to a judge's son.

For I believe. Like my father and his father before him. I believe in our salvation. I believe Those Above will save the world when our structures, and their offerings, are extraordinary.

On festival day so many structures will stand exquisite and sublime, fine pillars of worship and faith, employing nooses, blades, or fire. Crowds will weep, watching wood and bone burn to ash. They'll lurch to their knees, praying their loved ones die with their tongues stilled and their hearts uncluttered. Praying our dead lands again sprout rivers of green.

There'll be more imaginative designs than mine, other structures that gather blood untouched by earthly hands. But I trust the judges, and Those Above that judge us all, will favor mine.

I looked to the sky and made the sign. A light rain began to fall. My mother's voice called in the raindrops. Faint but audible. It said, *Life is sacred but self-sacrifice is holy.* It said, *Death is nothing to fear.*

The raindrops sound like her, soft and sad and strong, like her stories of her dead god, like her last words.

"I carry him with me always," she'd said, "churches or not." She'd pointed to my heart. "He's all that's left to save us. You need to carry him too."

And I have, in my way. The perpendicular simplicity of his cross and his sacrifice, that story stuck. That story I carried.

On festival day I'll place a propitiation to save us. The builder. Me. In the structure of my making. Self-slaughter was forbidden but I'll

138

die without a drop of doubt or fear. For my mother calls to me from above, in the rain, the wind, the stars, and the moon, just as her dead god was called by his father.

She will lift me to her unfathomable bosom and my offering may save the world. For Those Above will return and heal it.

And my mother, if she still has a face to do so, she will smile.

Gate 9

Jeffrey Ford

WE HAD LESS than a half hour to get from one plane to another. The airport was crazy with holiday travelers. I had on a backpack, dragged a small roller suitcase, and held my five-year-old daughter's hand. I walked as fast as I could and she ran and hopped to keep up. The thoroughfares of the terminal could be measured in miles. I watched those beeping carts go by and wished I had the courage to pretend to be impaired. Instead, my gut and bad knee and the cigarette addiction I was hiding from Suzie and the kids latched on like lead remoras and said, Not so fast. At one point in the scurry, Karlee tripped and fell. I managed to keep her from hitting the floor by grabbing tight and jerking my arm up. She dangled like a doll and I set her down easy. I stopped, let go of the suitcase, and kneeled to speak to her.

"I'm going too fast. I'm sorry," I said. She rubbed her eyes, still sleepy from the flight, and said, "Are we meeting Mommy soon?"

"No, babe, we gotta go on one more plane before we see her." She lowered her head, her bottom lip curled, and as her brown hair came down around her face, I noticed tears forming in the corners of her eyes. The kid was exhausted with the whole rigmarole and I couldn't blame her. I hugged her and told her not to cry, which is always a stupid thing to say. In that instant, a brainstorm moved in from my own North Sea, and I said, "Would you like to ride on my shoulders?"

Instantly, she perked up. Pushing back, she gave me a skeptical one-eyed squint but still smiled. "Up here?" she said and patted my neck.

I nodded. "You're gonna have to hold on tight."

"OK," she said.

I stood and lifted her under the arms, way up so she could get her legs around my neck. As soon as she was in place, I grabbed her right calf so even if she fell backward, I wouldn't lose her. For her part, she clasped her fingers under my chin.

"Giddyup," she said and slammed the heels of her sneakers into my chest. I laughed and, grabbing the suitcase, I struck out again for Gate 9. On our right, I noticed we were just passing Gate 53. "Shit,"

I murmured and tried to put on some speed. From above came Karlee's voice: "I heard that, Steve." Mommy was mommy, and even though I was her biological father, I was Steve and had never been anything else. I was uncertain if that conferred more or less grace upon me.

The only thing that had saved me to that point was electric walkways. By the time I'd cover the quarter mile between them, I was bent over, wheezing, on my last legs. Then, like an answered prayer, we'd be caught up and whisked along, smooth silence, for a measly hundred yards before being deposited back into the rat race of the concourse. Still, it was enough for me to straighten up partway and catch my breath.

I thought Karlee had fallen asleep. Her arms were still around my neck and her hands beneath my chin. I was just beginning to lose feeling in the hand I had clutched on her calf. We were passing Gate 32, and I was having delusions of grandeur of making the flight with minutes to kill wherein I could get a cup of coffee. That's when Karlee knocked on my head the way you would a door, leaned down to put her lips next to my ear, and said in a breathy voice, "I have to go."

I stopped dead in my tracks. My mind went instantly blank. For as smart as I always believed myself to be, I'd never planned for this contingency. The moment she spoke, all of the inherent issues were brilliantly evident to me. I never traveled with the kids without my wife. I thought, when I finally tell Suzie about this, she's going to shake her head and pronounce me a rank amateur of a parent.

To the left, a few yards forward was the entrance to a women's bathroom. On the other side of the thoroughfare was a men's room.

"Did you hear me, Steve?" she asked.

We were an obstacle in the flow of foot traffic. I walked on as far as the bathroom, Karlee wriggling on my shoulders. I had to decide something pretty quick. My first thought was that I could take her into the men's room with me. But I imagined what Suzie would do with our son, Munro, if they were in the same situation. I couldn't see her taking him into a ladies' room. He was older, though, by two years. Still, it didn't seem right, and I had a vision in my head of a line of guys at the urinals, who all turned to look at us and for some reason raised their right hands in unison as if an act from a Broadway show.

So that was out, and no one was going to be understanding of me taking her into the women's bathroom. If I'd had more time, I would have railed against the fact that the airport didn't have family bathrooms where Mom, Dad, and the kids could all hang as a nuclear unit while one of them took a piss. I needed quick thinking, imagination and action, all of which were in short supply in my travel-addled mind.

As we stood there, Karlee still on my shoulders, an older woman walked by on her way to the bathroom. She looked up at Karlee and waved to her with a big smile. Karlee let go of my chin with one hand and I assumed it was to wave back. At age five she was already a social creature like her mother, open-hearted and affable. My son was more like me, quiet and sketchy. Before I knew it, I was saying, "Excuse me, ma'am, would you mind taking my daughter into the bathroom? We're running late for our gate and she really has to go." I realized immediately I could have been more eloquent. My plea oozed desperation.

The white-haired woman stopped, looked us over, continuing to smile, but did not answer immediately. I lifted Karlee and set her down on her feet. She hopped around while we waited for an answer. I could tell right away the kid was fine with having this nice old lady escort her. During the pause, which lasted only a second, I assessed the woman to make sure I hadn't made a mistake in trying to enlist her help. Only as I gave her closer scrutiny did I notice that her brow and cheeks were rippling with wrinkles, reminding me of Pruneface from the Dick Tracy comic. I took in her necklace of hot-pink beads, like giant pearls from a black-light poster. Her dress was a shade of turquoise, and, on her breast, she wore a pin in the shape of an odd insignia—a stylized eye with a centered arrow pointing straight up from the top of the lid, and a mirror arrow on the bottom side pointing straight down. The pupil in the silver-wire eye was a perfect circle of green glass.

"Certainly," she said, nodding. She lifted her left arm, to reposition the strap of her big purse, and with the opposite hand reached toward Karlee. "Thank you," I told her. "You're really getting me out of a jam.

"Are you all right with this?" I asked Karlee.

"Steve," she said and shook her head.

"Relax, Dad," said the woman with a smile. "My name is Edna Gray, and I have years of experience. I'm a parent too. Two boys, two girls. They're all at least as old as you."

I mustered a laugh, but it didn't matter because the two of them were off, hand in hand, discussing something. They disappeared through the open entrance, and I realized I had to pee too. Not wasting a second, with my roller suitcase in tow, I bolted across the thoroughfare to the men's room. Despite my vivid imagining there was no chorus line at the urinals. It was empty. The place stunk of turnips and turpentine, and I wondered what poor soul had given birth to that stink. There was a definite chemical edge to it.

I relieved myself with alacrity and efficiency. There was no way Karlee was even on the bowl yet. She had on a pair of tights under her dress, which would slow things down. I gave my hands the most cursory washing, dashed out of the bathroom and across to the entrance of the women's room. No one was standing there, and I breathed a sigh of relief that Karlee didn't have to come out and find me gone. While I waited for them, I thought about how a cigarette would really hit the spot at that juncture—a little nicotine kick to help me run the remaining mile gauntlet to Gate 9. After that I checked the time on my phone. If she hurried, we'd have a good fifteen minutes.

Back in high school I had run the mile in a little over four minutes. It'd been twenty-plus years since then. Staring into the distance, I came up with a half-assed algorithm that factored in age, weight, general health, the tendency of my left Achilles tendon to blow out, and the cigs, of course. The number that popped up at the end of this evidence-based process was ten. I figured, even limping along, I could do a ten-minute mile. Nothing to be proud of but realistic. Right then, I heard a distant sound beneath the general hubbub of the airport, like a roll of thunder in the next county, and realized it was a toilet flushing.

I tried hard to prevent myself from picturing our arrival at Gate 9. I expected any second to hear Karlee's voice, and pictured Suzie meeting us at the gate in Columbus. Since my wife had a speaking gig in town for two days, she'd gone on ahead of us and taken Munro. That way we only had to have one kid in day care. I couldn't get away because of work, so it was me and Karlee. Suzie and I talked it over and she told me I could do it, no sweat. As far as bathing, dressing, feeding, I was aces. Suzie was just confident with the kids, though. No happenstance could distract her. She was imbued with steadfastness and courage. The difference between us was like the difference between a real parent and a wax parent from Madame Tussauds'.

I looked up and there was no little girl holding the hand of a wrinkled old lady exiting the women's room. Instead, a middle-aged woman in a blue dress, shoulder-length brown hair, came into view. I must have taken a step forward in anticipation of meeting Karlee, and in doing so had landed perilously close to the entrance. The woman in blue made a face at me and said, "Back off, creep." I put my hands up in front of me and stammered an apology. I told her, "My little girl is in there," and she shook her head before disappearing into the flow of the thoroughfare.

I checked the time on my phone, and a good four minutes had passed since I'd calculated that I only had a quarter hour left. "Jesus Christ," I said under my breath. "Let's get on with it." I paced back and forth, did a whole ten trips before I checked the time on my phone again. When I glanced up, I noticed a woman in a white business suit, carrying a briefcase, approaching the entrance. Her long blonde hair was spiraled into a bun on top of her head. She looked wealthy and for some reason—although in most circumstances I would think the exact opposite—I immediately believed she would be trustworthy.

"Excuse me," I said. "If you see an old lady and a little girl in there, could you tell them we need to hurry?"

At first, she looked put out by my request, but once she heard it all the way through, she smiled and nodded and I breathed a sigh of relief. She disappeared through the entrance, and in my imagination, I pictured us arriving at Gate 9 and its being completely empty but for an overexaggeratedly pleasant young man behind the counter who made a fake pity face I wanted to punch when he informed me we'd just missed the flight. As that was playing behind my eyes, I witnessed a veritable wave of women charge through the entrance to the bathroom. They came from every direction at once and they all walked swiftly and stiffly as if urgently needing to relieve themselves. I stepped back to let the caravan pass, knowing I had my agent with the briefcase in there.

Seconds passed, minutes passed, and the ladies of the wave began filtering out onto the thoroughfare. At this juncture, behind my eyes, I *was* punching the attendant behind the counter at Gate 9. Landed a couple dead center on his tractor seat of a face, a couple to the ribs. As he slipped down toward the floor, I heard a voice say, "Excuse me, sir." I came to as if I'd been in a trance, my heart pounding and sweat on my brow like I really had gone rounds with that obsequious gate attendant. The woman in white shifted her briefcase from one hand to the other. "I didn't see them. They must have been in one of the stalls. But I thought I might have heard a child's voice." With this, she turned and walked away.

That was it. I had no idea how much time was left. Trembling slightly, I took out my phone and dialed Suzie. She picked up immediately and in a harsh whisper said, "I'm in the middle of my panel on Trigonometric Reconstruction."

Fearing she might hang up on me, I yelled, "Wait, Karlee is missing."

"Hold on," she said and I could hear her leaving the lecture hall and going through a door into silence. "What did you just say?" she asked.

"Karlee. I asked this nice old lady to take her into the bathroom, and she did. But I've been standing here for a long time and they haven't come out."

"How long?"

"More than ten minutes. We're gonna miss our flight."

"Why are you calling me?" she asked.

Her question brought me up short and I didn't know what to say. "Can you tell me what I should do?"

Then her words came like a blaring horn in my ear. "What are you waiting for? Get the fuck in there and grab her, you idiot. Who knows what could be going on?"

I hung up quick and lunged toward the entrance. As I did, there was a woman approaching I didn't see at first. We nearly collided in the doorway, and I said to her, "I'm sorry, but my wife told me to go in here."

She looked at me with wide eyes and backed slowly away.

"To get my daughter," I added.

She turned and fled.

"Sorry," I called after her. Then I passed through the opening into a realm of gray tile. Gray tiles on the floor, all the way up the high walls, and around the sinks and mirrors. I looked down the row of stalls and its large emptiness made me slightly dizzy. There was some dark secret of a scent that stood the hair at the back of my neck on end, and the place was dead silent. The brightness of sun that shone through the semiopaque window at the far end, set high up by the ceiling, drained away as no doubt some massive cloud rolled in.

"Karlee," I yelled.

I listened hard. This time I heard a drip here or there, the secret whir of the water in a leaky tank. I had Suzie's mandate, so I let go the suitcase on wheels, dropped the backpack, and barged forth, pushing stall doors open to see inside. I went down the long row of compartments, and, hoping I could catch anybody who had been hiding and tried to flee, I walked back to the first stall in the opposite row.

145

Now all manner of visions swept through my head. I was frantic, expecting to see Karlee's body, limp in one of the stalls. My thoughts went back to her patting me on the neck earlier and saying, "Up here?" I saw her face—big green eyes, her smile.

I came to the last stall and it was locked from within. I rattled it and screamed for whoever was in there to open up. No response, so I got down on the floor and started pulling myself under the door. When I was halfway through, I heard the distant voice of the terminal loudspeaker announce that our plane was boarding. I was just going to have to forget making that flight.

I was out of breath from all the exertion, and it took a while for me to make it, but eventually I got in there. Somehow, the toilet was gone as if it had been ripped out of the floor, and in the dark, jagged opening where it had been, I could see a ladder running down into the underground. I realized Karlee had been kidnapped. It felt like somebody had a hand in my chest and squeezed my heart. My mind went into a tornado of confusion and I was blithering, choking.

What cut through the bullshit was a vision of having to confront Suzie with the news. In it, both she and Karlee were standing with their arms folded waiting for my explanation. I took out my phone and turned on the flashlight. There was nothing else to do but descend, which I did, nearly losing my step twice and plummeting thirty feet. I finally arrived on the ground safely, but not before a couple of bats flew past my face. Turning and scanning with the flashlight, I was amazed. There were actual stalactites and stalagmites everywhere, like a cavern instead of the airport basement I'd expected.

I walked forward to where the rocky vault opened wider and I could see that below me, down a sloping incline, there was a road through the underground darkness. Also a streetlight with an old brown Cadillac parked under it. I could definitely make out a figure in the front seat. I started down the hill, wondering what I was going to have to do to get Karlee back. I could already feel my Achilles tendon acting up. The fear that had built as I waited outside the women's bathroom had drained me and left me exhausted. Still, I knew I might have to fight to the death. It was ridiculous, but on some occasions, life does reveal its absurdity. Either way, Karlee's life was in danger. Old Steve was just going to have to reach back for something extra. First time in my life I ever wished I had a gun.

I approached the car. Both front windows were open and the driver was smoking a cigarette. I ducked down and she turned suddenly to look at me. "Hey, are you that guy whose kid was boosted?" she asked.

146

"You know about it?"

She flipped open her wallet and showed me some kind of badge. "Detective Sinch. I've been assigned to the case."

"Can you help me?"

"Get in," she said.

I did and she started the car. It was cold underground, like late autumn, complete with wind, and she wore a big canvas coat the color of an impala. Her face was ruddy with a nose like an eagle's beak and a crew cut. Not a minute passed between cigarettes; a chain smoker if I ever saw one.

We drove into the pitch-black of the underground. I don't know how she stayed on the road. "Got a source who tells me your daughter's kidnappers are holed up in an abandoned house out behind Spies Orchard."

"How did you find out about it?"

"We keep an eye on everything."

"Well, you didn't keep a very good eye on my daughter," I said, unable to believe I'd said it.

"That's the breaks, motherfucker."

We drove deeper and deeper into the dark and she leaned forward and pushed the radio button. The songs came and went. We were certainly driving farther than I'd expected. I asked if she had a plan.

She told me, "I'm just going in blazing. I'll mop these jackoffs up and then we free the kid."

"Don't be reckless," I warned. "You'll end up shooting her."

"Take five," she said and lit another cig.

A song came on the radio and Detective Sinch gave a whoop, turning the sound up. "Love this one," she said and sang along in a voice worse than mine, to the tune of "Your Violent Breath." There was banjo and pedal steel, and a lazy sweetness to it. The only lines I could remember were, "I lean in close, for a wanton kiss, and suffer a fifth of death. Your beauty is dangerous, but oh, my lord, that violent breath."

As the last notes of the song sounded, we came up out of the underground on an inclined ramp running through a tunnel that released us into a rural night scene. The moon was bright, and we passed miles of barbed-wire fences, behind which were lumbering shadows—cows perhaps, horses—that made strange choking noises. Returning to the world above made me yet more nervous, knowing we'd be facing off against the kidnappers soon.

"OK, here we go," said Detective Sinch, turning off the radio. She pulled into the opening of a dirt road that snaked through pine trees. The car slowed and with her free hand she put her index finger to her lips. "Don't do anything until I tell you to," she whispered. The car came to a halt. She turned it off and we cautiously got out. I noticed she had a gun in each hand, both some kind of 9-millimeter.

"You've got two guns," I said. "Can I get one?"

She moved toward the house. "Fat chance," she said. Once the words were out of her mouth, she took off running. Before I could even marshal the effort to follow her, she was on the broken-down front porch of what appeared in the dark to be a log cabin. It all happened so fast. I heard the door squeal open and then she shrieked, "Fuck you, shit heels." The shooting started and I hit the ground and prayed that one of those bullets hadn't hit Karlee.

I crawled on my belly toward the porch, the shooting went on and on, and then Sinch came stumbling backward through the door with a spray of blood coming from her neck. On her way to the ground, she took aim and shot her assailant, who stood at the door. A direct hit to the gut. He fell forward onto the porch. I got up and ran to the detective, but she was dead by the time I reached her. I grabbed one of the guns. I had no idea whether it was loaded.

Before stepping over the writhing body in the doorway, I kicked his gun away into the yard. He wasn't going anywhere. Inside, in a living-room area, there were two men, obviously killed by Sinch. I listened hard but didn't hear any other noise in the house. I went back to the guy in the doorway. "Where's my daughter? Look, you've got a chance to live," I said and aimed the gun at him. I wasn't so sure of what I was saying. Bleeding out all over the place, he shook his head.

I aimed as best I could and pulled the trigger. The bullet smashed through his shinbone and revealed a jagged white edge before the blood came and the errant bits of meat landed.

"Next I'm gonna shoot you in the balls," I said.

"No," he pleaded.

"Where is she?"

He forced a laugh.

I took aim.

"She's in the bathroom down the hall. I dragged her in there myself. She's been in there since we got here." Then he laughed more and pointed at me.

I shot him in his big balding head and shut him up.

Down the hallway from the living room, there was a body dead on the floor. It was Edna Gray, the old woman who'd taken Karlee into the bathroom. It looked like Sinch had drilled her through the left eye. Her glasses were still on her face, but one lens was shattered and covered in blood. In her open palm lay a .38 special. There was a fold-out chair next to the bathroom door, as if the old lady had been sitting guard. I breathed deeply and then knocked on the door. "Karlee," I called. "It's Steve. I'm here."

I almost tried the doorknob but stopped myself. After waiting a few more breaths, I knocked again. Silence but for the night wind outside. I sat down on the chair, thinking I'd just wait a while to go in. I had a picture in my mind of Karlee, curled up, asleep in the empty bathtub with a bed pillow under her head and a blue blanket over her. I waited and waited, fearing I'd lose the image if I moved.

The Baby-Monitor
Joyce Carol Oates

1.

IF YOU WOULD KNOW FEAR, bring a baby into the world.

2.

It wasn't the mother's idea to move the baby's crib out of the parents' bedroom after six harrowing months of sleep riddled with interruptions like hailstones against windowpanes. Nor was it the mother's idea to install a Security Optics Baby-Monitor System in the nursery adjacent to the parents' bedroom. Still less the mother's idea to upgrade the Baby-Monitor as soon as it was installed to include such luxury features as real-time audio with a seven-volume level/two-way talk system/digital zoom for ultra-close-up viewing/rechargeable battery/night-vision.

(Especially, ghastly "night vision" the mother would not have chosen. Had the mother had any choice.)

3.

Since the "nursery" was next door to the parents' bedroom, the mother insisted it was no trouble for her to make her way to the baby when he fretted or fussed or cried to be fed in the night or because his diaper was soaked. As her mother, and her mother's mother, and that mother's mother had not required a ridiculous electronic device to alert her to the visceral needs of her infant, so this mother protested that she preferred to be summoned to her baby in the time-honored way: roused by the baby's bloodcurdling cat cry or by the mildest baby whimper as audible to the hypersensitive mother's ear through the bedroom wall as giant crab claws scratching against the wall would have been audible. Instantaneously hearing such a baby sound, the mother is *awake*. Strike of a match illuminating the vast night sky, the mother is *awake*. Bloodshot eyes springing open out of a tangle of numbed ganglia, the mother is *awake*. Out of a yeasty-warm bed

150

leaving the obliviously sleeping husband behind like a mere mound of laundry or indeed a sodden insensate corpse, the mother makes her quick-stumbling-barefoot way into the nursery next door unerring as an arrow shot from a bow and within breathless seconds she is at the baby's crib preparing to lift the dense hot miracle weight of the baby gently in her arms to comfort the baby if he is fretting, to change his diaper or to nurse him if he is hungry (oh, Baby is always hungry!— the mother's astonishing heavy, aching breasts already leaking milk in anticipation of Baby's sucking lips) or if it has been a false alarm, no actual cry the mother imagined she'd heard, not to disturb the sleeping baby after all but to stand above him as her racing heartbeat slows and her quickened breathing returns to near normal gazing down at *her baby* with that helpless, swooning love that is indistinguishable from terror.

For one person alone of all the world living now or who has ever lived is *this baby's mother.*

4.

And that person: *her.*

And so, the responsibility to keep the baby alive: *hers.*

5.

Politely explaining to the father of the baby no, she didn't see the need.

Yes she understood, yes she was grateful for the in-laws' generosity, but no—not another electronic device in the house.

And this one, in their bedroom. Security Optics Baby-Monitor System! *Night-vision* screen! Ridiculous.

Telling him, the father of the baby, that there was something unnatural and grotesque about it: installing the Baby-Monitor in their lives. Instead of sleeping normally, or hoping to, lying in bed obsessed with keeping your baby alive and so compelled to watch your baby sleep in the blurry black-and-white screen through the long hours of the night like a sort of shell-less mollusk in a crib.

Timothy laughed, annoyed. Surely she had to be exaggerating?

Pointing out that there was certainly no need to stay awake staring at the Baby-Monitor. No need to become *obsessed* (her word, not his).

"You don't even need to look at it. We'll put it on my side of the bed. We can turn it off actually. Where's the harm? My mother only wants to be helpful."

In the husband's voice an air of exasperation, reproach. The slightest suggestion that Lori was being critical of his parents, especially his mother, the husband's voice thinned and rose an octave, a warning.

And so quickly Lori amended: Yes, of course she was grateful. His parents were so kind, generous. As always.

The in-laws who'd purchased so many expensive/mostly useless things for the baby, their first grandchild. Every sort of impedimenta relating to *new baby* they'd ordered online for months in an orgy of *new baby gifts* for the in-laws had money, and they had time, for each was retired from longtime employment and at a time in their lives when their expansive lifestyle was no longer rewarding to them, Timothy's mother was feverish with excitement in her new, much-anticipated role as *grandmother*.

She, the baby's mother, had to be careful not to offend. For if you accept your in-laws' "extra" car, if you accept your in-laws' financial aid in purchasing a house, you are not in a strong moral position to politely decline lesser gifts and bounties without giving the appearance of being a hypocrite.

Explaining to Timothy that she was grateful for the gift but concerned that they already spent so many of their waking hours staring at electronic *screens*. Much of the day at their work, computers. Cell phones, iPads. Their eyes were fixed upon simulacra of people and things and not actual people and things and surely their brains were being altered for the worse.

"Isn't it well known that these devices are spying on *us*? Recording *us*? Our lives are under constant surveillance and we don't seem to care, isn't that strange? *Why* has that happened?"

Lori, addressing Timothy, in her most reasonable voice, yet sounding nonetheless plaintive, pleading. Always there is weakness in pleading.

Timothy seemed unmoved. For all they knew, these were just "scare tactics"—that we're living in a surveillance state, or will soon be living in a surveillance state. "Collecting data is mostly for advertising purposes, I think. Targeting potential customers."

Timothy, long a vehement defender of privacy, individual rights, free speech, freedom of the press!—exasperating to Lori, hearing him speak now so negligently.

Because he's defending his mother. Never position yourself between your husband and his mother.

"... what I mean is, it's *unnatural*. Being with the baby in the daytime is natural but spying on the baby in the night is something else. No one in the past had anything like 'Baby-Monitors'—parents, grandparents, ancestors. . . ."

Lori's voice trailed off weakly. How inane she was sounding. How *fearful*.

Timothy laughed, as if embarrassed for her. Saying she'd never used to exaggerate so much. Lately now . . .

[*Lately now.* Lori is offended by these words. This new imbalance between them. As if giving birth, and before that the pregnancy that had seemed both ennobling and humbling, and interminable, have cast wife and husband in new roles for which neither is prepared and she, the designated/inevitable "mother," finds herself in the demeaning position of needing to defend herself against an earlier version of herself.]

Timothy points out that the Baby-Monitor is supposed to help prevent—what's it called?—"SIDS. Crib death. But how would the Baby-Monitor prevent that? If the baby just—stops breathing? In the night? Would it make any sound at all?"

At this Lori froze.

Why, *why* would a husband say such a thing. *Father* of an infant just six months old.

Seeing the look on Lori's face, stricken, frightened, Timothy reached for her hands, his wife's icy hands he squeezed, the chafed-skin hands he squeezed, hands that didn't feel like his wife's hands but like the hands of a stranger, somewhat coarse, unyielding, hostile to him as if to very maleness and the power to wound that is the power of maleness and so he laughed, tried to laugh, cajoling the woman, the mother, his wife to laugh, to laugh in the old easy-intimate way, the way of coconspirators that was becoming lost to them as a language not spoken becomes by degrees lost, indecipherable.

"Sorry, honey. That was stupid. How often do infants die in their cribs—must be one in a literal million, or more."

Closing his arms around her, to gather her to him. To console, and comfort.

"... just something I read in the brochure. Forget I mentioned it."

For of course Lori was right, they didn't need more gadgets in the household, more expensive devices to break down, and yes, there was something *unnatural* about it, any sort of *surveillance* about which the object of the surveillance isn't conscious, where you can see someone without them seeing you.

"We can keep the stupid thing in a box; my mother won't know."
Timothy spoke with husbandly passion, squeezing the hand of the
mother of the baby to assure her, *Hey, look, I am on your side.*

6.

No one is on your side. Essentially, you are alone.
Alone with your baby it is your responsibility to keep alive.

7.

Like loose-fitting rivets the days hold, just barely.

That night in the hours after midnight staring with fascination at
the small electronic screen at eye level several feet away as she lies
in bed in the darkened bedroom while beside her oblivious of her
insomniac vigil the father of the baby sleeps facing the contrary
direction for of course once the terrible words were uttered by him—
SIDS, crib death—it was clear that, following the principle of cosmic
irony inherited from her fatalistic Eastern European peasant ancestors, *of course the baby will die if the damned Baby-Monitor isn't
installed.*

And, yes, on her side of the bed. *Her side.*

In these hours after midnight the mother's glazed eyes are focused
upon the figure of the sleeping baby in his cradle inside the six-inch-
by-eight-inch screen. A shadowy figure as in an ultrasound. Reduced
and diminished so that it doesn't resemble a human baby so much as
an amoeba with rudimentary facial features—(shut) eyes, (very small)
nose, (snail-sized) lips.

Baby appears to be mostly head, torso, arms. Tiny hands resembling those flipper-hands growing from the shoulders of thalidomide
babies the mother has seen in ghastly archival photographs.

(But how is this possible, the mother wonders. *She* had not taken
thalidomide during the pregnancy, had she?—the era of thalidomide
was decades ago.)

In the darkened bedroom minutes pass with excruciating slowness. Soon it will be, should be, time for Baby's next feeding: a relief.

When at last there is *no possibility* of sleep, when Baby begins to
wail, a relief to be *fully awake.*

. . . stumbling into the nursery, baring the lesser aching of her
breasts.

When Baby slept in the room with them there'd been no ambiguity about Baby's need, which woke them immediately like artillery fire.

Now with Baby at a distance on the farther side of walls there is the likelihood of error. She has abandoned her baby, trusting to the Baby-Monitor camera installed in the other room above the crib.

Very tired, and her eyelids very heavy. Pleasurably tired. Anything to do with the miraculous birth is *pleasurable*.

After the fact, that is. Before, when the great effort lay ahead, there was primarily apprehension for *what if*.

(Out of *what if*, all fear springs. Purest terror.)

After a very long day of performing as the mother of a baby less than a year old requiring the repeated execution of a sequence of tasks focused upon the *baby body*—(changing diaper, bathing, nursing/feeding)—(changing diaper, bathing, nursing/feeding)—focused now in the stillness of night upon the glassy screen shimmering a few feet away in the dark.

Peering at the baby in the monitor, seeing to her relief that the tiny hands are attached to normal baby arms—of course.

And these tiny hands quivering so that the mother is reassured, *Yes, your baby is alive, don't be ridiculous.*

Safe for the mother of the baby to sleep now. Allow her heavy-lidded eyes to shut. Allow her hypervigilant brain to shut down. But disconcerting, how the *night-vision* screen is eerily leached of color like a scene in an old newsreel. Not clearly defined black and white as in a photograph but blurred and gauzy shades of gray like shifting mists in a perilous landscape at which the mother stares intrigued as if at a newsreel of another era, another lifetime in which the sleeping baby in the monitor isn't Baby but a stranger's baby for whom the mother need not feel any emotion other than a generic-human concern and compassion for an infant of her own species. In this case a long-ago baby, unnamed, possibly even a "foreign" baby, no longer living anywhere except in the newsreel and no longer recalled by anyone living for all who'd lived at that time are not living now.

One, among millions. And all perished.

Certainly, it is recommended that the mother of the baby sleep for as long as the baby allows her to sleep. A normal baby can sleep for as long as fifteen hours within a span of twenty-four hours, unfortunately not usually for more than a very few hours at a time.

The baby doctor recommended moving the newborn to another

155

room after six months so that the parents' sleep will be less interrupted. For each has been suffering from sleep deprivation and with sleep deprivation a certain edginess, shortness of nerves and of breath, a general anxiety heightened in their case since they'd delayed having a baby until the mother was forty years old and the father forty-four.

Recovery from the C-section is slower than anticipated. As the excessive weight she'd gained is slow to melt away.

Because you are not young enough. Why did you wait so long! Out of fear. Unnamed.

Still leaking blood into her underwear, most days. Ravaged uterus, slow to heal. If she moves too abruptly her pelvic area is wracked with pain.

Sleep is recommended yet the mother understands that she *must not* allow her eyes to close even for a few seconds. That is the trick, the temptation. *Must not* sleep for something is likely to happen to the baby that would (certainly) not happen without the Baby-Monitor to record it.

Lifting herself on one elbow, seeing that Baby (in the monitor) appears to be stirring.

Time for the 2:00 a.m. feeding?—she feels the *frisson* of dread, anticipation.

Heavy breasts like sacs filled tight with warm water. Beginning to leak at just the thought of nursing the baby.

Life in the body: so much *wet*.

Initially, nursing had been painful. Baby sucking at the mother's nipple, which is one of the most sensitive parts of the mother's body, almost unbearably sensitive to the slightest feathery touch let alone Baby's robust sucking.

Like the female genitals. *Clitoris:* almost unbearably sensitive, sheerly nerve endings.

The mother of the baby shudders, recalling. For *life in the body* is the challenge.

In the monitor, Baby seems to have shrunken.

Is this Baby, in his crib in the nursery, or is this the six-month fetus in the ultrasound photograph?—Lori remembers staring at it, being shown the X-ray in the doctor's office at the clinic.

For a moment, Lori is confused. Brain befuddled, confusing the image on the screen with the ultrasound: if this is the ultrasound of the baby at six months it means that the ordeal of the delivery is still ahead. (Frankly) not sure she can survive it a second time.

156

Contractions striking her lower body like bolts of electricity, she'd screamed for help. Screamed until her throat was raw. If she'd known what this would be, what the pain would be like, *no pregnancy no husband no thanks!*

Never forgive the man, for precipitating such an ordeal. Her very body, distended, twisted out of shape.

"Oh God!"—her eyes spring open. For a moment no idea where she is.

(Has she been asleep? How long? Despite knowing that *she cannot allow herself to sleep.*)

Seeing the luminous screen a few feet away. Remembering now.

But something has changed: shadows fall over Baby like the shadows of circling predator birds.

Trying to remain calm, she fumbles for the remote on the floor beside the bed. She will *zoom* closer to the baby, to see what this is. Something in motion, undulating shadows—*wings?* Has a bird made its way into the nursery, or a bat?—but no window is open, she is certain.

As if the undulating shadows have wakened him, Baby has begun fretting. He is not entirely awake but he is waking. Tiny eyes fluttering open, those astonishing miniature eyelashes. Pudgy baby arms, flailing. Lori can see, disbelieving, appalled, that the silhouette of a sharp-beaked bird has fallen over Baby's face.

Baby's mouth opens in a (silent, anguished) scream.

The mother of the baby throws off the bedclothes beneath which she has been lying on her left side observing the monitor. In frantic haste she has forgotten the father of the baby entirely, as during the long days when Baby and Mommy are alone together in the most exquisite intimacy excluding all others, she feels no resentment of him, no envy that he can continue to sleep heavy as sodden laundry in blissful obliviousness of her and of the baby for she has known from the start of the pregnancy that she is alone in this; in this matter of the baby, the responsibility falls entirely upon her, like a mountain landslide.

You are in this alone, you wanted this. You have no one but yourself.

Stumbling into the nursery panicked. Grateful for the low-wattage Mother Goose on the floor behind the crib, kept on through the night. Relieved to see that there are no birds, no bats, no wings fluttering above Baby—of course.

But Baby is certainly awake now and frightened and his crying is shrill as clashing cymbals.

Further relief: Baby is normal sized (of course) and not the freakish amoeba baby of the monitor. Not a long-forgotten infant in a newsreel. How ridiculous, Mommy's worries!

"Oh, sweetie! Stop."

Lifting the wailing baby from his crib. Out of the coils of sleep ganglia threading through her brain.

Twinge of pain in the uterus not (yet) recovered from the trauma of the surgical delivery six months before.

"No more crying! Mommy is here."

Her heartbeat is returning to normal. All of her senses aroused, rush of adrenaline as if she'd prepared to confront an (unknown) adversary but all is normal—of course.

Fleeting dreams, hallucinations. Still she resists taking medication; she will not succumb to weakness.

It looks as if Baby's diaper needs to be changed—of course.

The miniature lips blindly seek the milky breast, the hot little body quivers with appetite.

Mommy laughs; Baby appetite is so fierce! Good that Baby has just one small, soft baby tooth, which can't do too much damage.

Since she'd begun nursing, awkwardly at first, wincing with discomfort, she has been noticing sharp, stabbing, fleeting pains in her left breast. Torments herself thinking—*Not possible that I have cancer! That I have cancer too.*

Cruel cosmic irony in which, as an educated woman unencumbered by foolish folk superstitions, Lori certainly does not believe.

But it *is* some sort of irony, to be inhabiting a female body: (ravaged) uterus, (splayed) pelvis, (stubbly-haired) groin, heavy-hanging udders grazing her upper belly.

She lifts the baby's eager mouth to the fattish right breast, blindly pushing mouth and breast together. At once Baby ceases crying. At once Baby begins sucking. Remember to secure the nursing baby in the crook of her right arm. Support the baby's delicate head, neck. (Still, parts of Baby's skull have not hardened; he seems to have no neck at all. Slowest of magic, Baby's cartilage-soft knees are acquiring bone.) Though steeled for discomfort, the mother is never quite prepared for the shock of the sensitive nipple being so robustly tugged at, sucked.

Praying, *O God* the baby will not reject her milk. For a mother's milk *is* her.

Soon then, after an erratic rhythm is established, waves of pleasure, a dark sort of pleasure rooted in the groin, the mother's eyes roll back in their sockets and her breath comes short.

158

Dense-heated little body secure in her arms all of it *hers*.

Cobalt-blue eyes of heart-stopping beauty moistly fixed upon *her*.

8.

"Hey!—wondered where you were, hon."

In the morning wakened by a jarring, jovial voice. The man, the husband calling to her from the doorway of the nursery as if across an abyss.

Where she, mother of the baby, lies sated, sprawled on the sofa like one who has fallen from a great height. Sleeping Baby hot-humid in her arms, flannel nightgown smelling of her yeasty body tugged off one shoulder and a fat bun of a breast bared, wrinkly nipple encrusted with dried milk (*not* semen) so that the man in the doorway is made to feel uneasy, a voyeur, an intruder, inanely smiling, guilty faced, rueful at having slept through the night for the first time in a very long time and flush with gratitude even as he feels a twinge of revulsion for the slattern wife, a stranger to him, each day, each night ever more the mother of the baby becoming a stranger to him, with the pregnancy gaining weight in belly, hips, thighs like sponge rubber of the sickly-white hue of lard.

All this sweeping over the husband, who is also the father of the baby, in the instant of staring across the abyss at the woman asprawl with a baby in her arms.

Realizing: until the baby had come into their lives his (fastidious) wife had avoided being seen by him in any disheveled state: uncombed hair, rumpled clothing, slovenly posture. And now, swath of fatty thighs, striations in the flesh, swollen ankles once slim as a ballerina's exposed to the husband's startled gaze. How has it happened, Lori has become so *physical*? After twelve years of marriage there remains between husband and wife a habit of formality, reserve, unease at intimacy yet the husband feels now the shock of arousal at the sight of the wife, a sharp sexual stab in the groin, unmistakable.

Unless it's a faint nausea at the odor of Baby diaper, sweet-rancid dried breast milk wafting to his nostrils.

"Oh, hon. Look at you. *Love you.*"

9.

Except the thought assails her—*But someday you won't. You will abandon us.*

159

Where did this fear originate?—no idea.

For suddenly there are myriad *fears*, tributaries flowing into the singular river *Fear*.

Suddenly a rational person has become a *fearful* person, one with everything to lose: baby, husband, marriage. Baby.

That had been the start: the day, the hour she'd learned definitively that she was pregnant, in the doctor's office. In her haste to call Timothy her thumbs had so fumbled the numerals on her cell phone she'd wondered if she'd had a mild stroke.

For all that is given to you can be taken away.

10.

. . . a kind of experiment, she thinks. Harmless!

Alone in the house as late afternoon slides into dusk. On the CD player late-Beethoven string quartets. That their baby will *hear*, *absorb* such music.

Each baby *is* an experiment, in fact. But most experimentation is unintended, unconscious.

She positions the baby (securely) inside several goose-feather pillows, facing a tall window shimmering with late-afternoon light. She positions the Baby-Monitor camera close by, slightly elevated and looking down at the baby; hurries then upstairs to the bedroom where the monitor is positioned on her side of the bed.

No danger in leaving Baby alone in these circumstances because she can observe him in the monitor clearly and in full color: his curious, alert features, the movements of his baby hands, the remarkable roundness of his eyes, which resemble neither Timothy's eyes nor her own.

Each baby is an alien being. Each baby, a mutant.

She'd taken cello lessons in high school, she'd been said to have been "promising."

Hearing the cello played perfectly on the Beethoven CD she feels an obscure loss, and shame for that loss, that she'd aspired to another life, a lifetime ago; she'd loved the cello, or had thought that she did, but not enough, finally.

Baby would be her true accomplishment, she thinks.

This new fascination has come upon her, to watch the screen during the day, to observe carefully all that Baby does when she isn't in the room with him, how he frets, his forehead crinkling, how the cobalt-blue eyes dart about, the little fists flail. Baby *is not hungry*—

he has had a feeding recently. Yet, Baby behaves as if he is hungry in some way, that has not (yet) come into focus.

Also: to keep her eyes open and alert to that exquisite moment when the Baby-Monitor ceases registering *day* and begins to register *night*. Color in the screen disappears in the blink of an eye like a switch turned off, each afternoon a little earlier as the earth turns on its axis in anticipation of the winter solstice.

You are never quite prepared for early sunsets, Lori recalls. Turning the clock back an hour: darkness rising from the earth, ever earlier.

"Oh!—God . . ."

In an instant the screen seems to implode. Colors vanish, gradations of gray emerge, somewhat blurred, grainy. The baby is untouched and, yet, suddenly reduced, drained of color and diminished.

There is something shocking about it, this instantaneous change. She leans closer to the screen, squinting.

Just an ordinary baby, in that instant. No name, no identity. Gradations of gray, and not very clearly in focus.

If the screen were switched to *off*, where would this baby go?

It is hard for Lori to keep in mind that the baby on the screen, that's to say the image of the baby on the screen, so reduced in significance, is *her baby*.

Alone amid the pillows in gathering twilight, no idea where he is, who he is, why he is, who is staring at him he cannot see; no idea how his soul has been sucked from him, with the waning of light in the sky.

Still, Lori will hurry downstairs to be with him—*her baby*. Her head has begun to ache with concentration; she rouses herself from a stupor. Through the monitor come mewing little baby cries like pleading mice.

That evening Timothy will say he'd tried to call her in the afternoon, she hadn't answered, he'd left messages and she hadn't answered, was something wrong?—and Lori will say quickly, No! Nothing wrong, of course, she'd been listening to CDs with the baby, hadn't heard the phone ring, she's sorry. And Timothy will say stiffly he'd called both the landline and her cell phone; it's strange that she hadn't heard either.

Lori hadn't replied. Not wanting to say—*Why is it strange? What do you expect of me, beyond what I've given you?*

*

11.

. . . another experiment. Also harmless.

In anticipation of a night emergency when the mother of the baby would be less alert and clear minded if, for instance, these Baby-Monitor "luxury features" are required.

Baby in the nursery in his crib asleep. *Not night:* afternoon nap.

Mommy in the bedroom next door not lying in bed but calmly sitting on the edge of the bed.

Again, all of the house empty! *This* is luxury.

No longer resentful that the father of the baby is *away* so much of the time. Instead, rejoicing that she is *alone with Baby*.

It's day, the world is bathed in color. Where there is light, there is color. Waking from a brain-aching deep sleep after a night of sleep pockmarked as a rusted colander, she, mother of the baby, is assailed by colors piercing her eyelids like cymbals clashing.

November afternoon as light begins to wane (as early as 4:00 p.m.) and with the waning of light the waning of color on the Baby-Monitor screen.

Holding her breath as the exquisite moment approaches. She has never been able to predict how, at a particular second, and not one second before, the color in the monitor will shift to *night vision*.

Baby is sleeping peacefully and will sleep for an hour or more. No awareness of the camera trained upon him, attached to the rim of the white-wicker crib.

This is the precious time—Timothy's mother has told her.

They grow up fast. They can't wait to leave you.

Lori doubts that this is so. Lori doubts that Timothy couldn't wait to leave his mother.

Lori has reason to doubt Timothy has ever left his mother.

. . . *no matter how you love them, they grow away.*

On the glassy screen, in miniature, Baby's dreaming face. Lori can see, or thinks that she sees, the minute movements of Baby's eyeballs in their sockets.

Dreaming, which is *seeing*.

The baby brain, turned inward in sleep. Alive, thrumming with life. *She* feels nothing like this; her brain has grown sluggish, like (in fact) a colony of sleek, gray-hued slugs not usefully meshed together.

Fact: she who'd imagined that she would always be young has become a not-young mother at whom other, younger mothers glance

162

in Kemble Park, where she pushes Baby in his stroller each morning in good weather.

Fact: startled to see herself in mirrors in recent months and so she has begun to avoid mirrors.

None of that matters now: female vanity. Laughs at herself in embarrassment, to imagine how any *of that* had ever seemed important to her.

Attracting the male gaze: that the male sperm might be deposited in the proper moist, warm, labyrinthine place. And when the transaction has been made, everything preliminary fades.

I see that now. Nothing could be clearer.

But before—have to admit, I hadn't seen.

Fortunately, she'd never been a beautiful young woman. You'd have said of Lori—*attractive.*

Dark hair, dark eyes, slightly heavy dark brows, olive-pale skin.

And all that, irrelevant now. Might've been a cluster of cells, moist, fertile, impregnable.

Lori has managed to activate the digital zoom device: zooming in close to Baby, as close, or closer, than Mommy would be if Mommy were holding Baby, for there appears to be some magnification in the camera lens.

Perilously close, it seems. Vertiginously!

Baby's nostrils loom large, as the rest of Baby's face softens and loses definition. Something wet moves, snail lips wet with spittle. Close-up of Baby's (distorted, enlarged) mouth. A *rapid chuffing* sound, amplified baby breathing so suddenly loud, Lori has an impulse to press her hands over her ears.

Once that breathing has begun it will not cease for eighty, ninety years. The little heart mechanism wound tight, ticking away long after the mother of the baby and the father of the baby have ceased to exist.

Lori is having trouble adjusting the zoom lens. God *damn.*

Baby's head has become alarmingly small; now it is too large again. With difficulty the mother brings the baby head into focus.

Shuddering to think that anything so large and *bulbous* was ever contained inside her body!

No nightmare of her girlhood had prepared her for pregnancy, let alone childbirth or the aftermath: the twenty-four-hour, ceaseless, continual, eternal Baby. Imagining sexual intercourse had been the limit of her imagination and even with that, she'd much underestimated the act.

Joyce Carol Oates

Surprises that are unique to the body. You *cannot imagine.*
Well, it was all a mistake. Wasn't it!
Generations of babies born out of their mothers' fevered need.
Can Baby hear Mommy's thoughts?—somehow, through the two-way audio system? For Baby has begun to stir; the little eyes flutter open.
Hel-lo! This is Mommy, can you see me, sweetie?
Carefully Mommy positions her (tense-smiling) face in front of the two-way camera.
Crinkly-faced, comical as an elderly man with a wrinkled brow and a few scant hairs on his pale dome of a head who is also (somehow) an infant, Baby blinks and stares in frantic unfocus. Flails his small fists. In another instant he will draw a deep breath into the miniature baby lungs to cry for Mommy.
Hel-lo, darling! D'you see who this is? Hello-hello . . .
A storm is gathering in Baby's brow. Baby does not seem aware of (the image of) Mommy on the screen.
(Lori wonders if the infant brain can't process simulacra on screens? The infant eye isn't yet adjusted to interpreting such stimuli? Animals often seem incapable of "seeing" images on screens.)
Instead, Baby's attention has been captured by someone or something out of the range of the camera. To Mommy's disappointment Baby pays no heed to Mommy smiling, grimacing, waving at him like a fool.
He is alert, sharp-eyed, squinting at something beyond Mommy's face—what?
What, *who?*
Another camera is needed in the nursery, Mommy thinks. A camera to record what the crib camera is recording, from a distance.
The entire house should be weaponized with surveillance devices. The weakness in household security, Lori realizes, is the broken vertebrae of the marriage.
Is Baby frightened or is Baby just curious? Is fear inborn in the infant brain, or must fear be learned?—taught?
Baby's eyes are rapidly blinking; he is rapt with concentration. Smiling in a way that breaks Mommy's heart, for it is directed not at (smiling) Mommy but at another, invisible.
Astonishing: Baby is lifting his arms to—who? Surely this is the first time that the six-month-old baby has lifted his arms to be gathered into the arms of another. . . .
(But there is no one in the nursery! No one in the house except

164

Lori at this moment! She is certain.)

Yet, it's fascinating. To observe Baby in the presence of an unknown.

Baby has cobalt-blue eyes, so dark as to appear all iris. In the monitor, *night vision* has rendered them black.

In *night vision*, Baby is unidentifiable. Pale dome of a head, blurred face, indentations for nostrils, twitching fish mouth.

Distressed, begins to kick. Whimper, cry.

The familiar cry, which will heighten into a wail.

She'd heard, in the clinic. As the baby was removed from her dead-numbed lower body. A frantic wailing, piercing her heart.

Kicking the crib, dislodging the camera. A six-month baby can be surprisingly *strong*.

Only the lower left part of the baby's face is visible now. The head is weirdly magnified and distorted like something waxen, melting.

Lori hears herself pleading into the camera.

Hello! Here I am! Look at me!

You know who I am! Here!

I am your—

—the one who—

—died for you.

12.

Her idea. Not *his.*

A sudden fever in the blood, in Lori's thirty-ninth year.

Sudden the wish, the need to have a baby. Out of nowhere seemingly the mantra *Have a baby.*

Timothy had been surprised. Indeed, astonished.

For Lori had never shown any interest in having a baby. Nor had Timothy, whom she'd met soon after moving to New York City from the small Midwestern city on Lake Michigan in which she'd lived her entire life.

Childless has the ring of loss, regret. Lori had never thought of her situation as *childless* but rather self-defined, self-sufficient. The equilibrium of wife/husband in perfect balance that, inevitably, a child, a third presence, would upset.

For eleven years, the "childless" household. Wife, husband equally involved in their careers, which were intensely competitive careers. So equally involved in the household, neither could have said what the other's salary was for all checks were deposited in joint accounts: checking, savings, investments.

Abruptly then, after the (premature, unexpected) death of her mother, Lori began to obsess over *having a baby*.

Losing her mother had felt like having her spinal cord cut. With something like surgical scissors. Just—*cut*.

Not that Lori had been especially close with her mother. She would have claimed.

Timothy had asked—*Are you sure?*

Lori had said—*Yes! I am sure*.

At once, the equilibrium of the marriage began to shift. For their lovemaking, which had been impulsive, playful, sporadic in recent years, became functional, deliberate. Nothing more self-conscious than *trying to become pregnant*.

They'd consulted a fertility specialist, at Lori's insistence. And this too an imbalance in the marriage.

Timothy, the husband, had deferred to Lori, the wife. Out of husbandly kindness, magnanimity. Perhaps with some hesitation, at first. But decisively then.

Subsequently, the advantage would be his: whatever happened as a consequence of the baby in their lives would be Lori's responsibility.

Like Archimedes with his lever. So positioned, the lightest, feathery touch is all that is required to move the earth, otherwise unmovable.

13.

Mother: what a curious word! *Moth-er.* Rapidly whispering the syllables.

Strange hypnotic, slightly obscene word, a delicious word, a secret word, a fantastic word—*Mother*.

I am your mother.

I am Mother.

Mother, I am.

14.

. . . lying on her (left) side though her heart hurts, thumping. Isn't it dangerous to sleep on your (left) side. Isn't the Internet rife with warnings, don't sleep on your (left) side.

It has been advised by her doctor, the mother of the baby should sleep more than she has been sleeping. Turn off the (damned) Baby-Monitor, no need to keep it on all the time.

Luminous in the dark, like a miniature moon. *Yes I will sleep but no. The risk is too great.*

Can't relinquish the baby to the night. If she allows her eyelids to shut. But still, it happens. She falls asleep and is wakened by a hard-throbbing heart against her ribs.

On the monitor, the baby has shifted position. *Sleeping baby* has vanished.

Luminous face like a little moon and across the moon's face a smile, for someone is bending over Baby, someone who is *not authorized*.

This is not Baby's mother! This is an intruder.

For a moment wanting to think that somehow the figure in the Baby-Monitor *is* her. The mother of the baby who is (somehow) in the nursery, lifting Baby to nurse him, even as she stares at the glassy screen of the Baby-Monitor in the bedroom.

Dry mouthed in astonishment. For this is very wrong. Rising from the bed, unsteady on her feet.

The face of the intruder isn't visible in the monitor. Just the arms, lifting Baby. Singing softly, a lullaby.

Faceless predator bird. Black condor, crow.

Is it the mother-in-law? Daring to enter the nursery, against the mother's wishes?

The mother-in-law had volunteered to watch the baby in the afternoon so Lori could sleep for an hour or two. Or three.

Push the stroller to Kemble Park. Prepare the evening meal. Never fails to take Lori's (cold, unresponsive) hands—*You are looking so tired, dear! You must sleep.*

Such bullshit, the mother of the baby is thinking. They will say anything to disarm/beguile her.

They are in collaboration. She has no reason to know, yet she *knows*.

Magnanimous Timothy, the father of the baby, has offered to care for the baby in the night so that the mother of the baby can sleep. *He* will watch the monitor. *She* can sleep in another room. The mother's milk can be suction-pumped out of her heavy, aching breasts, stored in sanitized little baby bottles. The father of the baby can nurse the baby as well as the mother, perhaps better than the mother since the father is a calmer person, his hands are steady, and his eyes are not bloodshot.

He has practiced, it seems. She has gone along with the charade.

The *male role model* for the baby boy. Essential.

The mother has no intention of giving up the baby to the father.

What if the father causes the baby to choke, forcing the rubber nipple into his mouth, flooding his mouth with milk?—the risk is too great. What if the father drops the baby on his head? Fractures his (thin, soft) skull? Impossible to prove intention.

Gradually the plan has become clear to her: the mother-in-law will take Baby, and care for Baby, for Timothy. Something will happen to Lori, the mother of the baby. Perhaps it is already happening.

They will cajole her into taking an overdose of barbiturates. But they will not call it that, of course: they will call it *getting enough sleep*.

Sleeping pills scattered on top of the bureau in the bedroom. No idea how they'd gotten there; she is sure that the pills, which she'd never touched, were kept in the medicine cabinet.

Frowning he'd asked—*Are these yours, Lori? Should I put them back into the container for you?*

Or he'd asked—*Should I bring a glass of water for you, Lori? You can take a pill now; it should last several hours.*

She hadn't answered him; it was a trick. You could give the wrong answer. As a girl she'd done crossword puzzles in ballpoint ink, to make it serious. No erasing. If you made a mistake you could not undo the mistake.

Math homework in ballpoint ink too. To punish stupid mistakes.

Lori? Should I bring you a glass of—

Slapped his hand, several pills went flying. Chunky round barbiturates, clattering to the floor.

The expression in his face!—really seeing, for the first time, *her*.

But when Lori enters the nursery the black crow mother-in-law is not there.

No shadowy figure. No agitation of the air. No echo of a lullaby.

Just Baby in his crib, innocently asleep.

Lori crouches over the crib, staring at the baby. *Her* baby.

(Is he pretending to be asleep? Has the devious mother-in-law returned him to the crib, and departed?)

Her heart is beating frantically—a sure signal that she is in the presence of danger.

Yet: Timothy's mother has vanished, the house is silent and darkened. Not even a scent of the woman remains in the air, that familiar repugnant lilac-talcumy smell.

On the hardwood floor behind the white-lacquered wicker crib, the Mother Goose lamp exudes a gentle light, just enough for Lori to see that, yes, Baby is sleeping peacefully and no, no one seems to have interfered with him.

The periwinkle-blue woolen blanket as Lori left it tucked about Baby earlier that night.

It's only 1:20 a.m.; Lori would have thought it was much later, for she has been lying awake for so long in the other room.

How long, the nights! But days are longer, a vast Sahara of time broken into a succession of *baby-body tasks*. The mother of the baby makes her way as into a labyrinth, ever deeper and farther from the entrance/exit.

Windowpanes reflect the interior of the room faintly, not unlike the glassy screen of the Baby-Monitor in the other room. Beyond the panes there is only darkness: opacity.

No moon in the sky, no star clusters. Dense, corrugated cloud covering pressing low.

Lori reasons that she might as well wait in the nursery for Baby to wake, for his next feeding. She will lie on the sofa, just a few feet away from the crib. She will close her eyes, just for a few minutes. When Baby is ready for her breast he will let her know.

For hers is the only breast Baby can suck. *Hers*, the only milk.

What a relief! The mother of the baby could weep with gratitude.

It hasn't happened yet, I am still alive. They have not replaced me, yet.

15.

The father of the baby is asking, *Would you like to talk about it, Lori?*

Cannot say *no* for he will then accuse her of refusing to cooperate with him but cannot say *yes* for then he will interrogate her.

16.

Fear: a spider scuttling in the corner of your eye; you need not acknowledge by looking at it.

17.

She'd never been a fearful person. She didn't think so.

From childhood secure in her*self*. Knowing her*self* loved by her parents.

But now, since the pregnancy, and since the baby, that *self* has been replaced. Another *self* has intruded, innocently at first: in her naivete she'd welcomed it.

My cup runneth over—an expression she'd never much liked for its biblical piety. Yet, the feeling is genuine; it's as if she is holding a cup and rich, warm liquid (milk?) is being poured into the cup, spilling over onto her hands, and she laughs, saying, *Enough!* but the rich, warm liquid continues to be poured and continues to spill over onto her hands; there is no way to stop it, no pleas or prayers that will be heeded.

All that is required is that you give up your life for another.

Yet that might not be enough.

And you have nothing else to give.

18.

. . . lying on her (left) side. (Left) side, hurtful to the heart.

Lungs and other organs weigh upon the heart, forcing it to beat like a bird trapped in small quarters frantically beating its wings.

It's a relief to be alone—finally. In the bedroom in the bed in the dark in the night.

First time sleeping alone in more than twelve years.

Staring at the small luminous screen a few feet away in the dark. No pretense of trying to sleep, not in these circumstances.

In sleep, the mother of the baby is vulnerable. The mother of any baby is vulnerable. *They* will take advantage of her if she dares to shut her eyes.

The father of the baby is elsewhere. She has asked him to go away, or he has gone away of his own volition. She has no idea where he is; she has ceased caring. Love for any other *not-Baby* has become impenetrable to her, incomprehensible as a dead language. Probably Timothy is staying with his parents, who live only an hour's drive away, in another city.

Through the Baby-Monitor she'd heard them, by chance. When the mother-in-law was visiting for the day.

Unknowing, for the camera hadn't been turned on. Yet somehow their voices were picked up by the ultrasensitive audio system.

Near-inaudible voices. Whispers, murmurs.

She could not make out what they were saying. Listening so intently blood vessels stood out on her forehead.

Only just isolated words: *she, her. Baby.*

Danger.

Couldn't put the words together but certainly she knew; she'd known for months how they were plotting against her.

And how astonished they would be to learn that their (secret) plotting wasn't secret at all.

But now, that danger is past. *They* have been banished from the house.

(Unless they return while the mother of the baby is asleep, which it is possible they might do, if she is not cautious and allows her eyelids to shut.)

Here is the strange thing: the mother of the baby has become habituated to the Baby-Monitor.

She could sleep in the nursery if she wishes, or bring Baby into the bedroom to sleep with her, in her very own bed, now that she no longer shares the bed with another person; yet she has come to realize that the Baby-Monitor is not only an instrument of precision, a surveillance weapon, but it has remarkable powers she has only begun to fathom.

So long as the camera is fixed upon the baby in his cradle, the principal image on the glassy screen is Baby; yet, with the passing of time, particularly in the night, other images may intrude, she has discovered. *If she stays awake long enough.* The blurred and colorless *night-vision* makes possible much that, in the day, with only the mother's (ordinary) eyes as instruments of vision, would be undetected, lost.

And so it is happening now: on the screen Baby's (enlarged) head begins to melt as Lori stares, heartbreak-soft skin dissolving, frail baby skull beneath, a spider's web of tiny arteries, veins, nerves, ganglia; Baby's cobalt-blue eyes are gone, as Baby's little snub nose is gone, Baby's mouth, sweet hesitant Baby smile. There emerges something wet and raw, not a *living entity* but parts, scrapings as the sharp, brisk, rhythmic sound of a knife increases in volume hurtful to hear as the mother of the baby raises herself on one elbow to peer more closely at the monitor in appalled fascination seeing glistening flesh, miniature organs, a growing pile of scrapings on what appears to be a filth-encrusted chaise lounge. . . .

Everything dark as soot, covered in soot. Yet at the same time moist, liquidy. A look of being warm. Somewhere inside the scraped parts, a tiny heart. Lungs, guts. Fingernails.

She'd bled for weeks, unpredictably.

You can hear the scraping of the uterus clearly. Yet you can also feel the scrapings. Harsh, sharp, deft surgical knife.

She'd never told Timothy. She'd never told anyone.

She'd been just a girl, twenty. And for twenty, immature.

Why it's a chaise lounge, she remembers only vaguely. Of course it wasn't a *chaise lounge* but something that resembled one, or she was misremembering.

Groggy, delirious. Vision out of focus.

By now, the blood has calcified, turned black. The scrapings are no longer moist but desiccated. So long ago no color remains.

Did you think you could forget me?—I am always here.

On the sticky tile floor inside the monitor, undulating motion. As of myriad baby bodies.

With the remote, she tries to zoom closer to the image inside the screen: undulating, writhing things, not (human) babies but (she sees, staring) rats: seething swarm, dozens, hundreds of rats, covering the floor beneath the filth-encrusted chaise lounge.

A scream tries to force its way out of her throat but her throat is too dry and clamps shut.

19.

You seem frightened, Lori. What is it?

. . . our baby? Why is that?

Are you afraid that something will happen to our baby?

In the quiet of the empty house. Relief!

Morning. Sunshine. She could weep; color has returned to the world.

She bathes the baby, puts a fresh diaper on the baby. She feeds the baby. Straps the baby in a stroller and pushes the stroller to Kemble Park.

Her baby. Absurd to think that Baby is just any ordinary baby.

Are you afraid that you will hurt our baby?

Please talk to me, Lori!

Six months' maternity leave from the university, followed by a sabbatical spring semester. Soon Lori will set up her laptop in a sunny corner of the kitchen. She will scroll through the (myriad, unorganized) notes for her next project, at which she has only glanced in months.

Except: in the laptop screen there has come to be an (occasional) reflection that interferes with her concentration. Even as she reads through her own words, passages of prose she'd forgotten she'd written months ago, exciting to her, even thrilling, this reflection intrudes, distracting her so that she has to reread, and reread.

A miniature face. Miniature head. *His.*

As if the laptop were (somehow) connected to the Baby-Monitor. The camera in the nursery, (somehow) connected to the hard drive....

Lori laughs uneasily; she has forgotten what modest computer skills she'd had before the birth. Always they instruct you: turn off the computer, then restart.

Or pull out the plug; then, replug.

Not possible to call Timothy to ask for help. Nor a mutual friend who would (no doubt) tell Timothy, that they might laugh at her ineptitude together.

"No. I *will* not."

Lori shuts the laptop, pushes it aside. With relief hearing Baby making cooing noises, beginning to wake from his nap.

Too much quiet, solitude! Not good.

Is it time for Kemble Park?—it is.

A small neighborhood park: swings, slides, sandboxes. Picnic tables, benches.

Suburban park, occupied mostly by (young) mothers in the neighborhood, or their nannies, with small children.

Rarely men, and rarely adults without children.

It's a surprise to Lori; some of the children are even younger than Baby, hardly more than newborns. Others are toddlers, preschoolers.

All of us, off the grid. No Baby-Monitors in Kemble Park!

Lori does not make friends easily; she is a guarded person, yet in Kemble Park, where no one knows her, she has made an unusual effort. Several friendly acquaintances whose last names she doesn't know have greeted her warmly—*Hi Laura! Laurie!*

Timothy would be impressed, she thinks. Timothy would be *jealous*.

More recently, however, these sister-mothers have been cool to Lori. Perhaps they have learned (somehow) that the father of the baby no longer lives in the house with Lori and Baby. Perhaps the mother-in-law had spread lies about Lori when she'd brought Baby to the park.

Lori has noticed recently: the young mothers in the park who'd once smiled at her now seem not to see her. Intent upon their cell phones, iPads, Kindles. Even the nannies, distracted by cell phones.

. . . how old d'you think she is?

Forty, at least.

Forty-five, easy.

No!

Did you see her hands? Her eyes?

173

God!—the bags under her eyes . . .
D'you think she's—
Buzzing in Lori's ears, can't hear. Hurriedly pushing the stroller away in case Baby is listening.

20.

The beginning of the greatest fear, that you cannot keep another alive.
A far greater fear than your own extinction because, after you are gone, your guilt will be gone.
No one will be a witness.
Days so long stretching to the horizon. Sculpted by time as by wind arranging itself like sand dunes except these were *time-dunes.*
Daylight is the safe time; Lori is grateful for daylight. Might've been the baby doctor who'd promised her that nothing terrible can happen in sunshine because sunshine is full color.
Time-dunes. If she tells Timothy, he will be impressed.
Except no: Timothy is no longer impressed by Lori's clever way with words.
When love ceases, a light goes *out* in the eyes. Lori has seen.
Lori keeps the camera trained on the baby at all times, this is crucial. When she approaches the baby to lift him, comfort him, nurse him, scold him she takes care to hold him tight against herself so that his face is hidden. The camera will record just the back of the eggshell head with its scant, dark hairs.
She takes care to hold him *tight.* So that Baby does not slip from her grasp and fall to the floor, fracture the eggshell skull.
Recently, she has brought the Baby-Monitor into the nursery. So that she can observe the screen in the baby's presence, glancing alertly from the screen image of the baby to the actual baby.
Of course, it is the image of Baby, in the screen, that yields secrets. You could stare at the actual baby for long minutes, hours; you would never see beyond the exquisite heart-stopping beauty of Baby to what the baby *is.*
Obviously, another camera is badly needed, preferably at a height: in a corner of the nursery where the wall meets the ceiling.
This would need to be a more powerful camera than the Baby-Monitor camera, one equipped with X-ray powers.
(Except: these X-ray powers would certainly interfere with the household Wi-Fi.)

Also, the Baby-Monitor screen is absurdly small. It will need to be upgraded. Lori has to stoop to see herself in the screen, clutching Baby. Her head is cut off; no way to identify the Mommy. Could be any female clutching a baby to her bosom.

Tonight, Baby's sucking is more robust. Tugging at the nipple, impatiently.

Small, sharp baby teeth have poked up in Baby's gums. Clamping together at the breast, tugging and tearing. Lori cries out in pain. She pulls Baby from her; his teeth tear at her bleeding breast as he wails, enraged.

Her sides are streaming blood; desperately she throws Baby from her. But on the floor on hands and knees he springs at her, biting her ankle. She kicks him away, screaming—*Stop! No!*

With renewed fury and appetite Baby continues to throw himself against her.

21.

Knowing now what she must do. Extirpate fear at the root.

Taking the baby outside, for the first time beyond Kemble Park. In a hilly area north of the city, a no-man's-land along the railroad embankment.

Here, less than a quarter mile from the interstate, is desolation: stagnant pools of part-frozen water, rotted tires, broken tricycles, filth-stiffened old mattresses, washing machines with yawning, gaping mouths.

"Here we go! Mommy is taking us on a *hike.*"

Wanting to establish for the record that she'd never been a fearful person. Not even as a child.

All this, this fear, absurd and demeaning, this is new. This is *not Lori.*

As if prepared for their adventure Baby is sitting up in the crib, in the Baby-Monitor screen looming large, and in the nursery, sitting very oddly, unnaturally when she comes to get him—you might say *adultly.*

Good that this pretense is being dropped. *Baby* behavior, cooing and kissing. No more.

As an adult might be sitting with his shoulders purposefully back, to avoid giving the impression of slouching. Turning the coy little face upward to Mommy like a trusting moon.

Lori laughs, shaken. For a baby is *so beautiful.* . . .

No matter how the Baby-Monitor screen has prepared her, there is nonetheless a pleasurable shock lifting the baby from the crib: the weight and heat of the dense little body. A baby is all head and torso. She laughs: how droll it is that Baby has *no knees.*

Well, maybe now—maybe Baby has knees. The soft cartilage has been toughening. Ingestion of calcium leached from Mommy's milk breasts.

Baby certainly has baby teeth, and damn, they are sharp!

Lori shakes her head, laughing wryly. A tale to tell the other mothers in Kemble Park.

And you wouldn't believe, the little demon bit me!

Overnight, he'd grown teeth. See! His first baby teeth.

First, carries the hot, dense, little squirmy weight downstairs to the kitchen, where there is sure to be, at this hour of morning, a patch of sunshine warming the cushion of a chair at a window.

Yes, yes!—time for the breast. No cryin'!

Greedily sucking at the wounded breast, sucking the life out of her as a particular sort of spider sucks the life out of its paralyzed frog prey. (Lori has seen the video. Horrific!—but you cannot look away any more than the paralyzed frog can detach itself from the giant spider and escape.) But it's a pleasurable sensation, she has to concede. Giving up, sinking beneath the surface of dark water, shutting her eyes in ecstasy obliterating the world.

Next, she takes Baby outside, bundled against the cold like a spicy little sausage in his special casing. (Even Baby's face is flushed, red.) Not in the stroller but in Lori's compact little Nissan. Not to the familiar park, which she has grown to dislike, but to the desolate edge of town beside the interstate.

Lori has dressed warmly, sensibly. She will be hiking a distance from the road. A mile, two miles. In such stretches of uncultivated land close beside highways, parallel with housing developments, strip malls, a distance of a single mile is many miles. A distance of a quarter mile can be to the horizon. Everywhere are scrub trees; the horizon is foreshortened. She is wearing rubber-soled boots. She is carrying Baby in a snug, warm pack against her chest and with both arms she holds Baby secure.

Not once has Lori gone hiking with Baby. Not once in all these months.

Her muscles have atrophied! The strength has been sucked from her; she must suck it back into herself.

Baby is alert, wary. Baby is not fretting or whining. Baby's eyes are wide and round for Baby senses that something crucial is imminent.

What relief, to have left the Baby-Monitor behind! Off camera, off the grid. No more weapons of surveillance.

Whatever happens here will not be recorded.

They are on a faint trail, overgrown with briars. Leafless deciduous trees beyond the railroad embankment. No one can see them here though they can hear traffic on the interstate. From a hill, if she had binoculars, she could stare into the kitchen of a bright-white aluminum-sided Colonial with latticed windows, observe a harried young mother preparing breakfast for her children.

Binoculars, one-way surveillance. In fact, Lori has a pair of binoculars in the trunk of the car, a remnant of her old, bird-watching days.

Walking briskly though she is not very fit—short of breath and a cramp in her leg. Murmuring to Baby, nonsense syllables to comfort.

Crusted snow, soft mud beneath. Melting snow, mud. A smell of wet earth, deeply satisfying.

Already she has forgotten the Baby-Monitor. A camera positioned above an empty crib, a screen recording emptiness.

Years ago she'd explored this desolate place on foot, alone. While Timothy was elsewhere. Storm damage, debris. Up a steep hill, down an incline, a stream edged with ice.

Small boulders. Styrofoam litter. A sound of fast-trickling water that draws the attention of Baby.

Sharp ears. Sharp, shiny, dark-blue eyes.

Mommy pauses, thinking. What has happened in this desolate place has already happened. Needing now just to remember.

A baby lowered gently into such a stream: water would flow gently over it, very cold, numbing, merciful. The baby would shriek at first, flail its tiny fists. Short legs thrashing.

Like butter, like silk. Baby skin.

"Forgive me. You will be thankful, one day."

Baby has begun to fret, anxious. Her mistake is to look into the widened moist-blue eyes.

On a fallen log she sits heavily, amid a scattering of animal prints. Sharp indentations of deer prints. The log is a fallen oak out of which other, smaller oaks are growing, in miniature. At another time Lori would find this fascinating but she is distracted now. She is panting from the exertion, though she has really not come very far. At a little distance her old, lost girl self observes her, with pity, impatience.

Sitting with her legs outspread, clutching the baby that is *her baby* in her arms against her chest.

It will require some effort, to remove the baby pack. To set Baby down securely against the log so that he won't topple over and begin wailing. Effort to open her jacket, her shirt. A nursing bra. What an ugly undergarment! She has stopped wearing bras around the house for rarely does she leave the house these days.

She resents the cry for milk; she has been hearing it too often.

No one in sight. High overhead an airplane?—a droning sound.

Her chilled fingers fumble with the nursing bra, the baby. So awkward! Her face is smarting with embarrassment, annoyance.

Oh, why is Baby always *hungry*! The mother of the baby smiles wryly.

Pushing the nipple into the hot, sucking, ravenous mouth. Mesmerized by the immediate sucking of the mouth.

What pleasure, they are off the grid. This smell of water, wet earth. High trees, leafless. No one will find them.

High overhead, the little plane has vanished.

Four Poems
Shane McCrae

THE SPEECH OF THE THIN KING'S MINDER

The thin king bound in the fiery hollow shook

The chain by which his left arm was suspended

And from a hatch that rattled open just

Above his right eye dropped a demon like

A glass-winged gerbil, who immediately

Began to stab the thin king's pupil with

A dripping claw, and said, *Forgive me, king,*

For my unwilling violence. I bite

My paws off, but they grow back while I chew

So that I wonder while I'm chewing, Is

This still my paw I'm chewing, *and, forgive*

Me, king, but that thought helps me swallow. I

Shane McCrae

Was just now talking to the cook, I don't

Know this one's name, don't ask me what his name is

He's got a head that looks like, right at the top,

A knot in an oak tree. I think he must

Talk through the hole he listens with. I have to

Shout through his voice to talk to him, for all

The who-knows-what he tries to tell me. I

Don't like to stare, so when I talk to him

I perch on the edge of the knot and shout, so I'm

Too close to see the knot. Anyway, I

Was talking, and I had to pull my face

Out of the hole to breathe, and when I did

Forgive me, king. You know I can't stop stabbing

Your eye. You know I have to hold your eyelid

Open whenever you try to blink. You know

Shane McCrae

I have to hold it open with my teeth

You know I've tried to swallow them. Forgive me

Anyway, when I pulled my head from the knot

I saw a new sign hanging from the line

Above the stove, where the cooks drain the bodies

Hanging between two bodies, on a sinew

And the sign read, You cannot love your mother

And let your neighbor starve. _I saw the sign_

And heard a moaning sound approaching from

The knot, a moaning and a rasping scream

Both sounds approaching me together, and

I looked in the knot and saw what looked like eyes

A pair of eyes, furious, rising from

The darkness in the knot, not glowing, but

Their fury made them visible. I saw

181

Shane McCrae

In the eyes fury great as yours once was

Hunger more hollow than you could sustain

Now. They rose fixed on me, and as they rose

I noticed, at first sheathing, and then growing

From my claws, icicles of blood, that grew

Down toward the eyes as quick as the eyes rose

I lost my balance, and I fell from the knot

And almost into the tall flame the cook

Was using to make pancakes, but I stopped

Myself. Hovering there, above the flame

Beneath the knot, I only heard the cook

Humming a song I didn't recognize

Each long note slid across the knot, ice sliding

Across a pond the moment winter leaves it

I turned my head and looked up, and no eyes

Emerged, but each of the bodies on the line

Opened its eyes, but lifelessly, and only

To glance at the icicles now melting into

The batter, then each closed its eyes again

Forgive me, at that moment a thought seized me

And holds me still. If God's your mother—surely

God is your mother, king, who with the first

Made things was made—and loving God would free you

How many must you feed or else despair

The earth has not yet swallowed up so many

I think. I was just shaking my paws dry

And thinking when you rang. And here I am

Blood pearled at the wound in the eye of the thin king

Who eats the world and burns in the hollow center

Of the world. The demon bit the lid and held it

Shane McCrae

SEAGULLS CRYING

To the beach at where   at anywhere a beach is

But might have been   in Oregon unless my

Grandparents were afraid   I would be known there

My kidnapping   or there I would remember they

Kidnapped me   and say

So to a stranger   so and so and so and

At whom and for how long then would they have to

Smile to get free how   whitely nod and wriggle

To keep their black   pet smile at whom how far beneath

Them   the last smile on earth

Or to the beach at the Gulf of Mexico some

Several fewer thousand miles from Austin

And where the water looked unnatural colored

To me who hadn't then before   seen water not

Bound on all sides penned   caught

And blue kept   clean the influx there prevented

Of influence from other waters   said to

But said by whom who weren't themselves corrupted

Said to be water just the same as that which e-

        ven I   a child could see

Looked clean being blue   a child but taught to value

Purity   I was four   was five was six that

Child a hallucination now   my mother's

Parents it was summer took me there   and almost none

        Of it   most of it gone

Now   I remember almost none of it not

Even myself   a dream now I remember

Except the crying seagulls at the window

Of the hotel room in which we stayed   from which I don't

        Remember leaving once

Except to go back home the crying seagulls

Crying at our window at   no other crying

Until I threw them bread my mother's mother

Had packed a loaf of bread   I tore the loaf apart

      As fast as I could tear

It each   brown slice apart   and threw the pieces

To the seagulls who   is standing next to me   which

Kidnapper   smiling   a hallucination

Helping with the loaf   but will not let me leave the room

      Not even leave with them

Not hand in hand with them   down to the water

To watch the seagulls there that might not cry so

Hungrily there   and some would hover quiet

Above the waves   and some would settle on the waves

      And none would know my face

Shane McCrae

THE STAGGERING MAN

*—After Bill Traylor's untitled drawing commonly
known as* Man Carrying Dog on Object

I wear the anvil and the dog

I carry them, the dog atop

The anvil.   You might think the an-

vil a caulked basket, me an African

Carrying water home from the well

The river,   in a basket on

My head.   It is an anvil, cast

Steel, painted blue, like water.   I walked past

The river in a dream once, walked

Along the river, carrying

The anvil.   When I looked and saw

My shadow on the water, where the blue

Anvil, its shadow, should have been

Nothing,   the shadow of the dog

Floating above my head.   I woke

Sweating, afraid,   too eager, and I checked

187

The corner of the still black room

Immediately for my burden

I leap from bed and reach for the anvil

The dog bites through my hand before I can pull

It back, though   I had felt the cold

Pouring from the steel, and the wet heat

Of the dog's breath.   As you can see

I hold a cane in one hand, balance the

Anvil with the other. Now which hand for

Which?   Joy distracted me.   To have

Dreamed such a dream! To have survived it

My burden,   disappeared! But I arrived at

The answer.   With the healthy hand

I keep my burden safe, and with

The cane I hold   in the wounded hand

I punch my dripping blood into the earth

AFTERHEX 6

One's opportunities to be unhappy are

Corporate, yet disembodied, like a clown who works

Exclusively at office parties, here he comes

Carrying as he always does his bright red briefcase

And now you have another Team Esteem Bonds Builder

To fear, the script in somehow   it's a universal

Language no human being would ever speak, approved

By many human beings.   As far as going along

With something goes, are you still part of everybody

The everybody in your home, the office, your

City, your state, your country, where? How far from you

Do you become just you again? if you within

The boundaries of your body know yourself, and so

Within the boundaries of your body are yourself

Alone, and not relying on what someone told

You years ago a liver is, and what a liver

Shane McCrae

Looks like, and how a liver works, for whom, you?   What

Percentage of your life do systems live for you

You wouldn't recognize if somehow you could see

Them pulsing on a cluttered gurney by your side

Mixed with, they look   identical, organs from oth-

er people that would kill you were they stuffed in you

Your body would reject? Is red   healthy? You're paid

To laugh by someone paid to whisper   by the people

Who pay themselves, and speak as loud as, louder than

They want to speak, or think they want to speak, the people

Who think their need   to be more powerful than other

People, their organs pulsing redder on the gurney

Will one day free them, though it binds them tighter to

You every second of their lives, and always has, though

You're paid to listen   to their whispers redden warm

In the gut of the middleboss, a nest for day-long eggs

Good Night, Sleep Tight
Brian Evenson

I.

"THERE IS A SAYING," his mother had told him several times, just before sleep, when he was still quite young, "always three graves." She had taken the saying from a book he had discovered years later in college. The same book, as it turned out, from which she had taken many of the stories that, late at night, she had told him to frighten him. Even once he learned that, they still frightened him.

"Why three?" he asked her that first time.

She shrugged. "One for the father," she said. His own father at the time was already gone, buried. "One for the mother. And, well . . ."

She seemed reluctant to go on. She had been, he now guessed with the perspective of several additional decades, pretending this reluctance, but he hadn't known this at the time.

"Tell me," he forced himself to say, though he dreaded what he might hear. But wouldn't hearing it be better than imagining it?

She shook her head slowly. "I've already said too much," she claimed. And then she turned off the light and left the room, leaving him alone in the darkness.

Later, once he had a child of his own, he wondered why his mother had terrified him so when he himself was just a child. He would never do something like that to his own son. No sane parent would. Was his mother not sane, was that the problem? Or was she simply cruel?

And why was she like that only at night, and not even every night? During the day she was kind, loving. Most nights she was this too. Only one night in twenty would she terrify him. If he was asked what on the whole his childhood had been like, he wouldn't have hesitated to say *Happy*.

Seen in that light, what harm, really, had been done to him? He had turned out all right, had had a few frightened nights, but ultimately this had had little effect on him. He wasn't "traumatized," he didn't

191

need a therapist, he lived what to all outward appearances was an implacably normal life.

He was, true, still afraid of the dark, but even that was hardly an issue. Anything to disrupt the dark, even the blue dot on the wireless router across the room and beneath the desk, was enough to allay his fear. It was never a problem, his fear was always in check.

Or, rather, the only time it had been a problem had been once, years ago, when he and his wife had first bought the house they lived in now and there had been a power outage. He had woken up in the pitch dark not knowing where he was, and feeling he was back in his childhood room again, in that same dark, having just been told another awful story. This one about a man who accidentally drank a ghost.

He must have gasped, or made an exclamation of some kind anyway. Before he knew it his wife was awake beside him and was touching his side, which made him gasp again—he heard himself this time. And then she spoke. *Are you OK, honey?* she said, or *Sweetie, what's wrong?* He couldn't remember which now. Hearing her voice, he knew where he was and his panic began to subside. A moment later there was a beep and the blue light of the router came on again and everything was fine.

The strange thing, it seemed to him, thinking about it years later, *was that she tried to scare me at all*. She never did during the day, never even said *Boo!* to him, was never anything but kind. So why at night? Not every night either, not one night in ten. Perhaps one in twenty, but with no real regularity, so he could never predict when it might be coming. No matter the night, she would come in first and read to him—nothing scary, just a normal kids' book pulled from his shelves. She would read to him and then tuck him in, kiss his forehead, and leave the room. She would turn off the light on the way out the door. But on those nights when she was going to frighten him, even though she flicked the switch down as usual, the light somehow stayed on. He did not know how this could be—he had tried to make the switch do that himself but never could. And she always acted too like the light had gone off properly, as if she believed herself to be leaving him in darkness. "Good night," she said, "sleep tight," and closed the door.

But a few minutes later the door would silently slide open again and she would come back in, taking her place without a word in the chair beside the bed. She would remain like that for a moment, silent, hands resting lightly on her knees, and then turn to look at him.

"Do you want to hear a scary story?" she would say. And then, whether he said yes or no or nothing at all, she would tell him one.

What made her come back? Why did she return some nights but not most nights? He wasn't sure. There was no reason that he could make out. She just did.

He asked his mother about it once, when he was older, when he was in college—before he met his wife-to-be and long before his son was born. The two of them were in the living room that she generally reserved for company. But now that he was away at college he qualified, he supposed, as company.

In a lull in her recitation of neighborhood gossip, he had asked, "Why *did* you use to tell me those scary stories?"

She gave him a strange look, as if genuinely surprised. At first he read it to be surprise that he would mention during the day what they never acknowledged except at night, but then she said, "What scary stories?"

"You know," he said. "At night."

She made a little noise of disgust. "I never told you scary stories!"

But she had, he insisted. He went on to explain how she had left the room and then come silently back in shortly after.

"What nonsense!" she said. "Once I left I never came back in. Why would I?"

"But you did," he insisted.

She shook her head. "You must have dreamed it," she said.

He hadn't dreamed it, he was sure he hadn't. *Why would she lie?* he wondered, once back in his dorm room. Shame, perhaps. Or perhaps she genuinely didn't remember.

He lay on his bed, staring up at the flaking acoustic tiles. On the other side of the room he could hear his roommate talking to himself as he tried to complete his chemistry homework, mumbling scraps of formulae. *Or maybe,* he thought, *even at the time she didn't know she was doing it.*

One story she told was about a creature that looked human but wasn't. Mostly it couldn't be distinguished from a human but it was, so she

Brian Evenson

said, "capable of atrocious self-distortion." To him, very young, the phrase sounded like a spell. "It was capable, for instance," his mother said, "of growing as tall as the ceiling, and then across it, and then lengthening itself down the wall. You can walk into a room only to find it behind you and above you and before you all at once. The worst thing to do is notice it. If you notice it, well, what choice does it have but to fall all around you and do away with you?" She gave him a smile—or half her mouth did anyway. The other half tried to smile but failed. "Good night," she said, and turned off the light and left him alone in the dark.

Another story: this one told slowly, in almost hypnotic tones, about a boy. "A boy not unlike yourself," his mother said, and smiled. A boy who went into the woods and crawled into a hole he found there, and found, at the bottom of that hole, not roots and grubs and rocks, but a long, glittering passageway, illuminated by torches and lined down one side in mirrors. The boy had heard enough fairy tales to feel optimistic about where this passageway would lead. Walking along it, his reflection pacing beside him in the mirrored glass, he dreamed of piles of gold, enchanted princesses, witches and ogres and other villains that he would defeat with one deft twist of his clever mind.

He was so caught up in his thoughts that he did not notice that even though the mirrors had come to an end long ago his reflection still walked beside him, more and more solid, matching him step for step, indistinguishable from him in every detail except that the creature that used to be his reflection couldn't smile properly. Every time it tried to smile, it came out glittering and terrifying, little shards of mirrored glass in place of teeth.

His mother stopped speaking, rocking slowly in her chair, staring at nothing.

"When did he notice?" the boy finally asked.

"Eh?" said his mother, coming to. "Only when it was too late."

"Too late for what?"

His mother stretched, stood. She went to the doorway and lingered in it a moment, then reached out with what seemed an unnatural slowness and switched off the light.

"Let's just say," said her voice out of the darkness, "that someone who either was the boy or who looked like the boy came back down the passage a few hours later, spattered with blood. When he reached the part of the hall that was mirrored, it made no reflection of him at all."

194

*

His mother claimed to have never told him that story either.

II.

He was naturally thinking about this, couldn't help but think about it, when he and his wife and son went to visit his mother. Normally they stayed in a hotel, ostensibly so as not to be a bother to her, but the real reason, a reason that he didn't share with his wife or his mother, and certainly not his son, was that he was worried his mother would offer to read a bedtime story to his son, worried too about whether she would frighten him once she was done, just as she had done to him growing up.

This time, his mother had specifically asked for them to stay with her. "But we don't want to bother you," he said. It wouldn't be a bother, she claimed: when they stayed in a hotel she didn't see as much of them as she would have liked. She would, she claimed, sleep in the recliner. She didn't mind: most nights she slept in the recliner anyway. He and his wife could have her bed.

He protested. They couldn't do that to her!

But no, she insisted, they could. They should! And as far as their son went, he could simply take his father's old room.

Later, speaking to his wife about it, he found himself hard-pressed to know how to justify his desire to cancel their trip. "You're being ridiculous," his wife said. "She's old. She won't be around much longer. If she wants us to stay with her, so what? If it gives her satisfaction, we should say yes."

"But what if she tells our son stories?" he asked, hearing even as he said it how ridiculous it sounded.

"What's wrong with that?"

"Scary stories," he said.

His wife laughed. "Your mom?" she said. "That sweet old thing? She would never do something like that."

And yet she had, he wanted to say. She did it to *me*. But since he had never managed to say this to his wife before, he did not feel like he could start now. It would sound like a lie he was saying to get his way.

*

Brian Evenson

Still, when he called his mother back to tell her they'd be staying with her, he couldn't stop himself from telling her there'd be one rule.

"Rule?" she said.

"No scary stories," he said. "You can read to him and even put him to bed, but you can't scare him. Not like you used to do to me."

She made a disgusted noise. "This again!" she said. "You and your delusions! I thought we'd moved past them long ago."

"Promise," he said, ignoring her.

"Of course I promise," she said. "I'd never scare any little boy, and never have."

"What about—," he started.

"I never have," she said firmly.

"But—"

"I'm getting off the phone now," she said, speaking louder now. "I'm expecting a call. If you don't want to stay with me, then don't. But be honest about it. Stop making up these ridiculous stories to justify it."

But she had told him those stories, she had. Yes, it didn't sound like something she'd do. Yes, it was hard to believe it had happened *unless you had been the boy in the room forced to listen to them.* But if you were that boy, which he was, you *knew* she had told them, even if you couldn't convince anybody else.

It upset him that she denied it, that she continued to deny it after all these years. If she would just admit it, that would be enough. It hadn't damaged him, he wasn't traumatized, he didn't need a therapist, he was OK, he was normal, he was, he was, and yet this nagged at him, nagged and nagged. It stood in the way of him and his mother having a real relationship, and had been in the way ever since he was eight.

They went. They stayed with his mother, that lovely old harmless old lady who wouldn't hurt a fly, but who had periodically terrified him while he was growing up. And they weren't even her stories! She had stolen them out of a book! Did that make it better, or worse?

She made them a lovely meal and they sat at the table and chatted with her about the neighborhood gossip, until the moment his wife looked at him and said, "You're awfully quiet tonight."

He *was* awfully quiet. He was lost in his thoughts. He was think-ing about what he'd have to do to catch his mother telling scary stories to his son.

But he rallied, joined the chatter. Better to do that, better to do nothing suspicious, nothing to give himself away.

After supper, his son put his pajamas on, then sat playing with some action figures he had brought with him. Soon, he started to yawn.

"Somebody's getting sleepy," his grandmother said.

The man didn't say anything.

"Sweetie, do you want your granny to read to you and tuck you in?"

His wife looked at him when his mother said it, to see what he would do. But he still didn't say anything.

"Sure," his son said.

And there was his son, with his hand clasped gently in his grand-mother's hand as she led him away.

"Are you all right?" his wife asked.

"Fine," he said, his voice strained. "Just fine." He kissed her. At a little distance he heard the door to his former room open, then close.

They hugged, then separated. "I'm going to take a shower," his wife said.

"I'll be along in a little bit," he said. "I'm going to read."

But he did not read. Instead, he snuck into the dark hall that led to his son's room, stationing himself at one end of it. He would, he believed, be invisible to anyone coming out of the bedroom, and if not he could pretend he was just going to or coming from the master bedroom, which was at the other end of the hall.

He could hear his mother's voice, gentle, a distant murmuring, from his old room. He could see a sharp line of light beneath the door.

Some time went by. After a while, his mother came out.

"Good night," she said from the doorway. "Sleep tight." She walked toward him. And then, without seeing him, even though she came just five or six feet away, she turned out of the hall and into the living room.

I should have reached out and touched her, he thought. *Then I would be the one scaring* her. The thought made him smile.

Brian Evenson

But no, that wasn't why he was there. He needed to be patient, to wait.

From his vantage he could see his mother. She was in the recliner, sleepy, leaned all the way back. She was reading, but her head jerked a little each time she almost nodded off.

She wasn't going to go back in, he thought. There was no point waiting. They might have to stay with his mother twenty nights before anything happened. He had accomplished nothing. He was getting tired. He rubbed his face. He should have scared her after all.

And then, suddenly, he thought he heard something down the hall. His wife, maybe? He peered through the darkness and yes, there was someone there, near his son's room, and despite the darkness of the hall his eyes had adjusted enough to see that it was his mother.

How did she creep so quietly from her chair? he wondered. Almost involuntarily, his eyes flicked toward the living room. There, in the chair, was his mother.

Panicked, he looked back at his son's door. The light in his son's room was on now—he could see the band of light under the door. And there, outside of the door, was his mother too. She was in the chair and in the hall at the same time.

He took one shaky step forward then found, abruptly, that he couldn't move. He tried to speak but the sound came out strangled and weak, hardly a sound at all.

From down the hall, his mother was looking at him, her eyes glittering coldly in the dark. There was something off about her smile, even in the dark. About one side of her smile.

To the other side of him, in the living room, out of sight now, he could hear his mother, his other mother, snoring softly.

The mother outside the door reached out. It seemed to him that her arm stretched a little longer than an arm should be able to stretch before her hand closed around the doorknob. She eased the door open and silently entered his son's room, his old room, leaving him helpless, still unable to move, alone in the dark.

Studies in Mortality
Elizabeth Robinson

He decided he would die and then
drove through mortality,

a motorcyclist in heavy traffic. He
was afraid for his dog, which he had

loved and abused. The neighbor said no
to taking it, but he died anyway and

the dog—no one knows. Cigarette butts
and dogshit left in the litter of his lawn.

*

She was afraid she would die, as though
it were hypothetical, but of course
she would die. That inevitability

functioned as an ointment on a rash. The
unblemished skin of her sensibility: she

she decided, she was *not* afraid she

would die. She adopted the
end as a form of rationality.

*

He died a long time ago now, so it is
surprising that his death feels still so

sharp. In the months before his death, he told his
friend "not to fuck it up." Advice

whose pronoun lingers ambiguously. Who
was talking to whom. And only over the

phone could one hear his southern accent,
death being about distance, another geography. He

romanticized his determination not to
romanticize his fast-approaching death. Not

to fuck it up. What it means to die when
everyone is dying and everyone who is

dying is dying of the virus. His mother said
he drove her crazy, the way he died,

maddening, not in fear exactly, but
anxiety about the details. How

he checked in to a hospice, but then
changed his mind, got on a bus

and went back to where he'd lived,
as though he'd had a home and wanted

to die at home.

*

They loved each other and then they
made a child together and so it seemed

that all was seamless and they had nothing
to fear. But then their son became sick

and they feared his death more than
their own. He died anyway, in a halo

of dread, in his unfinishedness. He died.
And they feared the next thing, and the

next. They feared the anniversary of
his birth, but even more the anniversary

of his death, which proved all that they
most feared: that what they made with

their love didn't last. That he was
gone.

*

She was very old. Her step was
light and deft. She never

said she was afraid to die. She never
mentioned dying. But she was

afraid of betrayal. Her son who
stole from her. Her friends who

died and left her behind. Her
memory that crept away in

malice from her still-supple
body. Until all the lack that she

feared was all that was left. Betrayed
by her own mind, the trace

of her that remained. That distinct
laugh she had. The irony she clung

to: she remembered that she had
forgotten.

*

He would use a different
word than "fear." More like

201

Elizabeth Robinson

"apprehension," a word
that can signify unease

or gaining a grasp on
the matter. For him,

to be afraid is almost
a physical grace, a body

declining softly into its
ambivalence.

＊

She is afraid that others will have to
clean up after her. She is afraid

they will not retain what she wants them
to retain. She is afraid her children

will continue fighting after she has
died. She is constantly afraid

of becoming incontinent. She is
afraid that if she falls down, she

will not be able to get back up. With
a friend who is similarly

afraid, she practices lowering
herself to the floor. They

try and try to find ways to stand
back up.

＊

Now, she is different. She is
afraid only that, having

202

made the decision, having
"done a dry run for my death,"

she will not die efficiently. "Help,"
she says vigorously, "Help. Help.

Help. Help." And even a stranger
knows that she is asking for

help in getting it done.

*

He once was she, and the world
often forced him back to the state

that obtained before
the death of that she.

It scared him when he was
called by her name, his "deadname." The

name of a person who is dead but
whom the DMV, the clinic, the

police can conjure back into
existence, how *she* could kill

him over and over in legal
technicalities. Frightening

when no death suffices, when

every witness concurs: there's
been no death, no death at all.

*

First he says he is not ill,
and then not very ill, and
then that he will not die.

Anger is suspiciously
like fear. As is defiance.

But as he dies, it is as though
he is wandering a strange

room, considering it from different
angles, and at the end, sadness

instead of fear. Sadness and,
yes, some anger, but only

at the memory of the dog
he was forced to leave

behind in that room, that
hotel room, the dog waiting

as he left, always that
presence alert behind the door,

as he walked away into homelessness.

*

He believes he is not afraid
to die. He has been very ill

at times: it was interesting
how easy it was to be ill,

to feel living as irrelevant. But
he is afraid for those he

would leave behind, the ones
he feels responsible for. And isn't

this the animating delusion of
the world? That one is

necessary to the world? He
doesn't want to consider

that what he holds as
duty, perhaps virtue, would

more accurately be
named as fear.

*

What did she fear more? Her death or
her own rage? Muddy whirlpool of

control stirring loss of control. What did
she fear that she loved or hated? How long

is a text message if continuously written over
the course of a single frenzied hour? How

long is the walk after she's jumped
from the moving car, cursing her spouse

and her family? What is so frightening
about being wrong? Was she never wrong?

And who will ever know? How did she
die? In her fear, she left before

she could tell us. All
that we will never know.

*

Not long before he died, it was his
birthday. Mute—mostly mute—by then,

he nonetheless said, "That's
so good" as he savored
a piece of chocolate. To neither

Elizabeth Robinson

know nor fear that death is
impending. To be assuaged,

actually comforted, that death
is not pertinent. To rest

with the sweet in his mouth,
while his daughters looked

on in panic at his endless
passing.

Twelve Nightmares
Barbara Tomash

OF FLIGHT

have you ever seen a possum
drop from a tree deadweight
spirit chased out have you ever
heard a bone snap inside you
and waited as one waits for
music to start many animals
freeze or play dead when
touched if you or your child
cannot scream vocal cords
paralyzed stay perfectly still
change color swiftly there will
be a period of heightened
awareness more attention paid
the eyes increased coagulation
to prevent excessive blood loss
have you ever removed pieces
of gravel from your skull here
where gravity flung and
abandoned you like a log my
nights are not populated by
female horses though I desire
them to be I desire increased
heart rate violent muscular
activity leaping over submerged
cars in flooded cities galloping
unsinged in trailer parks on fire
I am isolated from the herd I
cannot overcome the wolves
fearful howling

Barbara Tomash

OF EXPOSURE

let me be clear I took my shirt off
I stood naked by the sea the
forest burnt I can't hear it
burning let me be clear the grass
grew poured forth stumbled on a
rock let me be clear I live in
honeyed light at the source of
nearly potable water the dining-
hall doors flung open what a dog
knows I want to know something
has stopped I took off my shirt I
stood by the exposed asphalt
hospital my igneous arms held
out in the shape of a stinging
pine the earth did not rotate I did
not feel it rotating remnants of
dry leaves browned the swales
some birds circled like smoke
some with camouflaged plumes
ran crazily in scrub let me be
clear those attracting red berries
could be poison the billowing
stopped

OF RITES

yellow is everywhere collapsing
I see dissolution as fringe or
feather preparation or thread the
bright orange slippage of my
forearm on the table unswerving
filaments of dried grass who
suspected light could be so fully
unelaborated   we   eat   that
delicate dish of dark smell
carbon burning stinging empty-

lot kiss of sugarcane mustard
fennel red ant hills didn't we
think we wanted ashes entrails
premonition wrested from
crushed petals our long bones
hollowed out from marrow
sucked from us by us until all
our lengths are flutes or
pounding sticks hands flung up
breaking into crackling light the
dirt-voice elsewhere of saying
sheets of rain

OF PASSAGES

we tacked up posters beseeching
for the missing it is impossible
to bring a memory to mind
without altering it people
dragged stones across vast
plains to keep track of the sun
and moon in the fear center of
my brain memories are
vulnerable to disruption trees
shift position relative to distant
hills a spinning top slowing
describes a cone-shaped path as
mine do I recall my body's
specific gravity walking
underground against a belly
swelling sorrow towers
demolished ineludible choking
if you travel south over a curved
surface the height of the north
star keeps decreasing long
before it touches my hair

Barbara Tomash

OF DISCARDED

you speak secretly with a
woman hidden in the wild a
dagger symbol placed next to a
name indicates extinction
fearful unreliability of witness
every modeled form will
dissolve the whole body
translated you do not waver at
the sight tell us about the
dinosaur lineages that still
flourish in the form of birds the
chain of forgetfulness which
exists in time rests in silence
square brackets indicate a gap
where writing once existed
discredited under ban post-
prophetic tell us the words you
remember which you know but
we do not

OF ART

scrawl scroll fresco in my dream
I chart the decay rate of uranium
becoming thorium the negative
space of handprints weight of
words birds herds nets traps
stick-legged animals in motion
dried-blood-colored spirals spit
daubed drawn I measure the
wingspan of my arms if I inhale
exhale through this beak how
will I speak here's the red ladder
symbol sepias of various
saturations blown through reed
the camellia branch quivering
on the wall sunlight flattens it

enamored of sharp detail a child
not asleep wakes with a
ballpoint pen in her hand the
turquoise naugahyde couch
drawn over with inky horses
arched necks overlapping we
have been human so much
longer than I thought my face
encrusted with calcite even the
deep sockets of my eyes

OF ILLNESS

underneath these harmless
noises see it thrashing the effort
to enunciate words huge pulse
always beating disfiguring the
structure of the wrist the arm of
the afflicted one who can do
nothing who forces open the
safety door and jumps to the
ground I am lingering on this
subject signs and symptoms
internal dysfunctions pathogens
the fiery serpents written about
in the old testament the parasitic
worm emerging from the thigh
the person who is sick takes on
"the sick role" the person who is
sick as a result of embarrassment I am lingering on this
subject fictitious health which
cannot be ignored *reality can be
lied about twisted and tamed*
you are really shaking and
shivering oscillating until you
exist only as a faint haze life
straining in ourselves *but
anxiety cannot be lied about*

211

Barbara Tomash

OF SHOCKS

the cake was baked but due to
fear of infection was not eaten
some faults might not slip
suddenly but rather slide in fits
and starts someone else sledge-
hammers the mold-covered
walls the edges unstick main
shocks always have after shocks
first you see the lightning then
hear the thunder you will not be
picked up as a shell from your
bed in the sand you will not be
found at a doorstep swaddled in
a clean or a dirty blanket we
sang happy birthday with our
microphones on mute

OF WALKING

disequilibrium greets the lifted
foot movement is a loss of place
how can I be sure a second
place exists to follow the first
how can I know whether I am
walking or falling whether I am
jumping out my bedroom
window swinging for the crow-
crowded power lines or off the
surface of a melting ice sheet
surprised by the staccato blue
ringing nothing that comes next
ice growing thinner pulled up to
my neck feeding ten rivers
sheltered from the cold
downslope winds arctic foxes
snowy owls reindeer in a
migrant delirium punctuated

212

by a landscape progressively
emptied of their long shadows I
walk in search of impossible
bodies appearing on another
ground

OF GAMES

we try scaring each other as fast
as we can it will not be limited
to a specific event or situation
you may be extremely fearful of
your own reflection you may
fear the mirror itself or ghosts
appearing in mirrors I may be
afraid of a highly polished car
or of some types of sunglasses
or of being dead or of the act of
dying you may fear deviations
and mistakes or pale when I
hand you my antique paper fan I
may fear the tent flap held down
by big humps of stones or the
raised trunks of the elephants in
the clouds we wrap arms around
our bodies rock from side to
side I ask for this clarification is
the path to hell really so very
straight and narrow

OF REALISM

the shape in the sky could be a
bomb blast or not isn't the
essence of form to subdue when
the river breaches its bank this
low garden will flood we need

213

Barbara Tomash

to build up our resistance to the
faulty dimensionality of things
the knife set in the kitchen sink
creates a new depth in the room
like a bracelet on a woman's
arm like a shaft blasted in earth
or my eyes in the mirror
whispering *open*

OF SPEECH

by the fireside or in the dark or
amid the foliage mothers put
their babies down *if you speak
truthfully to me I'll speak
truthfully to you* words are easy
to fake tongue-bone descended
in the throat everyone within
multidisciplinary earshot on the
exhale I am striving to read your
mind like beavers construct
their dams extended bouts of
mutually contagious screams
hoots barks a few movements of
the tongue and my head shifts
directly over my spinal cord
forcing out this melodic
expression of human symbolic
culture—am I not abandoned—
are we not capable of being
disentangled—*I wanna go home
I need to go home let's go home*
prompting other voices to chime
in with tongues bunched up in
deep vaulted palates

The Cult of Ciudad Mitad
Matthew Baker

ECUADOR, 2019

IN THE QUAINT TOWN of Lulumpamba, in the valley of Lulumpamba Plain, stands a grand shrine to the equator, Ciudad Mitad.
Legend maintains that members of the celebrated Geodesic Mission,
caught by surprise by a sudden storm, once pitched camp at the very
site, huddling together under wool blankets as hail battered the don-
keys and the horses out beyond the canvas flaps of the tent. By studying the properties of the equator, the expedition made discoveries
that led to the establishment of the standard unit of length, the
meter. I first read about the cult of Ciudad Mitad in a note scribbled
in faint pencil in the margins of an obsolete geology textbook, a first-
edition volume held in the collection of the Museo Nacional, in
Quito. Fascinated, I decided to travel to Lulumpamba, hoping to dis-
cover whether the cult was real. I arrived by bus the following day,
alighting onto a sidewalk in a cityscape of brightly painted shops
with charmingly faded signage, where bells were ringing in the
steeples of a local church. After securing a room at a guesthouse, I
went straight to Ciudad Mitad, a neocolonial monument rising beyond the central boulevard. Once merely a humble pole in the ground,
today the shrine features a majestic walkway lined by the busts of
geographers and geophysicists and geodesists who participated in the
expedition, all culminating at the dramatic centerpiece of the shrine,
a gigantic stone tower topped by a bronze globe. A line of radiant
yellow paint extends to the east and the west from the base of the
tower, separating the north and the south hemispheres. That morning the sunlight was warm, which made stepping into the darkness
of the doorway in the base of the tower feel pleasantly cool. I wandered the museum in the tower, inspecting exhibits about magnetism
and polarity and flux, climbing all the way to the balcony on the roof,
but while the exhibits were intriguing, the museum made no mention whatsoever of a cult. All that the guards were interested in talking about was Nikola Tesla. I spent the afternoon strolling around

Matthew Baker

the rest of the town, querying bartenders and merchants, looking for somebody with information about the cult, but nobody in town would admit to having knowledge of the cult either. By then the sun was sinking over the hills beyond the valley. I ate a bag of takeout from a café in a nearby plaza before returning to the guesthouse to continue the search the next day. Over the following weeks, that became my routine: visiting the monument each morning, interviewing the locals each afternoon, all in hopes of finding some new evidence or clue. After all of that time, I still had found nothing. Gradually, however, despite that there was still no sign of the cult, a feeling of intense excitement began to build in me. An equinox would occur that month, and as the equinox drew closer, I couldn't help but think that the cult might gather that day to observe the occasion. I dared to hope the cult might finally surface. I became convinced that the cult would finally appear. Admittedly, I was also excited by the idea of being there at the equator on the day of the equinox, when every shadow in the town would align with the cardinal directions. At sunrise the shadow of the tower would extend far to the west, following the painted line on the pathway, and then gradually shrink toward the base of the tower, vanishing at the stroke of noon, and then grow back from the base of the tower, following the painted line on the pathway, coming to stretch far to the east by sunset. I fantasized about being there at the tower to experience the event at noon: that almost mystical moment when every shadow within sight would vanish as the sun aligned directly above the town. The night before the day of the equinox, I was almost too excited to sleep. Yet when the equinox finally arrived, the weather that day was cloudy, a bleak indigo haze. I walked to the shrine anyway, but the sky was so overcast that the tower had no shadow at all, and the mystical moment at noon came and went with no visible sign of alignment, making the experience feel pointless. The cult never materialized. Disappointed, and strangely sad, I went to the café to sulk, drinking a glass of horchata alone at a table on the patio. I sucked at the straw without tasting, gazing at the boulevard in a trance. The patio faced out onto an intersection, and as a breeze rustled the leaves of the trees in the median, a pair of figures wearing panama hats approached a pink-haired figure standing at the curb. Each of the figures took out a brass compass. I had witnessed similar interactions at that intersection before, which had amused me, seeing people consulting compasses for orientation in a town famous for a landmark that was essentially a compass. Watching the interaction happen yet again, however, I suddenly realized that the scene had the appearance of a ritual. After the figures nodded at each other in recognition, then briefly examined the compasses, each of the figures bowed with clasped hands, as if in thanks or relief. Goose bumps spread down my arms. A sense of revelation. My heart had begun pounding. I rose from the chair. Dogs bolted into an alley. The pair of figures in the panama hats had already strolled off down the boulevard, but the pink-haired figure noticed me approaching and turned to confront me.

I tentatively took out the compass on my key ring.

"You seek the truth?" the pink-haired figure said.

Adriana was employed as a bagger at a supermarket, spending shifts diligently packing groceries into fluorescent bags, projecting an attitude of nonchalance, but even when at work she possessed a secret truer vocation, serving as a devoted acolyte of the cult of Ciudad Mitad. We drank horchatas together on the patio as she told me about her life. She was mother to a pair of thankless children. She had been a teenager for both pregnancies. She didn't believe in marriage. She did believe in love. Her soul mate, regrettably, was a famous movie star who had never known she existed and had died the year before. She wasn't surprised that none of the others in the cult had wanted to speak to me. The cult wasn't exactly social. Ultimately, taking the time to explain the teachings of the cult to a foreigner wouldn't make any difference in the final outcome, the apocalypse was nigh, doomsday was obviously inevitable, so why even bother. To be honest she was only talking to me because she found me attractive. I shouldn't take that as a compliment, she emphasized. She was only attracted to people with strange faces. Anyway, she could take me to the gathering the cult was having that night, if the world hadn't ended first.

We met later that evening at her apartment, where her older son stood singing melodramatically into the microphone attached to a karaoke machine, ignoring her younger son, who sat at a table in the kitchen scribbling on credit cards with a crayon. A telenovela played across the screen of an ancient cathode-ray television distorted by warped bands of color. Adriana was applying eyeliner at the mirror in the bathroom, dressed in a beige robe. A matching robe had been laid out for me on the toilet. Wearing a robe to meetings wasn't required, she said, but wasn't exactly not required either. Literally every other person there would be dressed in one. But whatever. She didn't want to pressure me. She wanted me to feel comfortable. I put on her spare robe, which had a desiccated wad of chewing gum stuck to the

217

back and smelled strongly of sweat and semen, which she explained was because she'd had sex so many times in the robe and washing the robe had always seemed pointless. We left her apartment just after nightfall, hiking through town under the light of a full moon. Adriana took me by the hand as we walked. The air was cold. The streets were deserted. As the shrine came into view in the distance, she began talking about the ritual with the compass. The cult was as old as the shrine, she said, had existed for nearly a century. At the time, identifying the precise location of the equator had been possible only by using the magnetic field of the planet for orientation. And yet as useful as the geomagnetic field was for navigation, the geomagnetic field served a greater, far older purpose for humanity. Generated by the cryptic movements of massive currents of molten iron flowing through the core of the planet, the geomagnetic field was modest in strength, a mere fraction of a tesla, and yet was staggering in scale, extending thousands of kilometers into space, where the energy of the geomagnetic field was what shielded the planet from the tremendous force of the solar winds released by the sun. Without the geomagnetic field, the magnetized plasma of the solar winds would have destroyed the atmosphere of the planet, rendering the surface of the planet as uninhabitable as the surface of the moon. Basically, the geomagnetic field was essential to the survival of life. And over the past century scientists had observed a startling drop in the strength of the geomagnetic field, a sudden weakening, which had recently begun to accelerate at a frightening speed. By all appearances, the geomagnetic field was in the process of dying. That was the universal truth, Adriana said. Thanks to the inverse square law, building a magnet powerful enough to replace the geomagnetic field would be technologically impossible. Even the most powerful magnet that humanity had ever created was pitiful in scale compared to the magnetic field of the planet. Faced with climate change or an asteroid impact or the eruption of a supervolcano, humanity possessed technology that could give the species a chance at survival, but humanity had no control whatsoever over the magnetic field of the planet and had no means of protecting the atmosphere if the magnetic field of the planet faded. In summary, the human species was doomed, and the only real mystery was how soon the end would come. Members of the cult obsessively consulted those brass compasses not as a method of orientation but to check whether the geomagnetic field still existed.

"Humanity is helpless. Whether the end comes tomorrow or next week or in a hundred years, all we can do is wait," Adriana muttered.

As she rapped on a hidden door in the wall that surrounded the shrine, I thought about the magnetic field moving all around us, through the palm trees, through the pine trees, through the restaurants and the cantinas and the shops strung along the avenues, through the rubber in the stacked tires and the nylon in the colorful flags hanging over at the go-kart track, through the concrete bridge over the river, through the laundry pinned to clotheslines, through the bicycles leaning against railings, through the fabric of the curtains and the fibers of the rugs and the beds and the chairs and the luggage on the floor in every room in every guesthouse where all of the tourists were peacefully dozing, through the titanic amounts of earth that the hills contained. I felt worried suddenly. I hadn't taken the talk of an apocalypse seriously. I had assumed talk of doomsday was just pessimism. I hadn't realized the magnetic field was weakening. The lock on the door to the shrine rattled, a hooded figure peeked out at us, then the hooded figure motioned us in and the lock on the door snapped shut behind us as we slipped down the walkway toward the tower.

The foyer in the base of the tower had been transformed for the ceremonies. Above a wooden altar lined with dazzling plasma lamps loomed an ancient painting of the Geodesic Mission, flickering with shadows that rippled across the canvas like the twisting bands of an aurora. Eerie panpipe music warbled from the speakers of a decrepit cassette player. Near the stairwell, a masked figure stood drawing scientific iconography on a magnetic writing board with furtive movements. Other cultists had already arrived too, scattered throughout the chambers of the tower. Most were dressed in loose beige robes, although some reclined in dramatic positions that caused the collar to slip over a shoulder or the hem to slip over a knee, exposing a chest or a thigh. Gloomy figures in hooded robes brooded nearby as squatting cultists flung handfuls of iron filings at gleaming lodestones. Crying quietly over a glimmering cluster of neodymium spheres, crouching figures plucked spheres from the cluster, then gently released the spheres, watching the spheres snap back to the cluster. Sobbing cultists huddled together around a levitating ring of bismuth. By the steps to the roof, a middle-aged colossus with big ears and a drooping mustache sat clutching a horseshoe magnet with a look of palpably existential desperation.

Drifting around in the borrowed robe, faintly shivering at the chill, I contemplated the atmosphere of abject despair that permeated the shrine as magnetism made objects leap and cling and hover in the air. From my daily visits to the shrine, I recognized a pigtailed guide who sometimes led tours of the tower, along with the hunched groundskeeper who tended the gardens. The guide and the grounds-keeper were both too busy weeping to notice me.

"Humanity has existed for millions of years. Imagine being there to witness the end of such a long and beautiful civilization. To be one of the ones to witness the moment of extinction," Adriana whispered. "All of us here have accepted the truth. That the loss of the geomagnetic field cannot be prevented, and that without the geomagnetic field life cannot survive." She tightened her lips and flared her nostrils and visibly swallowed, as if picturing a possibility that made her profoundly emotional, and then glanced back over at me. "I have a secret, though. I never look at a compass hoping the needle still points north. I cannot wait for the end to come. I want to be there. I would like to watch."

Beyond the balcony on the roof, stars glittered in the sky, releasing tremendous storms of magnetism on worlds throughout the galaxy.

"You aren't afraid of the end?" I whispered.

Tears were streaking down her cheeks now as she blinked, smearing her mascara, but though the others in the tower radiated a terrible sadness, I was amazed to see that the expression on her face was one of eager anticipation, and that those tears on her face were tears of joy.

Remember When We Were Holy
Tori Malcangio

I. THE SYMMETRY

IN THE BEGINNING, they told us that only babies born with a her-
ringbone of downy fuzz running the full length of their spines carried
the gene. Then it was the nostrils: if one was larger than the other.
From there, it grew into a hysteria of symmetry. If one eye was squin-
tier the baby was a carrier. One ear higher. One testicle smaller. Left
side of the labia fatter. Oh, how Richard squirmed at this. To think
of his daughter having labia; such a prickly word for his pure baby
girl whom we'd designed one night on a whiz of bubbly wine and
goat cheese, right down to her delicate parts. That area I engineered,
being the woman and inherently more attuned to shades of pink,
shapes of flower petals, and all. But, still, nothing was guaranteed.
We'd upgraded her with Gene Purification, but so had the Kims and
their baby never got to sleep in the room we'd helped them paint a
dreamy color called Apple Flesh.

II. THE SISTER'S SISTER

By the second month of pregnancy, I convinced Richard to touch my
belly. He didn't believe she was in there yet and said it seemed a
counting-your-chickens thing if he was to pour on affection without
some hope it'd be reciprocated down the road. I'd married him for his
chronic hesitancy, his safety-first insistence that one must approach
every day as if it were a shoddy bridge on the brink of collapse. I supposed my attraction was a product of growing up in a family of believers. Any crazy conspiracy shuttled over tepid tea in the Together
Hall of Sacred Heart Parish they believed. Quickly, though, I learned
blood-born doubters like Richard doubted to the same belligerent
end as believers believed. Even when she kicked at four months, he
insisted it was indigestion. "You've been drinking powders again?"
I had. A chelated mix of dehydrated cow hide and natural human

growth hormone. Patti Marks in Book Club said a bunch of people including her older sister's sister-in-law had taken it, and the fontanel, the soft spot on a newborn's head where the two tectonic skull plates haven't yet met, had been completely closed at birth. A blessing! Miracle! All this frantic intervention because the Doctor in Charge had announced that The Factor was no longer linked to faulty symmetry but to a too-pronounced fontanel. This determined carriers. Without a semiflexible head, labor obviously was more difficult; pushing out a bowling ball was no longer hyperbole but the new reality and rightfully shocking to mothers who'd delivered a baby before The Factor had become the ravage du jour. Though what did pain matter if we got to keep our babies? Richard doubted the link between food and our baby's health, but even he was willing to gamble on this one.

III. THE FONTANEL

You never could be sure who was on what side. You'd pin someone for a Factor denier, then the next thing you know they're saying The Factor is destroying common decency and How about you join me to march for stricter testing because Factor kids were slipping through like crazy. Problem is, they said, too many mothers are giving birth at home and dodging the system. Richard and I weren't deniers. We knew The Factor existed, just look at his nephew, an almost mute teenager with a cartoon girlfriend he himself coded. Look at the Kims. Their second baby had it too but somehow wasn't caught; she's now a kindergartner who can't stand in a line or sit quietly and paste. Here's the kicker: those were exactly the people I couldn't confide in; any inquiry would reek of information gathering, illegal preparation, fluffing the nest to raise a Factor child. Really, the only people besides Richard whom I felt safe around were the Book Club crew: Jane Fontaine, Melissa Zu, and Patti. Jane was married to a sexy advertising career she refused to sacrifice to motherhood. Melissa and Patti had older teens about to leave for college; they worried about their future grandkids. Melissa gently questioned the tactics of the Doctor in Charge: I heard his grandkids' fontanels weren't measured. Patti said she read nurses were keeping Factor babies and that some were getting auctioned off to science to pay nurses a doctor's salary. It's what they're earning now, you know. Jane, being creative, covered the qualitative. It's all suspicious, she said. What if the nurse measuring has blurry vision, isn't eating right, is in a hurry to clock out? What if there's a whole other world where these babies are going and a countercivilization is underway to someday overtake us? We all laughed, though me least believably. It was a swelter outside and Patti's air-conditioning was on the fritz, which left me sweating under the new layers of flesh I'd been hiding with baggy clothes. Didn't they know the phones were listening and that talking brazenly like this might cause trouble? Baby Girl was counting on us to do the right thing. "Can we please talk about how stupid the plot is in this book?" The book honestly was as unimaginative as my wardrobe: rich grandees drinking dirty martinis and having nonsense outbursts, and, in the end, everyone flees the snooty little suburb. They agreed with me, except Jane thought the dialogue was fantastic. I asked who talks like that and she said everyone she knows. Not me, I told her. And without verbally agreeing, she agreed. Then somehow they drifted back to the fontanel and the new parameters the Doctor in Charge had issued yesterday, unbeknownst to me. Richard was usually the one to keep us updated. The plates cannot gap more than the width of a needle, Jane said. And not a knitting needle, a hypodermic, Patti added. As they debated, I read the Factor App alert I'd somehow missed: *and if an acceptable gap presents at birth, it must give to the touch no more than a firm mattress and no less than an apple.*

IV. THE TEENAGER

Toward the end of my second trimester, Baby Girl kicking as if someone were going to come snatch her soon, Richard and I threw around the idea of moving. Or I did, and Richard shot it down. Where are we going to go? A bunker? My parents' attic? True. My data had already been uploaded to the Pregnancy Collective; I was getting pushed maternal memes, invites to church services near me, my daily radon and viral exposure count, ads for therapists who treated Factor-related grief. Nowhere was off the radar. Remember the von Trapps? he said. What about the Souters? I added. They'd spent Janice Souter's entire pregnancy in a remote Costa Rican hut, only to be arrested after the baby wailed during Will Souter's unmuted Zoom call. In a funk after our conversation, I turned our last two shrunken zucchini into bread and delivered a loaf to our new neighbors across the hall, Lyle and Ivan Cook. Handsome men, a pairing I told Jane I'd be happy to wriggle between. They'd moved in a week prior with a teenage daughter who we knew off the bat was a carrier. The downcast eyes, shredded clothes, a frightening indifference to the general inertia of the world. I told them one day how lucky they were to have had their daughter when they did, insinuating that in today's scape she'd not have made it to a nice apartment in Parkview Village. In their rapid, silent nodding I read that they'd had this conversation before and it'd actually been a fight. One day at the community pool, I asked the skinny teenager her name. She merely lifted her eyes off her device and tried to look at me, but was off by at least a foot, her empty gaze locked behind me, likely on the magenta pool raft. Factor kids were drawn to bobbles, instant gratification, jarring colors—things absent on a human face. I never did get her name, but I got a look into what Richard and I would be dealing with if our girl was born a carrier and then I wasn't sure who was luckier, Lyle and Ivan, or me and Richard.

V. THE BLOOD TEST

Richard, who'd either started believing in the power of food or was just resigned to doing something other than fretting silently, was pan-frying pasture eggs when the alert came over. The Doctor in Charge announced an update to The Factor diagnostic criteria: a blood test would replace the fontanel measure. Immediately headlines hailed the breakthrough. *Science Speaks for Our Children. The Factor: Going, Going, Gone.* The Doctor in Charge said the blood test, though more expensive than a new set of brakes and not covered by most health insurance, would substantially eliminate false positives, which critics nailed at or above sixty percent. Over 22,000 newborns had been wrongly diagnosed due to improper needle placement and other not-yet-specified human blunders. Richard spanked the spatula on the pan. "Now what are they looking for, Ellie? A T cell mooning the camera?" He swept the phone out of my hand, grazing my belly for the first time in a few weeks. Are you listening? he said. Obviously, yes, but Richard needed confirmation. I nodded. Are you OK with that, he said, this arbitrary culling? Richard and I had never cried together, but it felt like something we should have been doing more often. I'm not OK with any of this, I told him, but I'm scared as hell. Do you want a kid like that girl? I looked at him, his burble of curls up front, that pronounced nose a girl would need to get fixed. I guess we want different things, he said.

224

VI. THE SECRET MEETING

We were perfect candidates, our New Doctor said, for clinical intervention. He had nice things to say about our dispositions. It's not for
everyone; some soon-to-be parents aren't equipped to raise a Factor
child. But you are. He looked primarily at Richard as he made this
final analysis based on a brief questionnaire that included a query
into our sunsetting sex life. Factor kids, he reiterated, often have no
boundaries and will walk into bedrooms unannounced, make insulting remarks, and send scathing texts with zero remorse, even tell a
parent where to park, when to go to bed. The doctor explained that
dealing with them puts tremendous pressure on parents, breaks up
marriages, destroys the family dynamic. This is why we've ended
up here, he said, with God no longer at the wheel, as they say. But
not for him to judge; he was neither a God person nor a people person,
only a justice person. He would make arrangements for a "clean"
blood draw at the hospital. In other words, even if your baby was a
carrier, nobody would know. She stays with you. Richard, unfolding
and refolding the nondisclosure paperwork we'd had to sign before
entering the doctor's mid-century–designed meshed Faraday cage,
requested specifics. What kind of nurse? Where does the blood come
from? The answers appeared to appease Richard: A well-compensated
nurse. From a pig. But what if our girl turns out to be a carrier, since
as you know, the telltale signs don't manifest until around puberty?
I asked. The doctor assured me that he was friends with at least a
dozen excellent therapists.

VII. THE BUCKETS

We'd made it through the entire hour of gushing over our new favorite unsappy memoir, *The Saddest Story Ever*, when Jane brought
out her phone. This, she said, is where they're going. She pivoted her
screen toward us. Looks like a ranch, I said. Jane said, Wishful. It's no
more a ranch than you're a farmer. The rest of the photos—taken by
a hospital nurse turned whistleblower—I still can't describe in detail
without wanting to die and wake up a simple life-form on another
planet. Ruddy newborns staged under fluorescents. Tubing snaked
through every tender opening. Nurses draped head to toe so as to
evade identification. Melissa and Patti suggested I seek preemptive

counseling in case mine ended up there, as it did appear, judging by the rich flush in my cheeks, that I was going to birth a carrier. I asked how they knew I was pregnant and Jane said when I stopped wearing my slutty skirts, but the dead giveaway was my hands, one writhing inside the other, whenever the subject of The Factor came up. Melissa said initially she supposed it was probably hard to let go of a baby, but in recent weeks her mind had opened; she'd been reading a lot, watching a lot, and had decided it was the right thing to do, considering one Factor child equaled too many Factor kids down the line. Patti said her friend's cousin was grief-stricken in the first few months after her baby was taken but had since become an advocate and wrote beautifully about the grace of letting go when things weren't meant to be. And have you heard, Melissa asked, the Doctor in Charge is proposing early rapid tests? This way nobody would have to endure nine long months only to go home empty-handed. Jane, pushing back her cuticles, said, I just feel like we're running around mad with buckets catching a thousand drips when what we need to do is repair the fucking roof. Metaphor was clearly lost on Patti and Melissa, but not me. Exactly, I yelled. It's the devices. I felt like Jane and I bonded a second before a tsunami of heat floored me. I'd dangerously exposed myself. In a gross sweat, I flipped to the chapter where the author described her face after her disfiguring accident as "kindergarten art only my parents could ever love."

VIII. THE MORAL COMPASS

In the beginning, they thought it was charming, this generation's viral vanity. Kids were merely superexpressive exemplars of confidence. Look at them: dancing for strangers to watch and sharing innermost thoughts and family cancers on live feeds. How brave! How vulnerable! For at least a few years the talk cycle leaned positive like this and then it didn't. Richard pinned the quick switch in sentiment to the tragic moment when America's Digital Sweetheart filmed her suicide. The GoPro she strapped to her head when she jumped from the Golden Gate sold at private auction for millions. Headlines streamed: *Gene Linked to Virulent Apathy. Humanity in Danger of Losing Humanity. Now or Never: Feds Act to Halt Spread of Genetic Factor.* Shortly thereafter, most of the nation, my parents certainly among them, formed a moral coalition—I forget the formal name, it's since gone under—and so began the construction of the

Moral Compass, which sits today in the dead center of the Reflecting Pool at the National Mall. Two hundred thousand pounds of concrete and rebar blessed at the Vatican and cast into a giant forefinger pointing at the new magnetic north: heaven. The bronze plaque's inscription, before its defacing by a counter group, read: *From him we hail. For him we cleanse.*

IX. PRETTY FORGERY

In the seventh month, Baby Girl was a fully hearing person and Richard's and my bickering was surely compounding her worry. The Doctor in Charge had expedited an experimental rapid urine test, and despite the widespread shortage and steep price tag, Richard had pulled a back-alley, totally uncharacteristic renegade move to get his hands on one. Just pee on the stick and we'll know in fifteen minutes, he said. We'll know what? I said. There were only a few things I wanted in fifteen minutes: dinner, my car serviced, and a back massage from Richard. I didn't need a quick answer to my baby's fate, which might or might not be the same fate Richard had in mind. We were afraid of different monsters. We were becoming afraid of each other. We'll know if we even need the "clean" blood draw, he said. Maybe we won't have to cheat the system if we know she's not a carrier, and, anyway, I'd rather play by the rules. I conceded that I did too. Rules were made to keep everyone safe, I added, though how he didn't detect my pandering I have no idea. He was too trusting and I should still be paying penance for taking advantage. Which had become more habit than I'd like to admit. In fact, the night we coded her, when he turned away to clear bubbles from his throat, I'd entered both BEY and GEY for her eyes. I wanted Baby Girl to come out with one of my blue and one of Richard's brown. I'd also coded for dainty feet and paid extra for the Disney princess nose, which Richard adamantly opposed, but I'm a homely experiment in natural gene selection and rightfully obsessed with pretty forgery. Will you please? he begged, wagging the test package at me. I looked out past our balcony into the parking lot where the cocktail-hour sun beamed off solar towers. The skinny girl was sitting on a curb weeping, her two fathers circling the asphalt around her, talking, cheerleading. She stood up as tall as both of them stacked and threw her phone at the handsomer one. It struck him in the mouth and as his husband tended to the blood, she sped off in their truck. I looked back at

Richard, who was plucking stubborn gray hairs from his forearms,
looking like a scared man who could use a yes. Fine, I told him, for
you. But even if it comes back positive, promise me you'll keep cooking good food.

X. THE WING

I recall Richard being a bit off all the next day, all day. We'd been
invited by his boss to a F*@k the Factor fund-raising gala. This was
the guy who hadn't given Richard a raise in five years, but Richard, I
guess, admired the implicit bolshie attitude. As we pulled up to the
Natural History Museum, where gala attendees would gather on
the rooftop for a starry night of forced natter, Richard started to
hyperventilate. Should we do another test? he asked. False positives
happen. Your urine might have been too concentrated. I hardly saw
you drinking water yesterday. I told him maybe all the tests were
rigged. Have you considered that, Richard? Oh, he said, now you're
a population-control conspiracy person? You said it yourself first, I
said. I could tell he was in his head practicing the biofeedback he'd
been studying. Finally, he caught his breath. Do you feel something
weird in there? he asked, gesturing at my belly. I told him that that's
what being pregnant was, a constant state of weirdness. He shucked
off the nice linen jacket he'd rented and slung it over his forearm.
With his free arm, he grabbed my hand and led us back toward the
museum. We'd been living with the news for only a day and while I
suspected it all along, it'd thrown Richard for a loop. Anyway, it was
easier letting Richard do the worrying. Sharing my fears would translate as a bad audition; I'd spent my life neutralizing hysteria and every
true mood muscle in me had atrophied. At the museum's double
doors, which were fabricated into prehistoric jaws, he stopped us.
People might know, he said, running a clammy finger under the
strap of my tight blue gown. True. Factor babies were typically carried high, and Baby Girl was up under my ribs. I suggested we take a
walk around the park and Richard looked as relieved as he had the
night in bed I promised him he'd never end up with a wife in a mom
bod. Implants, metabolism vaccines, fat relocation—whatever it
took, he was guaranteed an enduring hottie. Under a canopy of fiber-
board maples strewn in white market lights, we walked hip tight. A
homeless family waded in the illuminated Piazza de Angela Sagrada

Fountain. The fortune-tellers and glass-jewelry makers and henna-tattoo artists and snow-cone carts had all been put away for the night. The tourists were hunkered down in their hotels until tomorrow rang in bright and promising again. I thought of Jane's adding to her comment the other day, Why don't we just shut off all the devices and see what happens to The Factor? Yeah, right, Patti said. No way would that fly, Melissa said. Everyone despises daylight saving time and we couldn't even vote that out. I looked at Richard looking at the gull bopping aslant down the footpath. It had a bum wing and seemed to keep forgetting that it couldn't fly. I'm sorry, I said. For what? he said. It was a cool night for November, much like my Novembers as a kid, and for a minute I was unmarried, unpregnant, kneeling in the Del Mar sand, trying to dig my way to a hell a little less hellish than what I was living. I said finally, Sorry for us having a Factor kid. We don't have a Factor kid, he said. You understand? And if you say it again—he put his jacket back on and walked ahead toward the car.

XI. THE PROBLEM

I had no intention of telling Jane. But of course she could get anyone talking carte blanche and by the time you realized you'd succumbed to her suave powers, all secrets had been spilled. Jesus, that's awful, she said. But the good news is, you know. You can prepare, or stop preparing. Shit. I'm not saying the right thing. Sorry. I told her not to be because we had a plan. I should have shut up there and not shared our doctor's name or the details about the scheduled clean blood draw, a sidestep she'd not heard about. Thank God there's an option, she said, her foot wagging to a bass beat playing on the stereo in her flat, and then she gently nudged my mind elsewhere—another gift of hers. So, pig blood? she said. Makes you want to stop eating them if they didn't crisp up so good like they do. A false laugh; Jane only played liked she was shallow because past the facade I felt wholesome, deep thought at work. I told her pig red blood cells are almost identical to humans'. She made a face before dropping a hint that she knew I was skeptical of the plan. I think all this is Richard's wish, she said, not yours. Contributing to the problem isn't you. For as long as I've known you, you've been a problem solver. She'd only known me for two of my thirty-seven years. Nor had I solved more than a handful of problems in my entire life, most of which she was unaware of. Cutting ties with my family was the first, followed by becoming a AAA gold member, then figuring out where on the balcony to put my hanging plants without blocking our view. Just think about it, Ellie, she said. It's not just about you.

XII. THE DISMANTLING

In my eighth month, Richard stopped eating. One night, while I finished off the hamburger casserole (loyal to the bone, he'd kept his promise to cook), I told him death by starvation was the slowest route possible and that it was no way to protest anymore since people did it on the regular every day. Celebrities were paid millions to shed half their body weight to play prima ballerinas or cancer patients, and Factor teenagers were virally documenting their paths to anorexia. He said that he simply wasn't hungry and the problem with society today was a colossal failure to listen—to intuition, to our partners, to our parents, to our bodies. Stomachs rumble, he said, to cue you to eat and mine hasn't made a peep in weeks. We'd met with the New Doctor again that morning and he'd assured us that the few couples who'd been caught cheating on blood tests and arrested had been careless, hesitant. You must insist that the nurse with the red bow in her hair draws the blood, he said, before gelling up my belly to listen to Baby Girl's heartbeat. That's your nurse, the only nurse. You got me? We both nodded, my nodding the most emphatic to make clear to Richard, who stared blankly, that I wasn't backing out. That I wouldn't do what I did in the final hour before our wedding and swap the "Wedding March" for "Purple Rain." I heard his stomach and offered him my last bite, which he took reluctantly. The plants on the porch swiveled in a wind forecast to bring an inch of rain, a joyous pattering on the roof we'd heard only once in our six married years. But something besides hunger was on his mind. "You got a raise?" I asked. His boss had kept him late at work; it wasn't a tone-deaf question. No, he said, I've been pink-slipped for that piece I wrote. Richard had penned an op-ed for the *State Enquirer*. The gist was we've made a terrible mistake in punishing children for The Factor and it's not too late to pause and rethink strategy. He used the analogy of an airline pilot not turning back in bad weather because he's committed to landing at his destination. A combination of ego and investment in time and fuel blinds him to the real hazards. The plane crashes. Richard said his boss was upset by the aviation metaphor, since the company was, of course, the largest manufacturer of jet turbines, and perhaps cruise ships would have been a safer bet. Richard ran his finger through the tomato sauce on my plate, then wiped it clean on a napkin. I haven't told you, he said, but I've been talking to the skinny girl across the hall and she's perfectly normal. I'd have probably believed him in the beginning, but by then I was heavy in doubt. I was doubting Richard, his increasingly more extreme stance on The Factor. His grating insistence that so many smart people—doctors and scientists and top government officials with families—could be steering us so wrong. We were at odds, and isolation had historically helped me make terrible decisions. Though, still, what he wanted was far more dangerous than what I'd decided was best. While he was sleeping that night, I poured out the last of my chelated powders and then dismantled Baby Girl's room. Ripped down her polka-dot drapes, yanked one abstract shape at a time off the mobile dangling over the crib. The "You Are My Sunshine" decal tore off in almost one piece, only the "ne" stayed put, which for me meant Richard and I were destined to remain a twosome. When I finished, it looked like a kind of artwork only its creator could love. On the balcony, staring at Lyle and Ivan's empty parking space #302, I called the girls.

XIII. THE COMMITTED

In the beginning, I could never have guessed how it would end. Certainly Richard didn't anticipate waking to an apartment empty of his agreeable wife. Wishing for morning dew, moisture of any kind, to revive my chalky mouth, I met Jane, Patti, and Melissa at the mini-mart on Garden Road. Each of us bought an antibiotic-infused water and a pack of the cigarette brand we smoked occasionally in college with men who went down on us every night. From there, Jane leading the way in dawn's early light (the feeling was undeniably patriotic), we walked to the barren field behind the old Beanery Coffee. As of last year, it was the last standing roaster in the country before it too was deemed a place of excessive nonwork gathering and then shut down. Yet you could still feel the buzzy brainpower of legions who'd sat and typed to the grind of beans. Dotting the field like crop seeds once did—so many pregnant women, a swath of protruding bellies and swollen ankles and sounds of sore backs. Melissa whispered that her phone said over a thousand were attending. Jane whispered that I was doing the right thing, and how empowering to take matters into my own hands. I don't normally support this sort of thing, she said. It reminds me of those cult people who put on white shoes and drank rat poison while waiting for a ride on the Hale-Bopp comet. But this is so different, she added. This makes so much more sense, Patti said. You're restoring righteousness to the world. You're a savior, Ellie, Melissa added. Right then, I wanted to tell Richard the same thing. I supposed he always wanted to hear that from me and while I thought I was generous with compliments, I knew then I'd failed him in that department. "What are we waiting for?" I asked. The three moved in close to me, very sisterly. "They'll call your name," a woman behind me said. Her voice shook but with what I sensed was relief. The wait was over. I felt it too. One in five babies, despite the blood test, despite a negative rapid test, was getting diagnosed after birth and whisked away. Women who spoke up were disappearing too. The Latina actress in that True Crime Series, won a bunch of awards, gone days after suggesting that The Factor might not be a condition kids were born with, but a syndrome we were creating. Nurture, not nature, is to blame, she wrote. An easy fix was Richard's unscientific take. Turn off the goddamned screens, he said. And I'd suggested he try to remember when we were holy. Remember those days? He looked me up and down as if I were an icy mountain he had to climb. So I spelled it out. Richard, take a look at the skinny girl who had caused her fathers such grief. They'd had a fistfight at the pool one afternoon over her refusal to make eye contact, and the handsomer one, who argued it was important to see his daughter's face, fell and hit his head on the deck. He was still in a coma and I thought of him again as I stood in the field. I thought of which one of us, me or Richard, would end up with head trauma if we had this baby. With my foot, I drew an infinity sign over and over in dirt so lifeless even ragweed had stopped trying to root. They called my name. Jane nudged me forward and I took my place in a long, winding queue of women, most of them in loose-fitting dresses. I tried to stand as still as possible, to appear confident. Therapists were standing by to remove anyone who fidgeted, who appeared to inhabit the mindset of a questioner, a doubter, a dissenter, a fearless speaker-upper. Only sympathizers. Only those who pledged allegiance without saying a word. Only those not cradling their bellies in fear were allowed the cleaner field option. When it was my turn, I opened my mouth as wide and hungry as an orca anticipating her squid and the Lieutenant Doctor in Charge placed the flat, thin pill on my outstretched tongue. While he chanted the inscription at the Moral Compass, I hummed "Purple Rain," already feeling Richard split off from me. A dizzy rush, a cramp and release, and there he was, I could see him so clearly, back at home watching our plants sway in their crochet hammocks as the rain came, listening to the patter alone, wondering, like me, what belonged to us anymore.

Four Poems
Bin Ramke

FEAR OF LIFE WITHOUT WATER
—For Lorine Niedecker

When it comes it does
come in pipes and bottles for
a price now rarely falls as rain as snow
at times it comes. It weeps
from plumbing and machinery
it seeps.

      I was a boy of boats
swamps and marshland views
of rivers lakes and bayous brimming.

We, my people, are turning off
the Gulf Stream.

The zinnias need it so too
the gooseneck loosestrife.
And babies with their binoculars
looking into fear.

The water I miss most is brown
and various with dazzle
usually in the morning
and to the east of me.
It had fish and history.
Had a sound of grass beside it.

The country believes it is young
but all has dried into a froth
of despair around the lips.

HISTORICAL TRAUMA

Tomorrow morning mourning will begin
again but tonight I weep for my only own
reasons private, unprincipled

I dressed for it, thin pajamas
worn to near translucency although
such bodies a punishment to watch

and nothing much to live in. A frightening
smell of food comes through the walls
from the kitchen, the empty kitchen

the pronouns. Cut loose grammatical
they prowl, they accuse, they hiss
under your breath as you speak my name.

Do not speak the name, the nature
of the name is false, falseness,
the obverse of obvious declensional

inending, provisional always providing
providing. An ending.

SAINTS OF THE LATER DAYS/THIEVES AND MURDERERS

A way to see if not the world
the interiors of the worlds' houses
to see minds at work awake
to the chance you offer them

or would if they would let you
in in spite of the time the darkness
as you walk the streets looking
into yellow-lighted interiors,

other people's minds in the night.
Poverty is next to homelessness,
and cleanliness kills as surely
as despair. When the end

comes it will be close to noon
on a sunny day. God wants a witness.

THE MORTALITY OF FRIGHTENED CHILDREN

I, afraid of him the child
at whose birth I wished dead to stop
her pain, would sacrifice gladly
to Abraham's god any Isaac.

> . . . and said, My father: and he said, Here am I, my
> son. And he said, Behold the fire and the wood: but
> where is the lamb for a burnt offering?
>
> —Genesis 22:7

*

Then came sounds from the far forest, hints
of burning small creatures hidden
by night scrambling in shrubbery both
predator and prey of pretty emblems
feathery furred and furious

were years and after
came agonies of age
of knees and fear of secateurs;
walking among hollyhocks clicking
a pair in my hands thought of films
in which threat to digits
feels, feels about to happen;
carry small tools of torture
we who garden, cook, eat.

Movies frighten with small
methodologies: knives inspire fear
more than do heavy cartridges clicked into
Glocks—that comforting sound,
the way pistols feel
well made, fitting palms
like the sound of a bell to an ear;
but a knife threatens quiet
in its scabbard, scary word.

*

At a certain number of years a child
may turn, a mind rearrange dendrites;
excess of synaptic pruning
clicking of syllables (*secateurs*) hiss
of it all, the grandeur. A
grand disease, ancient in splendor.
A split against the world
a rage for order.

*

Our last visit to Lost Creek that fall
on the way to Fairplay we walked among aspen
bright in the light of season, soon
to be bare but for the moment golden.
The path itself a joy an accomplishment
like love; others passing paused
to be company, be kind.
We brought out
our lunch and sat on a downed limb
shared the final
sacrament of the season.
                    A woman
with a lion passed us, or perhaps
 a dog trimmed to resemble nobility.

237

Bin Ramke

*

Among the horrors this: your child
strapped onto a bed calmed chemically
as he cries with voices in the halls
head reverberant of voice.

*

Fear of sage grouse. *For*
not *of* the bird but of its passing
its sound recorded resounding
a depth of time and timber
if one generation replaced
the other like the song of birds in the forest   (Kierkegaard)
loss any irrevocable vocal
absence enrages echo in
the memory. Ordinate and abscissa,
there a point of crossing as
if the world worked as it sometimes does
for lovers and those who feel
the fall coursing forward, waft
of new air against old leaves
furtive trees and inhabitants.

"The *swish* sound is produced when the rough feathers
on the neck pouch are dragged through his wings,
and is only heard when the bird is close.   (allaboutbirds.org)
Following the wing swishes is a short series
of low, clear cooing notes, then two booming pops
in quick succession from the yellow air sacs." The rest
nestless movement followed by silence.

Ghost Soliloquies
Rebecca Lilly

DARKLING

"There's no proper dwelling for soul,"
spoke my doppelgänger, darkling entre-
preneur of the necropolis, "only phan-
tasmagoria, faces in the Rorschach, our
unintelligible psychobabble." Staring at
inkblots, I monitor the bottom-feeders
in my words, more afraid of the Reaper
than Lucifer. The devil's a panhandler
in the afterworld, while the Reaper's a
busker in an alley with little foot traffic
where I'm afraid his concerto rips open
a hole: he hides where the underworld
opens to a field of willow herb, where
desires are moths afraid of dawn.
Lately it's been crickets trilling in this
field that unsettle. Every tree's a
specimen from Genesis, and a grief
from eons ago lives under a fear,
equally old: its soft autumn wind passes
through the umber leaves, as rooks
disperse shadows to the rocks. Only the
Reaper has ever understood my solace.

Rebecca Lilly

ALIASES

The darker *me* has no biography, nothing in particular I'm proud of, only a
memoir of self-help recently begun
with diagrams of tarot card arcana. By
way of aliases, the drawling minions of
talking heads pole up my fortune-telling
booths outside tribal tents smoking
with opium. A cloud-forest of fears
whistles by like a twilight of owls, the
shadbush basking in moonlight. My
memoir got left out on the rainy tarp of
desperado afternoons! White flowers in
racemes, it blew from a hollowed
biography of sicklepod and fireweed, the
dark held carefully in a polished
bone cup with black jasmine tea. I'd
cleared my own path, so as to plant
bulblets from the lily family, but the
darker me insisted on personifying a
Celtic warrior, not Mother Mary. By
the forest, I peel bark off hickories and
oaks I knifed with graffiti in Bible
school, the backyard shut to truants.
The heartwood reveals the seasons I've
been gone, the fear forests where
foundlings vanished off-trail in
memoirs, blowing rainfall in mirror
shards, soul. Staring Death in the eyes,
you might be spared. *Bon Voyage.* Love
isn't a chronicle.

GOLD LEAF

The house of curious doors had flames
shooting out—my head alive with the
tarot's Falling Tower. I pulled the
blinds as I switched off the fire of
knowledge. "Clarify your object," said
the sorceress who photoed the flames
with fingerlike wands. It's too bizarre
to look: each fear of mine, a crystal
curio, a moon haloing a notebook's
leaves where I'm sitting by the tower
window. Now the fire's out and Death
is hardwired to a blown bulb. While I'd
prefer its switches were trans-
cendentals, intense cold blows as easily
through tower stone as through a hole,
so I study the snowflakes closely as
gold leaf scatters over the sill. "I
apologize. I mistook, in my poem, the
moon for the sun. I've honored false
auguries," I confessed to the forest,
and it answered, "No, it's the leaves
you've collected. Remember, it's
autumn."

Rebecca Lilly

GRAVITAS

It's the fear of bad *bling*, the ruby eye
in cataracts of rainless clouds. It's
about seeing myself *now* versus *then*,
reading by a lanternfly, the algae-
covered pond blurring its demonic
body. Without reflection, the devil gets
disoriented in a mirror, his bearings lost
in our ordinary world, a seesaw of
light. And should the mirror shatter
with gravitas ... picking up shards
afterward, it's very quiet, and the light,
sharp. It's difficult not to think of body
parts and a guillotine hammer under the
lanternflies who wink off the last sand
through the hourglass like the
Sandman's French kiss. One afternoon,
on a whim, I gifted the devil a photo of
himself (knowing, for the undead, the
mirror's no help), as I reassembled the
puzzle of glint. From the ceiling, the
devil grinned, disappointed his photo
didn't show his plump red lips! The
photo's graininess and overexposure
didn't matter to him: with a nail-clawed
hand, he snatched it back, scratching its
premonition. Death has flashbulbs for
eyes, I reminded him—why my ghosts,
colorless, slip through the hourglass as
dust, the white sands of time.

242

NIGHTSHADES

Lucifer unnerves with reminiscences of petty sins, and the guilt trips—even so, I'm thankful for the visits: I learned to identify the devil's approach and know the critical differences between Death and the devil. Death is a jaguar, while the devil's an old she-goat grazing on bristled weeds, almost invisible. *Why do rose petals wilt when the devil squints at them closely, aromatherapy from a bowl of water on my windowsill?* In the forest, wind's a disembodied otherworldly howl forking at the trailhead where the devil trampled petals of other flowers: angel's trumpet and mandrake. When I follow the devil, I admit it's not to know a destination—faith is no aegis—but to discern the shadow's missing edges. My impulse is a knife that cuts a stone in half, a subtle knife of white diamond, one every forest king desires to possess. Dark arrives in wheel-barrows of weeds uprooted by the gardener, but remember: even if the night blooms collude with you, your nightmares are harmless.

BLACK INK

Freddie, my doppelgänger, studied
obituaries, sparing me the queasy
stomach, butterflies in my gut, so I
could sit with him at breakfast in a
sunroom, sipping coffee, nodding off to
the idea I'd see it coming when
everyone I know has bit the dust. "I'm
always fear friendly!" He speaks with
an onstage drawl, a morbid lackey of
the devil. "My *God*, I'd never drop
names of those prematurely slated
for . . . you know." As a poet and lover
of bookshops, I've minded my own
invisibility, staying clear of family
plots. "You're on the wrong side of the
fence," Freddie said, bowing like the
master of ceremonies for Gothic
poetics. "You're tipping an old hat!"
It's the dark magic which denies me the
possibility of any death management.
The irony of a jester and sidekick who
intensifies my miserly habits—Freddie,
the unwitting oracle, puts a lid on the
inkwell whenever the cacophony of
crows cracks a window. If fear's
opposite is love and not courage, I'm
holding up a graveyard bouquet of pink
plastic roses, hydrangea and baby's
breath for Freddie to inspect. I admit
I'm envious of those who died inhaling
no scent of themselves, floating in a
hole that, shoveled out, matters little.
(The Gothic deconstructs, as often as

not—the esprit de corps of a symbology that treats neurotics.) Freddie prides himself a philosopher for poets, while I hide out with ghosts to clear the butterflies from fields of pink and purple cosmos. Per my request, the ghosts and I compare notes. I try to stay detached, striving for naturalistic observations of epitaphs, but anxiety kicks in with crumpled flower wrappers in an open hole. I ask which psalms should be passcodes to heaven, and which adages rewritten. Freddie's here too, doing bed preparation where the weeds were mown. The ghosts, out of loneliness, repeat their soliloquies—but each hears only its own.

THIRD EYE

In the small hours I've often thought of my breath as a posthumous wind, my only SOS. Intuition tells me to breathe deeply, but cautiously, as a witness, since silence has a history with the living, but a somewhat different one with the dead. I know well the silence of repression. The devil, who hunts us relentlessly, has to follow noise, such as a cough or footstep on gravel, in dark. Without a lamp, our breath must show irregular patterns of panic for the devil to track. Breath fogging my bath mirror has a particular quiet like a lepidopterist pin balanced on my fingertip. Butterflies in my stomach migrate to the country in my third eye as the silence bridges horizonless distances inside my mind. Somewhere along the path, I halt if I fear the devil overheard this little talk with myself, pressing my heels into ground, and snapping my mouth shut. Butterflies cloud the valleys full of willow herb as my eye glances off, attempting to catch them, but their direction's askew. Fog glitters into nothing because the wind's so fierce. Only the heart's compass could tell the truth.

A PLAY IN THE WOODS

I keep a journal so as not to remember:
oddly enough, an inscription lets the
memory disappear. "Fear burns on the
pyre of your presence." (Those words
aren't mine, so I'll remember them.) I
study late works of mystics and seers,
and admire how their sentences, like
chameleons, change color with reread-
ings, or even with repeat re-
membrances. I hear echoes in the
inscriptions as well, like birds fluttering
—never songbirds, but crows or
vultures with raw-throated calls. I sit in
the woods, wondering what the sound
is for darkness, as well as the light in
my heart. Having been close a long
time now with mystical works, I've
been dead longer than I've lived. While
I'd like to catch the wind's sound in
snow and ice in the woods, I'm caught
up in the sun's flights of fancy, in
verifying personhood, and in transmit-
ting messages to the dead via the
crows. My living seer isn't a mystic but
a dramatist—a hermit by the rock
where I journal. *Brother of the sun*, he
told me in a poem. (I had to run off,
marry the moon, and live in a brick
hovel for a while, howling like a wolf.)
"Faith is my aegis," he said, "and truth
is a dare, a chameleon in the greenery,
my friend, or, if you prefer, a tiger who
will never be tamed. Never!"

Gimmer

Genevieve Valentine

THEY'RE ON THE WAY to visit Carol: Thursdays, four to six. Bea looks out the window—closed, always; Mom fought with Carol over it once, how the wind tore at her hair, Carol snapping she was going to be sick and their father scowling at the scene, and by dinner he'd coded them out of the control panel. The morning clouds are breaking up.

"Maybe we can take Carol into the garden," she says.

Her father says, "Let's see how she's been."

A leftover answer. It's a long time now since she's been anything.

He wouldn't hear about them having any pets, so Carol just read fairy tales where princesses had animals, like that was getting him back, sitting up in bed with her voice bouncing out the always-open door into the hall like Bea had even asked for a bedtime story. There was no end of it—the princesses listened to swans and married bears and greeted all the sheep of the field that raced out to meet them. Even when one princess or another was brought low by schemers, her geese never gave her any trouble.

"That's not what a pet's like," said Bea once.

"No," Carol said, hopeful. "A real pet bites."

Sheep bite, it turns out. It doesn't matter.

The doctors were careful with Carol. Whenever they visit, the nurses (always new nurses, it feels like) are delighted at how deft the doctors have been. Of course Carol remembers what day it is, they say, sounding half surprised it's true; of course she loves craft hour. No, the nurses have given up the reading lessons, but she's perfectly happy looking out at the garden. Of course they can see her paintings; no, it's not much—her hands aren't what they used to be—but the colors are so nice.

(Mom doesn't look at the paintings even when she bothers to come; after the first time, she set them down with shaking hands and smiled like she was holding in a terrible sound, and started finding something else to do until the nurse had locked them back in Carol's art cubby.)

They've put Carol in one of the visiting rooms to wait for them— Mom got upset the first time they saw the room she sleeps in. Carol smiles tenderly; it's nothing like Carol, which was what Dad wanted, so Bea doesn't know why he always looks like he looks. She tries not to think about it. He doesn't like her screwing up her face.

Her bedroom door doesn't have a lock. He'd taken away Carol's whole door after he found her diary; Carol flushed his watch down the toilet and asked him how he liked other people touching his things, a screaming fight that scared Bea into the closet in her room until it was over.

He never found anything in Carol's room again, which made him even madder. Not even her memory drive. Carol got punished for being sullen and keeping secrets after that—couldn't prove you weren't keeping secrets, could you—but Bea could tell his heart wasn't in it. Whatever he'd wanted, he hadn't gotten.

Bea's room is the way it was when she was twelve—the pink plaid border and the blue sprig comforter, the bookcase with little vases in a line, screen background of a castle, nothing on the walls but the poster Mom got her from the museum they almost visited for her birthday. (Women got outcoded that weekend because of some protest incident inside; Mom convinced Dad to authorize buying it online. Almost as good.)

Bea never kept a diary. Not one sideways keystroke on the memory drive. She never touched the floorboards, either—she'd thought about hiding a little paper journal there like a girl in a novel, but then Dad had found Carol's money.

When Bea brought Carol's daily meal up to her bedroom, Carol was always sprawled across the bed, back to the corner, looking through what used to be the doorway.

"Just apologize so you can come out," said Bea every night, and Carol said, "Thanks for the food."

The sixth night she was rubbing her thumb over her wrist, pulling the skin tight over the chip. She said, "Leave the fork."

Bea went cold. "No. I'll get in trouble. Stop."

"No," said Carol, like she was promising.

Bea hated her too much to give her the fork, but she also didn't tell Dad when she brought the tray back downstairs still full. Not that night, or the next, or the next. After three weeks Carol's chip flagged the Family Department, and Dad got a lecture about malnutrition from a pair of doctors as Carol lay grayly in bed. The room alarm came off the chip after that. She had to follow a meal plan and strip for the nurse at school checkups for two months, but she got out without apologizing. It must have been worth it, for a little while.

Dad doesn't bother to search Bea's room anymore. That's something.

Of course they can go into the garden. There are no tantrums anymore.

"You're so big now," says Carol.

Mom's mostly stopped coming; she thinks the nurses are paid to lie and that Carol doesn't remember anything, and that's a very useful thing for Mom to think, since it keeps her from making the kind of scene Dad won't put up with.

"We were here last week, sweetie," Dad says. "Bea's only a week older."

"Too old," says Carol, and Dad and the nurse laugh. Bea doesn't.

When she came out of the aisle of medical books, he was chatting with the librarian who'd helped her with the Dewey Decimal numbers. He was smiling, calm. He asked if she'd found what she was looking for.

She couldn't answer, but he said, I'm talking to you, Bea, and so she settled on "I couldn't understand it," which must have sounded true enough that he didn't say I wouldn't lie right now, Bea, which was the one to avoid at all costs.

Once she was buckled in the back, he looked in the rearview and said, I trust I won't have to come looking for you again.

He didn't have to. She gave up lingering in the stacks or bringing home things that raised his eyebrows—history, romance—and soon he was taking her every weekend. She appeared at the appointed time, handing him the books to review as she got in the car. He barely looked anymore—there was never time to get too many. Still, the library almost whenever she wanted. It was something.

*

"Why are the cubbies locked?" Bea asked once, as Carol looked mournfully at a watercolor the nurse was sliding into the space above her nameplate. "Couldn't she just come get it later?"

It's to keep everything safe, the nurse said as he swiped the staff ID and talked brightly about ceramics classes and outbursts that ruined papers, sad little accidents that patients had sometimes, and how careful they wanted everyone to be. They didn't want anything breaking.

A girl across the room had stopped painting; she watched the access card like a hunting dog, one thumb pressed to her wrist.

Once she tried the window on the way to visit Carol. She sat in the back; she'd barely moved her wrist over the panel, so he wouldn't see, so it would look like a mistake if she got caught. Locked. There was no getting out until he opened the door.

She felt sick, suddenly. When she asked for permission he said he liked the quiet, without the wind in his face. You'll be fine, he'd said. You've always been too sensitive.

She keeps her hands folded in her lap now. You have to be careful if you want to stay free.

It was so easy. Easier than thinking about college for Bea, which had been pushed back another year. They didn't have the money—Carol's facility was so expensive—and Mom didn't want to hear another word about it.

The doctors explained the lobotomy to Dad like a fix to a faulty carburetor—not responding, quick to lock up, fighting direction. On Thursday, Carol had hit a nurse and made another run for it. On Monday they put her on the phone, to show how well things had gone; the nurses said, Bea, it's Bea, Bea in baby voices until Carol said it too, but like a letter, not a name. Carol didn't say anyone's name, after; whatever had been cut out of her, she'd cut it out of everyone else too.

"I'd like to take driving lessons," Bea said. Not like a conclusion. It had to sound like a daydream. Like the pink room had come down

251

to dinner. "Then Mom wouldn't have to interrupt her day to come get me from school."

Her father blinked. Your mother has plenty of time in her day, he said, and more experience.

Bea didn't look at her mother. She could feel her staring just fine. "Well," she said, pushing a smile onto her face, "I could get more experience from lessons before I start driving on my own."

He set his fork down. We'll decide when you're ready, he said. You clearly have plenty to work on here before you start something new. Like manners.

She bit her lip and didn't answer until she felt her mother's heel, pressing on her toes hard enough to hurt.

"Yes, Dad," she said.

He blinked again, but she supposed he didn't hear that title very much. God knew Carol wasn't using it.

Maybe it was better, she thought. Maybe it would be better to just forget it all. Maybe, when there was nothing you could do—not even hold silence—the only way out was to forget it all so deep that your grudges sank. That your enemy didn't have the pleasure of seeing you flinch.

The first time he'd driven her back to the library, it was because he'd come across a sheepdog competition on a sports channel over Christmas. He was so charmed that he talked about it over dinner, so charmed he said yes when she asked.

I'd think ranching's too much work for someone who's never had work to do, he'd said, opening the door for her; Bea was careful not to frown. I'll be right here, he'd said.

He laughed at her armful of books. You look like a farmer's wife, he'd said, sounding not unhappy about it; Bea was careful not to smile too wide.

Sheep sounded like a lot of trouble for something so easy to lead. Half the advice was about how to stop them biting the dogs.

It was slow going, confusing just because there were so many ways to call a sheep, depending what you wanted to do to her. Culls too old for anything but meat, lambs not yet put to work, drafts brought from the hills to the lowlands to calm themselves, gimmers old enough to breed, gelts not suited to the ram for some reason that must be obvious when you were on the hills in the first bite of spring.

She'd always thought sheep were hopelessly stupid—that sheep had no enemies because they forgot their whole lives as soon as they lowered their heads to the grass—but they knew how to fight a dog at least.

The dogs were the only way to keep yourself in sufficient sheep, and teaching them was rough going. You had to wait until the pup was old enough, because if you started too young it would be too afraid to listen and the sheep would trample it to death if it didn't bite them first; sheep could see much wider than people, so they were hard for a dog to surprise. You had to build its confidence so it could face down the toothy old culls that didn't want to move, but you had to make sure its interest was only in the work and not the ewes. (Sticking, they called that—the dog started thinking about the sheep, frozen staring, and then it was all over. A sticky dog wouldn't take orders anymore.) Lessons three times a day, directing it to mind you with a few sharp words, until you'd trained the thing to sew up the whole hillside like a mending stitch at nothing but a whistle, feeding sheep into one pen or another to die or to breed, cull or gelt or gimmer however you liked.

Her father asked if she'd learned anything, in a tone that hoped she hadn't.

"You were right about not having pets," she said.

They hadn't told her about Carol until after it was over. "We worried you'd be upset," her mother said, and she was too angry to hear the warning there until she was screaming—it wasn't right, there was nothing wrong with Carol, they were monsters—and her father said, We'll have none of that. Then she heard.

"School?" asks Carol.

The nurse coos that it isn't school time right now—later, he says, you can go a little later. This one never got the memo about pretending that Carol remembered things.

Bea says, "Yes, I'm still going."

"How long?" asks Carol.

Bea looks at her father. Carol doesn't. Never does.

"Just going to finish senior year," says Bea, hot faced, when Dad says nothing.

Carol frowns. "No," she says, tender.

Yes, promises the nurse. That isn't long, he tells Carol; she'll be done before you know it. Then she can come here any time she wants!

Carol looks only at Bea. Carol says, "No."

Brandon asked to walk her home after choir last year, and she'd never even thought about Brandon, but the idea of walking home was so thrilling that she half gasped before she said, "I can't."

It was enough for him to keep trying—she had to say it two more times across the parking lot before she got to the car. Brandon was frozen halfway, watching her with a strange look on his face. Maybe she ran from him.

"You're late," Mom said, and Bea meant her "Sorry"—the car sent a report if they weren't back by three.

It was quiet a while; they didn't have much to say to each other. A few blocks from home, her mother flexed her hands on the wheel and sighed. "You wouldn't."

It sounded like something Mom was only telling herself, but still Bea promised, "I wouldn't."

You never let a boy close enough to get you in trouble. Getting knocked up was a thing only girls with no future did: girls who didn't care about the family's reputation, girls debasing themselves just to be oppositional. Pregnant was the worst thing that could happen to a girl—the very worst—except for getting rid of it, which was somehow so much more terrible than that; so terrible that your father made a phone call, and you never came back.

To keep Dad and Mom from looking in her room so much, Bea did her homework in the kitchen. It was full of geese, and Bea hated it.

At first it had been just a goose cookie jar, but every Christmas there was something else from Dad, and so now there were goose tea towels and salt shakers and a napkin holder and a brass paperweight that kept a cookbook open.

Mom always cleaned it in the afternoons, long swipes of the counter and polishing handles and glances out the window at the road that ran just past the trees in their yard. She asked about homework the whole time. Bea couldn't understand what she did all day when Bea was in school so that Bea was stuck working on geometry over the sound of Mom washing the glass jars with goose-head stoppers.

They'd held things, to start with—candy, cookies, roasted almonds you could smell even with the top on. But then Mom was on a diet, and then somehow Bea was too, and one of the almonds had gotten some shell stuck to it. Now Bea had a porcelain molar, and the glass jars sat empty, the sun cutting through them, the heads guarding nothing.

They stay for dinner. It's crustless sandwiches and warm green peas and applesauce and a pressed-starch spoon that starts to sag three bites into the peas.

"A fork," Carol asks no one in particular. Bea's spoon melts to nothing in her grip.

At Christmas last year they'd brought presents. They hadn't given up on the reading yet, so Bea had saved up her allowance and bought a book of illustrated stories. Carol made a happy little noise when she saw—took Bea's hand in both her hands and squeezed. Mom excused herself, thick voiced, and hit the bell until the nurse let her out. She'd still be in the hall when it was time to go.

Bea read, Carol's eyes on her as the princess took dresses from birds and fell asleep for a hundred years and solved riddles. Their father sighed and went out.

Carol kept looking at her, tender, bruising. "Very nice stories," she said. "I know them?"

"You do," Bea said, and Carol's fingers dug tighter. "I still have the one you left me at home. It's safe there." Dumb luck he'd never thought to take it. Child's things in a child's room.

Their father opened the door. Carol looked only at Bea; she held on and held on and held on.

Dad must have thought Mom was more like Bea than like Carol, but they found the halves of the old credit card behind Mom's section of the closet, in a box of tampons. Mom's name on the account, the letters raised like her name was trying to escape. Carol gripped the pieces like they weighed more than she did.

255

Genevieve Valentine

"Let's get a snack," Bea said, which was code for We Need to Go; the house recorded audio. But Carol was so far away she had forgotten Bea was there. It went on forever. Twice she touched the halves together and held her breath, like something would happen. Anything.

Carol asks for a story, and after the nurse unlocks Carol's book from the cubby, Bea reads about a princess and some animals who love her.

Bea thinks about the flock of sheep smart enough to see the dog and know where they're being driven—two hundred terrified hooves thundering toward the long-haired maid, who is either the most beloved of the dog, or who is dead.

"She combed her golden locks finer than spun wool," she reads, and then, "Sheep bite, you know. They have to train the dogs for ages, or else they get bitten to death."

Carol doesn't look up from the book. She says, "Good."

He's never mentioned any more about driving, but it's a long way to visit Carol, and by now she can feel when it's time to switch gears, the car sighing and sliding forward in relief. She could do it herself, probably, someday.

Along the road, the wind shakes the tips of the trees. She wishes she could feel it, but the sun is warm, and that's something.

Don't Look Now
Terese Svoboda

I saw that film, sitting under a tree in Sudan in the company of an Italian priest and the man I was with, she says.

She rearranges her legs, since that matters so much in a shrink's office. Dr. K is new, young—well, anyone's younger than she is—and, she presumes, has read all the books on the shelves behind him.

What am I forgetting? she says. Nicolas Roeg, he was the director. The most frightening film I've ever seen. Back then you would've seen it because everyone saw everything that came out as soon as possible, there were so few new films.

She lapses into silence to see if Dr. K will prompt her, or if he's one of those who will wait forever.

A long minute later he says: What was the film about?

A couple travels to Venice, she begins, because they are grieving the death of their daughter and the husband is restoring a church. They meet a clairvoyant who says their dead daughter is trying to warn them of danger. The film was the color of the pigeons that were always flying up, and red from the bad dwarf's cape.

Dr. K isn't bothering to take notes; he will improvise. She stares at the papered-over window behind his head. The dwarf had a knife, she says. Inadvertently the husband becomes a suspect in a murder case. Cunnilingus was involved. Surely the priest was scandalized.

He smiles. She's taken aback: shrinks don't smile. She always tries to make them smile but most of the time they keep a straight face. But scandal is always amusing.

The man I was with made it a point to talk about the film and the sex, she says. The priest was handsome and friendly. I was embarrassed. Did I turn the embarrassment into fear? I was definitely afraid of the man I was traveling with, that he would turn on me.

She looks again into the opacity of the window but doesn't see it this time. I could hear the bloodsucking bats settling in the trees above us during the credits.

Very Graham Greene, says Dr. K.

That sounds like a compliment but she doesn't say so. Dr. K has gray eyes, not unfriendly, needs a haircut.

The priest was so handsome, she says, even collared and wearing khakis. The collar must've been hot. I thought even then about what that symbolized with regard to sex, a choke collar. That decade was all about sex.

He scratches his nose. Bored already? Or uncomfortable with the topic?

The priest's English was as bad as my Italian, she says, not looking anywhere near Dr. K. The man I was with loved to pretend he could understand whatever language even if he didn't know a word of it. About the same age, the two of them enjoyed each other tremendously while piecing out the movie all over again in the dark of the night, long after the projector was packed away and the wind had died down. Especially that one scene.

She looks down at her hands. That part when the dead girl turns out to be the dwarf. Donald Sutherland was the lead.

What did you do while they were talking?

She finds the question dull, surely a sign that it might lead somewhere she doesn't want to go. I had lunch with Donald once, she says, and visited a rare-book store with him, trying to get him to act as host to a project.

Did you succeed?

I did. I had just become a blonde and had blisters in my scalp from the bleach, and I had balls. I find that hard to imagine now.

Dr. K appears to be listening, but a little too intently. Is that what you want back? he says. That kind of imagination?

Well, she says. Sutherland never did the work.

He nods as if she's answered the question.

What I find hard to believe, she says, is that I have any memory at all of the monastery courtyard, of the Sudanese who came and went while the movie ran on. How few stopped to watch. I couldn't understand why they weren't riveted. Sure, it wasn't their language but nearly everyone in Khartoum spoke English or Arabic, along with six other languages. But why were we watching the film in a monastery?

Maybe the priest didn't know about that scene.

Unprecedented, a shrink offering an answer.

The priest ran the film series. He had a mission to fulfill, she says. Colonial conversion?

He observes the cockroaches dying on his wall, says the shrink. Gives them the last rites. Escape, that's what people do when they're out of their element.

I'm not talking about fate, am I? How we had to see that film in that context then.

The idea of fate isn't very useful in therapy, he says.

She nods, and waits for the wry expression on his face to return to professional.

The priest was funny, she says, and sad. He came from Naples and said in his terrible English that he was a spy before he signed up to become a priest, a spy in the Algerian War, for the French. It was so twisted, he said, though no one would have said twisted then. He was doing penance in Sudan and had nearly forgotten why, teaching hordes of Sudanese girls in the high school. You see, I was listening. Maybe I listened like a shrink while the two of them talked. After all, whenever I said anything, the man I was with repeated my every word, and only then did the priest respond. There was no point in talking.

You were made invisible, says Dr. K.

Like you? But you have power. When you repeat me, you magnify what I say.

He nods slightly. The requisite tissue box sits on the far end of the bookshelf. She would have to get out of her seat to get one, or he would have to dispense one. More power.

I remember how the endless, claustrophobic alleys of Venice in the movie quite captured the feeling of being lost as a tourist. I felt the full terror of that after we left Khartoum, of being unable to read the Venetian signs and getting irredeemably lost. The man I was traveling with often went on ahead. I was pregnant by then.

Dr. K clears his throat. As I remember it, the film's about the psychology of grief and the effect the death of a child can have on a relationship.

You did see it?

Yes. I remembered it when you mentioned the claustrophobia.

Mistaking the dwarf with the knife for a child, that's what really undid me. A sort of precursor to my son's death. An accident, she says, not due to a murdering dwarf.

I see, says Dr. K.

Nobody does. She looks at her hands again because there they are, sitting in her lap. The film was about how nobody understood each other, nobody understands what it's like to lose a child. The terror.

She can't tell the shrink that all she wanted to do was have sex after the child died, just the way the couple did in the film, or he'll think she's trying to seduce him, and drop her. But isn't a shrink like

Terese Svoboda

any audience, and you have to seduce them a bit to make them listen? I remember the guns in the Sudanese museum we visited the next day, she says, stacked up so gaily, celebrating the vanquished, their ammunition, their tanks, all the photographs of the dead.

Dr. K pulls his hands out from under his desk. They begin to move to signal their session is finished, move like an Italian's, with eloquence. Or does she just imagine the nationality of his raised palms?

Next week.

She plunges into the snow of New York that has piled up during her session, taking care to follow the footprints others have left before her. Do they all go in and never come out? Across the street is Madison Square Park, and dogs chase after balls despite the snow, their leashes, and their owners trailing after them.

She hadn't heeded the film's warning; she should have resisted the man she was with that night and never gotten pregnant. And to have been so lost in Venice—at every turn she faced another baffling decision. She remembers how the priest couldn't quit talking about the movie afterward, how he had called out the title as they were leaving: *Don't Look Now.*

But despite her fear she has to.

In the Woods behind the Market
Rob Walsh

WE CAME UPON THE MAN in the woods behind the market and put a dollar in his tin, waiting to see how he responded before we moved ahead with our proposal. Even in those days a dollar wasn't much money, but around here there were still a few places where it could get you a cup of coffee. When he replied that even drip coffee was like three bucks, we decided not to mention the specials they ran sometimes in the market you could almost see through all the trees and shadows. He didn't look like the sort of person who wanted to be corrected about anything.

Though we only had a few questions about the REAL VETERAN sign planted before his shelter, it seemed to bother him that we'd bring up the sign and ask for his confirmation number, the outfit or department or whatever number veterans used to confirm their service. He lifted his shirt and gave us a few scars to consider, "the kind that veterans have," and overall seemed like a pretty good candidate, so we asked, "How would you like to earn a hundred more of these?"

There was a bit of wind that day so the new dollar was scuttling back and forth as we waited for him to ask a follow-up question, or at least thank us for the offer. But he just looked at the dollar we'd extended and sat there patiently, as though established members of town regularly brought proposals to these ragged edges of the forest and he could pick and choose which ones to accept. "We'd gladly do it ourselves, the job in question," we explained, "but we don't want to get on the wrong side of the police."

"I'm no criminal," he said.

"You won't need to get your hands bloody or even dirty. Like I say, we'd do the job ourselves if we weren't already on such good terms with the local police department. All we need is for you to scare someone."

He began to withdraw inside his tarp-covered shelter, whose door flap was so small he had to bend to fit inside. But then he looked back and asked, "Any touching?"

"Not if you can be scary without laying hands on her. But you may want to consider that she's quite attractive and any man would be fortunate to be touched by her, even prodded or bumped into from behind. Some say she's the best-looking female in town. He says that," I nodded at Boyle, who hadn't said anything yet. "He loves her. But she broke his heart."

The man grunted in a manner that suggested he was more interested in the story now, but it could have also meant he just wanted us to leave—we didn't know enough about him, only his REAL VETERAN sign and the tattoos on his arms that seemed to be just a long list of crossed-out names.

"This woman," we continued, "strung our friend Boyle along for more than a year, agreeing to dates with him and never paying for any of her food, ritually ordering seafood and wine, accepting every gift and encouraging him—through her positive reactions to the gifts—to buy her more and more, increasing in price as Boyle's feelings increased."

"So now you want to give her a good scare," he said.

"It's not revenge, but yes," we replied, "it would be great if she imagined for a moment that her world had come crashing down, and then she might regret for that single split second how she treated a nice person like Boyle."

"What makes you think I'll be able to scare her?"

We didn't want to say anything about his tattoos or his missing teeth, or that his clothes were really dirty. It wasn't until he asked this question that we really looked at him closely and began to feel sorry for him and wonder what decisions had led him to this point. But he seemed to detect that we were feeling sorry for him and kind of firmed up suddenly and said we'd better not be here when he returned and went off a few steps to urinate in the bushes.

We walked away and kept our eyes averted until the noise ended and then came back and tried to pick up where we left off. "Middle of the night would be best, don't you think, when you tried to break into her condo or something? I mean, you could set it up however you're most comfortable."

He looked at us for a while or what seemed like a while, maybe only five or ten seconds, but in some situations that amount of time can feel longer. "I want two hundred," he finally said.

Boyle had spent so much on her already, what was another two hundred? we argued until Boyle surrendered and counted out the money. So it was done. The plan was in motion.

The man said we could meet back here tomorrow for a status update.

When we returned, there was no sign of the man and no sign of the shelter. There was some evidence that he'd been there but we don't know if we should describe what or how, specifically, well, how he'd urinated before but now he'd done the other one, and Boyle was so upset that he almost stomped on it before he caught himself and wandered back to the parking lot and kicked the truck—my truck— in the tires. "This was your idea," he said, "and it didn't work!"

"It was all of our idea."

"You were the mastermind."

Normally I'd be OK with that label, but in this case I refused it. It was clear Boyle blamed me for his failed plan. Also, I realized much later, after so many things had changed that it was only possible to look back on what happened that day through an alien fog, that Boyle probably blamed me for introducing him to Yeonhee in the first place.

I didn't know Yeonhee very well at the time. I worked at the car dealership and she bought a used car, little red one. Yes, I introduced her to Boyle, but I also married her, and this was only a few months after that scene on the side of the road with Boyle kicking my tires. I can talk about the wedding if you're interested in that sort of thing. First, however, I think it's important that we give Yeonhee a chance to explain her decision to let Boyle buy her dinner so many times.

"He seemed like a nice enough guy. Lonely, but haven't we all been lonely? If you know what it's like to be truly lonely then you know the cost of a meal is not so unfair for an evening respite. Plus I was in graduate school and had like no money. I was working on my thesis. It takes all your concentration to write a good thesis. On many nights I wasn't capable of saying much or looking up from my plate. I was so tired from reading books, taking notes, and so on. But he kept asking me if I wanted to have dinner, no strings attached. That was how he would sign off his emails, *No strings attached, Boyle*. And I knew that if I was going to get a master's degree I'd need a few breaks along the way. Takes a lot of hard work, accomplishing one's dream. I remember opening up one night and talking for hours about the limits of hard work and how the universe was nonconsensual, meaning that most dreams refused to materialize without a lucky break. My thesis was related to this topic so I had a lot to say about it. That was when the gifts started, really nice pens and leather-bound notebooks and some other things that were meant, I assumed, to be a kind of materialization of the lucky break I had mentioned to him. I still have all the gifts. Does Boyle want them back?"

No, he doesn't. After the wedding I showed up at Boyle's house with all of the gifts piled in a cardboard box.

"What am I supposed to do with these?" he asked. "Return them? I don't have the receipts!"

"Some places might give you store credit."

"Yeonhee will do to you," Boyle warned, "exactly what she did to me—that's who she is."

But Boyle was wrong. Now Yeonhee had a master's degree. She had a good job at the Center for Public Outreach. Usually it was she who paid for our dinner. I was a lucky man and happier than I'd ever been. But I needed to conceal the full measure of happiness around Boyle.

"You just don't know what her angle is yet," Boyle warned me.

"She has a good heart, and you might be able to see that," I argued, "if you looked at the renovations the Center for Public Outreach has made to our town, like the safer playground with the sandbox refilled after she learned how dirty sandboxes can get, because feral cats use them for a litterbox?"

There's a reason I mentioned the children's playground. Minsu and Junho, our boys. Once we had the boys, Boyle abandoned his series of warnings. Now he accepted that our relationship was legitimate. This bothered him more than anything. "I can't believe you let her give them those names," Boyle said.

"I like the names. We chose them together."

"What do you think would happen," Boyle asked, "if I told her about what transpired so many years ago—is it ten years already?— between us and the homeless man, the plan that you crafted and spearheaded, the one I haven't said a word about until now?"

"Are you threatening me?"

"Think she'd take the boys?" Boyle wondered. "And only let you see them on weekends? That's usually how it goes."

Versions of this threat began to surface more often. It occurred to me that maybe I should be the one to tell Yeonhee what happened on that dark day so many years ago. But if I did tell her what happened, maybe I should change the version slightly. In the new version, it could be Boyle's idea. I could be the one trying to talk him out of it.

This is what I was thinking about when little Minsu brought me the picture, a monster killing another monster, and like the rest of his drawings I put it on the fridge and knew it didn't matter what the picture was or how skilled he was as an artist, only that Minsu had made it for me.

One day when the fridge had even more drawings on it I took out a beer and drank most of it while standing beside the fridge and trying to appreciate their work, trying to keep my mind from wandering back to the forest behind the grocery store and the tarp-covered shelter, the mist-clad trees, and the scars the vet had showed us in response to a pretty insensitive question, I realized now, since I was a father and an altogether different person.

The place I used to go for drinks after work was off-limits these days, since Boyle hung around there. "Maybe today is the day I'll give Yeonhee a call," he had threatened last time I went for drinks. "See how she's doing after all these years. Catch up on old times." The bar was overpriced anyway, I realized, and I was happier at home with my beautiful family, watching a movie, heaped together on the sofa. "I wonder if she still remembers me?" Boyle said. "I haven't changed much, have I? Some people change a lot as the years go by, forget who their real friends are and how much they still need those friends to guard their secrets."

The other day Boyle showed up at the dealership. He wondered if we might have a friendly chat in my office. I closed the door behind us. "What?"

"Aren't you going to offer me a coffee or soda first like you do for somebody who can't make up his mind about a car?"

Boyle tapped the soda can's lid for a few seconds to defuse the carbonation, and though I'd read a magazine article that reported how this had little to no effect on spillage, I kept my mouth shut and waited for him to finish tapping and explain what he was doing there.

"Here's what's going to happen," Boyle said. "A young lady is going to visit this dealership tomorrow. I have all the info you need about her in this." He held up an envelope. "Since she's a graduate student, you're going to show her a cheap used car and suggest a test drive. Instead of driving around the block, I'm going to need you to take her out by the cliffs. Halfway through the test drive, you're going to say, 'What's that sound—do you hear that?' She's going to say, 'Uh, no?' Because you're only pretending that you can hear an eerie rattling or whatever type of sound you'd like to make up. At that point, you two are going to switch spots. 'I'll drive this back to the dealership for safety purposes,' you're going to say. But then you speed up toward the cliffs and say, 'My God, the brakes, the brakes, my God—' "

"I'm not going to scare this poor girl," I told Boyle.

265

Rob Walsh

When I read what was inside the envelope, Boyle said, then I'd understand that she was another cunning grad student who thought she could order whatever she wanted on their dates without ever going home with him and extending a proper thank you.

"I don't care. I'm not doing it."

Boyle slid the envelope across the table and tapped it much harder than he had the can a few minutes ago. "It's either this or I'm calling Yeonhee. Take your pick." His eyes were cold, hard, and a moment later I got sick of his eyes and turned away before I could see enough to describe them properly. "Four, oh, four, nine, oh, oh, nine," he said as he left the room, which was Yeonhee's phone number except that the last nine was a six, but I couldn't depend on something like that to keep him from getting through to her.

There were nights when I lay awake beside Yeonhee and some pretty wild ideas entered my head, ways of getting rid of Boyle that wouldn't have occurred to me if I was sleeping properly. After a few more years, however, Boyle just kind of faded away. Everything ends, material things as assuredly as our ideals and desires, Yeonhee quoted once, and though I don't remember where the quote came from and don't normally pay close attention to the bits of wisdom she likes to recite, given that we don't read the same kinds of books or materials— but anyway, for whatever reason this one seemed to kind of swim around inside me and grow larger the more I thought about it, and is still there even today.

This is where I had planned on finishing my story, with Yeonhee's quote and its banishing effect and Boyle, like so many problems we think are going to ruin us, growing dim and quietly fading into nothingness.

I wasn't planning on the detective. He stopped by the dealership a few weeks ago and asked if I'd ever seen this man before, the one in the photograph he placed on the desk between us. It was the same man. The homeless man. Not the detective, I mean, but the picture.

The detective was sitting there watching me, exactly where Boyle was sitting last time. It seemed like the detective could see something crawl past my expression when I considered the photo. That's why he produced another full-length, shirtless photo taken against a bare concrete wall full of nightmarish cracks. I only glanced for a moment at that picture before saying "No," since it clearly displayed the man's scars. The next photo was taken from a distance, so it looked like a big figure was dragging a little figure across a gray field. But like I said, it was taken from a distance and there was no way to confirm the little figure was innocent or helpless. Also, I was only glancing at the pictures for a second or two. "Any reason to believe he visited our dealership?" I asked. "As you may already know, we have cameras that span the full lot. Since this must be related to something that happened at the dealership, it'd be no trouble to pull the footage for you." I probably shouldn't have opened my mouth again, but I added, "What he did, was it serious? Like he's the kind of guy who'd get some idea in his head and not be able to stop himself. . . ." But then I said, "Don't tell me. There are rules and regulations. Privacy concerns. I shouldn't have asked. Besides, this has nothing to do with me."

That night after the boys went to sleep, Yeonhee sat down next to me on the couch and showed me their latest drawing, a joint effort—both boys had signed their names in the bottom corner. It took a while to focus on the drawing and forget the images the detective had shown me, and since those images kept wrapping back and overlaying things, each one now had the boys' signatures.

I had to close my eyes for a minute. The last thing I wanted to do that night was consider more pictures. If you're feeling the same way, then I guess you have the option of taking a break and coming back to this part later, when I opened my eyes and saw the cliffs high and black, studded with pillars that looked like monster teeth, wavy and blunt and of a single piece, as the boys were too lazy or couldn't focus long enough to draw each tooth independently. They used monster teeth in every drawing I had seen. All people and creatures had them, as did the materials they needed to survive. It was a versatile technique, used to represent hungry cliffs or ripples in the blue water at the base of the drawing, as well as the waves of orange fire eating the crashed car. The fire looked unfinished, like the boys might have run out of orange and would come back to this when we bought them more.

Messages
Mary Kuryla

SHE HAD SEEN IT from the bedroom window. No trace of an owner, it was swaddled in the leaf mulch, fingers curled as if to catch a ball. It looked like a man's large hand. She could walk to the eastern edge of the planked porch without setting off the bracelet strapped to her ankle, and was halfway there when the fingers transformed into the stunned front legs of an animal. The palm of the hand was now the white furred belly of a hare. Someone had sliced across the fluff of throat a clean line, another slice ran the length of the belly, meeting at the slit throat. The long jawbone of the hare, the black that outlined those notorious ears, the nose and the mouth, dashing. Ants, the yellow eyes were flecked black with them.

She backed away, worried the dead thing held contagion, when something she saw on the snout brought her to a halt. Though her mind said no, her knees bent into the earth alongside the hare, and she moved in for a closer look. It was the whiskers on the hare's snout. They had been cut down to nubs. Taking away a thing's whiskers seemed indecent in a way the slicing had not, or not entirely. Leave it, she told herself, let the woods take care of it, wasn't that what the woods were good at? Instead, she softly poked a twig at the flaps on the belly. The sliced pelt formed a pair of shutters. Not liking herself for doing it but helpless to what seemed an invitation, she pinched open the flaps. The hare's hind legs sprung open upon pink hairless babies curled and still behind the membrane. Hinds over heads, fur matted in mother's wet, the open eyes of the unborn stared at her. A sob lobbed at the woman's chest, and it hurt.

She thought of it as her husband's house because that was how she felt inside it, unwelcome. Of course, she never told Earl this—it would have disappointed him, and hadn't she disappointed her spouse enough? The house fell to her after Earl died, and there was not a chance she would live in it. She had taken instead a room in the apartment of an old friend who was content to her marrow. But she had held on to the house for Earl's sake, passing bad checks to pay for the costly and relentless upkeep of a house in thrall to the elements. It was the only address she could supply to the parole board that met the requirements for the felony of check fraud, and now she found herself trapped and alone inside Earl's house. The surrounding woods were as much to blame for her unease as the house. Too much among the trees, too accommodating of the uncanny cycles of the natural world, the house quivered when the rain pounded the roof or the winds lashed the walls. It leaked, and not just rain, honey, sometimes sap. She had served six months of her sentence here, avoiding most rooms of the house, no different than when Earl was alive. His disappointment in her was the air she breathed.

Through the kitchen window, across the gully, on a high dead branch, a hawk stared at her. She stared back and then shut her eyes, sure the hawk would take off. But when she opened them, the hawk had flown closer, watching her now from the bough of a sycamore. Was it trying to get a message to her? The feeling that the animals were trying to tell her something had gotten worse since Earl died. At the same time, other woodland creatures ignored her altogether. Deer idling on the hill just beyond the porch, squirrels lounging on the cushions of the garden couch, did they scatter when she opened the door? Instead, they hardly budged. She had to shoo the bobcat with a paw on the spine of a mole from her stoop. In the victim's flat, enormous eye she had seen her own image, how small she was, tinier with each day—Earl's house, her home, this was what she had become.

To be nestled amid the wild of the woods, that was the feeling Earl had designed into the house. Insect to rattlesnake, every living thing was OK with Earl, her amateur naturalist. When the owl called from the pitched roof of the house to the owl on the bowed oak to the one on the well shed up the hill, triangling the property in a fence of hooted breaths, he had said it was the hour of the owls. "Hear the echo of the coyote's call down the canyon walls?" he asked as they lay in bed not touching—there was not an inch of skin on his body that did not hurt; the treatment had swelled his flesh until he swore it would split open. "The grasshopper mouse screaming at the moon?"

Humming and whispering, distant graffiti, so many lived to be heard in this house. The buzz and flutter noise of wings around her pillow woke her most mornings now, but did she ever see the moth? What about the coin-sized bites taken out of the window screens? Nibbles along the weather stripping? It was all the messages of teeth marks to her. But Earl just laughed. "You put such faith in a thing's ability to get to you."

Her parole officer knocked on the door, saying he had gotten her message. A tuft of combed hair stuck up at his crown like a feather. She walked Rogers to the end of the porch to show how on the hare's belly was sliced a T. "Someone leaving it here, like this, feels like some sort of message," she said. "A message to me. I hope, you know, I'm wrong."

He bent over and his thick hands fumbled with the flaps to get them to close over the babies.

She was on her knees without knowing it, slapping aside Rogers's hands. "Don't you know they're afraid of the dark?" she said, surprising herself. She sounded just like Earl. "Leave them be. You'll scare those babies."

Rogers backed off, murmuring something about dead things better left unseen. He was right, of course; no one should have to look at those creatures. But it was she who had done the uncovering, an act she could not explain beyond a troubled feeling that the hare and her babies were not so much dead as becoming something else.

The woman heard Rogers snort. She looked up at him from where she knelt, directly up the nostrils of his formidable nose. He had trimmed the hairs. She got to her feet and hurried back into the house.

Rogers followed her to the door. He stepped closer to the threshold. She hesitated, that old uncertainty rising in her chest. What point was there to invite inside the person whose job was to keep you from coming out? "Please, have a look around the property, Officer. Someone could be using the woods to get to me."

She could see Rogers was not in the least concerned, not for her, not for the hare. What became of a parolee in her own home went way beyond the limits of his duties. Still, he lingered on the doorstep, his nose twitching like he smelled something nice. Maybe the coffee brewing on the stove. It was a good smell. She thought about offering him breakfast.

"I would look myself, only I might set off the alarm." She waved at the bracelet on her ankle.

Rogers smiled, which she guessed was really a way of trying not to laugh. He asked if she had reason to believe she could be harmed.

Her husband had once taken her to a local animal sanctuary in the hope the wounded would awaken her heart, but the eye socket sewn shut on the cougar's face and the resuscitated roadkill that was still putting on what face the tires did not take had horrified her. Over and over, she had failed the one she loved. The sun crested the tree line, and Rogers's face blackened. Sunbeams spangled from his head. On the threshold at his feet, the woman swooned. Rogers caught some of her shoulder before she hit the floor.

She came round to find herself in a chair in the kitchen. Rogers's hands were on her. She observed those hands, how they held her upright as if without them she would not be chair material.

"Hands off," she said. What the hell?

His hands came off slow. He stepped back out the door but leaned in to let her know he would check on her tomorrow, make sure she was all right.

She stood before the closed door after the man left, listening to his government car chop down her driveway, rattling the loose grill over the culvert, until the sound of the engine softened into the branches. She opened the door back up and ran to the edge of the porch. Officer Rogers often complained that the canyon walls dulled the signal on her bracelet from reaching all those transmitters orbiting earth. If she was fast, if she was lucky, if she kept her head, she could be back on the porch before Rogers got to the main road and the signal was restored. Back inside she would study what the camera traps had caught of the things traversing the woods, just as Earl had done, wedging his computer between their dinner plates to show images of radiated cottontails ghosting about, birds stabbing aside leaves, a spider picking across the thread of the night's web. Maybe she would catch a glimpse of whatever had done that to the belly of the hare. Earl would approve—she was taking matters into her own hands, ensuring no other animals got hurt.

But her feet did not leave the porch. To oak, to sycamore, to walnut, her husband had strapped the camera traps, and she could see the traps from where she stood. Really, she did not like the cameras. They brought the woods eerily inside. What did she want to know about animals and their doings while she could not sleep at night? It was bad enough fretting over what the creatures inside the house were doing as she stared at Earl's form in those nights without moon, her fingers hovering over his beard, which seemed to grow thicker as he diminished, becoming less a man than a form a shadow a thing.

271

And in the dim tossing of worry, she would hear the animals. First a creaking talk that might have been bats inside the walls, males greasing out from under the eaves on one side, the females greasing out the other. Earl explained that the males and females lived separately. Mice squeezing out more mice, and maybe that was it, the sound of mice giving birth in the venting, or was it the gopher snake that slicked the dirt cellar floor black, and the ants, the ants, ever in lines with the earth's poles? Could be, it was the sound of termites carving their grooves into the wood of the window frames? When she had despaired at the appetites of termites, Earl had told her to think of the grooves as letters written in their language. "I see letters," she said, "whole sentences, Earl, and that's the trouble."

Earl wondered if her sensitivity to the natural world and the animals inhabiting it had given her the gift of tongues. If she wanted to, if she tried, Earl was sure she could speak and hear in the tongues of all animals. The woman decided her husband was having himself a good joke and had laughed along.

But at some point each night Earl would rise from their bed—her silent panic finally nudging him out. I'll check the cellar, honey, he would say and go. She would scoot over to his side and sit with her arms wrapped around bent knees, listening in the dark to his descending steps, his mattress going cold beneath her. That last time, Earl came back to the bedroom waving a sour-smelling storage lid inscribed with faint pink cursives of urine. "Here's a few messages, what do you think? Warnings from mice?"

Whether it was from fear of setting off the bracelet or of entering the woods, the woman never crossed the boundary of her porch to collect her husband's camera traps. But the next morning when she opened the door to holler at a woodpecker drilling the boards of the house, she tripped over something on the doorstep. A camera trap, one of Earl's, camo colored and mono-eyed black. She startled, leaped back, looking around to see who would have done this. There was nobody. Only trees. The oak that bowed almost to the ground no longer had a camera strapped midway up the trunk.

She sat at the kitchen table. She hit the space bar on her husband's computer. She had not wanted to look at what the camera on her doorstep had trapped, had left the camera where it lay, but by the dull yellow light of dusk she relented, picked it up by the strap and brought it inside. The camera had been set there for a reason. It was a message to her. Soon the tight reluctance to look became restless distraction. It took patience to get through all the images the camera had captured, and she was losing it. Until this one. A thing had come too close to the lens, flaring the corner white. An animal was not in the picture. Its whisker was. Thick but tapering, down pointing, stiff, whatever belonged to it rendered inchoate by the blast of the camera's flash. Raccoon was her first thought. A raccoon had snuck up to inspect the camera, then, at the click of the flash, startled. Whiskers are to a mammal as antennae are to a bug, she could hear Earl telling her as she trimmed his beard, which he said had begun to hurt his face. Whiskers picked up signals that the nose and eyes and ears could not, lengthened the knowing, stretched beyond the body how things felt, making of it a whiskerier self.

She studied the image. This whiskered thing may have been of the woods but it did not belong to anything that trod the woods. The whisker seemed to violate the nocturnal hour caught by the camera. It was doing something not quite animal. She had seen the whisker before on the dead hare supine at the edge of her porch. The cut whiskers of the hare were not the whisker the camera had trapped, but their goneness spoke, like a phrase lifted from a sentence that had only found form by the absence of the phrase. The hairs on the woman's arms tingled with transmission. Keep looking at that whisker in the image, her arm hairs said.

She snapped off the table lamp, the only light in the room now, and leaned forward, closer to the image. The aperture opened and, in the letting in of light, the whisker filled the whole bottom portion of her terror. She could see the fear and the fear was in the whisker. That's what she had sensed in the lit follicle—a harming. Now the whisker squirmed, a pinned thing, and jigsawed into the outlines of a form she could not make out. A shape or a shadow, a whiskered presence spreading and sticky, and it had a face, a face not yet joined to the skin of its face, and it was breathing a wet force, a man, maybe, a man hurting that whiskered thing? Or was the whiskered thing becoming a man, or was it something awfully in between?

She played for Rogers the bit with the whisker when he came back the next evening. He glanced at the image then looked at the woman, perhaps frustrated that she had bothered him with it. Something in her expression made him look back at the image. She could see the effort Rogers was putting into looking and was grateful not to have

273

to shoulder this alone. The numbness in her chest eased and she could feel her breath at her ribs in a way she had only ever felt when pressed against Earl's chest. But then Rogers made a gagging sound. His brow glossed with sweat and his cheeks reddened, as if he blushed. He stepped back from the image on the screen. She closed the computer to have something to do, to cover her fright at the disgust the image seemed to have aroused in him. Rogers glared at her over his hand covering his mouth, but when he lowered his hand, his mouth hung open, tongue fat. A light at the back of his eye sparked in excitation. She heard him whisper, What are you showing me this for?

"You didn't believe there was something out there. I'm trying to show you something is." She stepped toward him, and he seemed to appraise her, his wet lips pressed together. But then he turned away to look out the window, or maybe he just wanted to stop looking at her. He thrust his hands in the pockets of his trousers. The skin of his elbow poked through a hole a worm had gnawed in his sweater. Instead of naked and shiny on the bone, the skin sprouted long, stiff hairs.

"Look around outside," she pleaded. "If it sees you, whatever it is, maybe it will go away."

The woman stepped around and met Rogers's profile. His face was a nose, and maybe this nose was what got him into things. The wrinkles in his nose seemed to say he was getting into it with her, and it smelled off. A parolee begging for his protection when he was really supposed to be policing seemed to rend him open. She should offer to sew the hole at his elbow. That was the sort of domestic gesture that reassured. Rogers should feel taken care of before going out there. But instead of offering, she pointed uphill at the bowed oak whose branch bent like a forearm pressed to the ground. She told him the camera that trapped the image of the whisker had been strapped to that oak.

Rogers snapped on his flashlight and ran the beam across the porch and upslope to the woods beyond, but the beam fell off before reaching the oak. He looked back at the woman, shrugged, stepped off the stoop, and crossed the porch, and she swore she heard in his gait now a Western flair. A few more steps, and Rogers was no more than an outline behind his flashlight. She took a couple of deep breaths to slow her eyes and she saw a little more. He had stopped by the oak to look up the hill as if to see what the camera trap had seen. But she could not be sure. Rogers was a firefly light.

"See anything?" the woman called from the doorstep, not a little ashamed for sending him to look, but also cold and fear bitten by whatever it was she had seen that liked its animals hurt. She could not help but sense something behind the fear, something the fear was covering.

Rogers said nothing.

The wind rose to tease and reshuffle the oak leaves, as if it were toying with Rogers, ha ha ha. But maybe she heard wrong. Maybe the wind was moaning. Was moaning how the wind sounded when it laughed?

Another camera trap strapped to a tree farther uphill, it saw something in the dark. She knew because its signal flared red. Had the laughing wind fooled the trap? Her eyes strained into the darkness to see what. A white burn of flashlight, and Rogers's face flared into shape, like someone had drawn it then smudged the face with the heel of their careless hand. Now Rogers bent over as if to pick up something. Oak leaves crackled under his boots. His flashlight swung and pointed down, rocking side to side, light swirling with the swirling leaves on the ground. No further sign of the man, only the long shadow cast by his flashlight of a single leaf sprouting from the otherwise dead branch overhead.

The house tensed and shuddered, and she slammed the door shut but remained standing behind it, listening for Rogers's steps on the porch, his knuckles at the door, the sound of his voice telling her to open up.

Only the leaves scraping against the house, only moans.

She stayed there, grateful for the bright lights inside, thinking she should turn on every lamp in every room, make the house burn with life and light, but her legs had begun to buckle under how tautly she stood there. The sound of teeth crunching on something echoed loud from a heating duct. The phone rang but went to voice mail. The message was all static, as though bees were talking, such noise. Then the lights in the house cut. The one on the porch too. The hum of the refrigerator silenced. Had the wind done it, whipping branches, snaring electrical lines? This would not be the first time the lights went dark in these woods. She peered out the window above the kitchen sink, trying to make out lights in her neighbor's distant house, but there was no telling, enclosed as it was by a line of cypresses. Had the power only gone out in this house?

No power and Rogers still out there.

Maybe parole would call, and when they did, she would tell what happened and beg for help. But now she understood that no one would call—no way to get through without electricity. She would have to check the electrical box. It was in the cellar. The batteries in her flashlight were dead. She lit a candle and went down the steps to the cellar.

Earl had said in those last days that he was not really dying. He was renewing himself through the good aid of the woods. One, two, and up, and she had lifted his head from the pillow to cut the beard thickened at his throat, wetting the tips of her fingers to catch the hairs falling in the gap at his neck. For then, they were newly married, Earl awkward and bony in a pressed suit, skin clean shaven and shining, crushing her bouquet in his embrace. She must take a breath. Her foot felt for the next step down. Earl's whiskers grew faster than she could cut them, unfurling along the moonlit sheets and on out the window to wrap around the branches of the trees.

She did not know how long she had been standing inside the cellar. She only became aware that she was there because of the sounds. Quiet and greasing, humming, whispering, the messages circled and nudged the walls of the house that might as well be her ear, where she felt carvings against the drum and the purr of deaf fear, a thudding cacophony silenced by a knock.

Light filled the cellar. Her hands were inside the electrical box, her fingers on the main breaker. If not for her hands, she would not know who was responsible for getting the electricity back on. She closed the latch on the box and turned back to the door of the cellar. She would find her phone and call parole, but she was stopped by a white storage lid that had not been there a moment ago. It lay in her path. She went down to her knees to read the faint pink cursive of urine across the lid. It warned, *Don't disappoint him.*

The woman ran up the stairs and into the kitchen. Rogers stood before the refrigerator. His back was to her, his head moving up and down at the refrigerator door in a licking motion. Rogers was tonguing the refrigerator hinges, catching the yellow liquids leaking out. It was sweltering in the kitchen. The foods in the refrigerator must have spoiled. How long had the power been out? The door of the refrigerator opened, and Rogers started moaning and sniffing for a disturbing while the putrid insides. He looked over his shoulder at her and said, Very good. You put the animal in here.

The woman slammed the refrigerator door on the dead hare shoved in with rotted carrots on the top shelf and stood with her back against the door. "I didn't do it. It's you. You must have put it in there."

The man gazed fondly at her, smiling. He was still Rogers, and he was not. He behaved as if nothing was wrong, except everything about him was wrong. He still wore the same sweater with a hole at the elbow. It was Rogers's nose. But his mouth shifted under a face poorly pasted on top. The mouth lined up under the other mouth, the canines pearling above the blood leech tongue, but with the tilt of his head, the mouth would congest with moth-eaten fur.

Rogers told her she should try to thank him. He had done what she asked. He had gone out and had a look around and come back. The woman caught a whiff of leaf mulch on his breath and something fetal. The smell was as pleasing as the faint scent of cheese on the crown of a newborn's head.

"My God, what happened to you?" This was all she could manage to say.

Now Rogers's face opened like a pair of shutters, the horizontal lines shaping into stiff whiskers that poked through the other skin. Rogers wrinkled his nose, like it hurt. His hands came out of his trousers to shift the skin on his face, as if adjusting a mask. The skin sponged beneath his fingertips, still wet, stretching and settling into place. It would take time to get used to himself, the woman heard Rogers say.

It was Rogers in his parole-officer skin, and it was a thing behind Rogers, an animalized other thing. It was Earl. She backed away to the front door, opened it, ready to run. But she knew it was too late. She had stayed too long in the woods. Her legs shook and twisted beneath her, and she fell to the floor. The sun rising through the branches of the trees cut a path of light from the open door to the woods. She loved Earl and had failed him. Animals were harmed but she had never allowed herself to be.

One eye in Rogers's face let leak a black line that greased down the nose. It seemed he was crying, and she reached out to touch him. "I won't disappoint you this time," she said.

Behind the Curtain

Troy Jollimore

The sleeping and the dead
Are but as pictures. 'Tis the eye of childhood
That fears a painted devil.

—Lady Macbeth, *Macbeth*

THE STORY GOES THAT in 1896, when the Lumière brothers first showed their film *Arrivée d'un train (à la Ciotat)*, audiences, believing that a real-life locomotive was bearing down on them, panicked, abandoned their seats, and fled from the theater. Recent historians have cast considerable doubt on this account, however. More than considerable, in fact: there is a complete lack, it seems, of supporting evidence.

The familiarity and ubiquity of this story, whose spread was in no way hindered by its being almost certainly false, says something about our feelings about movies. We are inclined, it seems, to associate movies with terror. And to doubt people's ability to distinguish between real objects and products of imagination and artifice. It seems only right, only logical, that early crowds would think those were real people, a real platform, a real locomotive. And that they would be afraid. It seems only to be expected that mere fictions, patterns of light projected onto a flat surface, would be taken as physical actualities. From the early days of cinema's existence, it seems, we have found it natural to assume that one of its primary functions would be to strike fear into our hearts.

*

The first horror movie I remember seeing was surely *The Wizard of Oz*. I am confident that I am not alone in this. How many children suffered through and were traumatized by that surrealistic Technicolor nightmare, that terrifying collective hallucination? It was supposed to be entertaining, amusing. Perhaps that is how some children experienced it. Maybe if I had been older—ten or twelve, rather than

278

five or six—I could have been a bit more skeptical, more detached. But I was young, and a sucker for movie magic. I threw myself head-long into cinematic spectacle. So it all felt real to me—the yellow-brick road, the flying monkeys. The witches, as terrifying as those in *Macbeth*. And, of course, Dorothy's fear. That, more than anything, moved me and got inside me: how frightened Dorothy must have been that she might be unable to return home. Just imagine—and I was precisely the sort of child who was able to imagine this, in vivid detail—finding yourself in a strange, luridly colored realm, where you did not know anyone, with no real idea of how to get back to where you had come from. That this was Dorothy's predicament was all too apparent to me. Even if Dorothy herself seemed, much of the time, able to forget the existential terror of her situation so as to be able to enjoy her adventures in this bizarre land—such powers of for-getting were beyond me at that age. To be honest, they are beyond me still. The older I get, the more the world feels like Oz: bright, fake, candy colored, and profoundly unintelligible and irrational. The older I get, the more I feel like Dorothy, and the less confident I am of being able to ever find a way back to some place of comfort, some place that makes sense.

*

But I should say that it wasn't merely the uncertainty about whether Dorothy would be able to get back home. It was the deeper uncer-tainty, the irresolvable issue regarding whether Oz actually existed. An uncertainty that cast into some real doubt the very meaning of "going home." Of what it is to have a home, to leave, to miss, to long for home. A certain degree of doubt as to whether Dorothy had ever left home at all. Visually, after all, the land of Oz was presented to us in a manner that made it nearly impossible to believe in. It wore its artificiality on its face, as if to ease the mind of the young viewer. You couldn't really be frightened if you didn't believe in Oz to begin with. But I did not find this comforting, because it was clear to me that we *were* being asked to believe in the reality of Oz. It wasn't as if Dorothy could just end her ordeal by wishing the whole damn place away. If it was some sort of dream or hallucination, it was one that she was inescapably mired in. And the audience too, along with her. That possibility was for me the most terrifying of all: that Oz was both unreal and inescapable, that it was a creation of Dorothy's imagination and yet entirely beyond her control. The possibility that

Troy Jollimore

Dorothy, for most of the duration of the film, was a prisoner of her own mind.

*

Like a person returned from a near-death experience, like those believers in religion I sometimes encountered, Dorothy was certain that another, higher realm existed, even if those around her could not perceive it. So Dorothy was, for me, an early lesson in just how fine the line is between religious conviction and insanity. And the more she protested that it was real, the more she sounded as if the person she was really trying to convince was herself. Add to this the weird doubling effect of the parallel realm, the fact that the primary figures there were doppelgängers of "real" people in the "real" world. What were we to make of that? It seemed that there was another world, one that was surreal, preternaturally creepy, at times downright terrifying. A world in which every ordinary thing had its unordinary double, into which one might slip at any moment, with no guarantee of being able to return. And it was impossible to know whether this other world had a real, external existence, or was something one's own mind, having gone off the rails, had invented.

*

I first saw Joel and Ethan Coen's fourth film, *Barton Fink*, in 1991, the year it was released. It had been decades since a movie had caused me such intense fear. So much so that, even as I grew more fascinated with the work of the Coens, and watched and rewatched their other films, I put off rewatching this one for years.

The film is weird, creepy, and has some disturbing images, but compared with most horror films it is fairly nonaggressive. Many don't even consider it a horror film. Rather, like most Coen films, it draws on a number of genres. *Barton Fink* doesn't go out of its way to frighten, or so you would think. It is at least as funny as it is scary. Indeed, John Turturro's frazzled and wide-eyed performance, as the titular playwright who is lured away from the comforts of New York to try to make some easy cash as a screenwriter in Los Angeles, is profoundly funny, and some of the supporting performances—most notably Tony Shalhoub as a slick, fast-talking movie producer—are hilarious.

280

Yet the film disturbed me in ways that conventional horror films don't even aspire to. I avoid conventional horror films, not because they are too frightening, but because they are so boring. They tend to adhere closely to the conventions of their genre, and are designed to provoke a fairly narrow set of responses. *Barton Fink*, it was clear, was aiming at something deeper and far more interesting. It got under my skin. Its images stayed with me. The terrifying desolation of the Hotel Earle, with its empty hallways, lined up and down with empty shoes. Its peeling wallpaper. The sticky goop that lay beneath that wallpaper. The thinness of those walls, and the inscrutable, often alarming sounds that came through them.

*

The Coen brothers wrote *Barton Fink* at a time when they were supposed to be writing their third film, *Miller's Crossing*. Having begun *Miller's Crossing*, they got stuck, mired in the intricacies of its complex plot. So they gave themselves a break and turned to a different project, assuaging their anxieties about writer's block by writing a film about an anxious writer suffering from writer's block, caught in a dismal hotel room with peeling wallpaper and a neighbor who just might be a maniacal killer.

The terror of writer's block is the dark flip side of artistic inspiration: you don't control it, your head. The ideas, images, everything of value, all seem to come from elsewhere, and that connection is insecure, our access intermittent. We don't really control our thoughts. Writing, when it is going well, when it is going poorly, or when it isn't going at all, reminds us how little we are in control. The anxiety provoked by writer's block is not confined to the fear of being unable to produce one's next work. It is also a far more generalized fear, of losing control of one's mind.

*

When Barton, fresh from New York, still cheered by the success of his latest play, arrives for what he believes will be a temporary stay in Los Angeles, it is at the Earle that he finds lodging. After passing through the eerily deserted lobby, he rings the bell at the front desk, which calls forth Steve Buscemi's Chet, who rises from somewhere *beneath* the hotel—like many of those we, and Barton, will meet, Chet is heard before he is seen—to emerge through a trapdoor in the floor. Chet asks, "Are you a trans or a res?" but Barton at first does not understand the question. Then he is unsure of the answer. I would be too. Take a long enough view and all of us are transient. But then again, maybe dying in residence is what establishes you as a res.

The Hotel Earle's motto, as we see from its stationery, is "A day or a lifetime." As if the two were equivalent, as if there were no difference.

When I watched *Barton Fink* a decade and a half after first seeing it, I discovered that more of it was set outside the Hotel Earle than I had remembered. Several scenes are set in brightly lit offices, or poolside, or in an outdoor park, all of them illuminated by the penetrating sun of Southern California. One might have expected at least one night of heavy rain to complement the film's noiresque atmosphere but the sky remains clear and the streets dry. (Then again, from inside the hotel it is pretty much impossible to discern what might be going on outside.) But other than the final scene, the scene on the beach, the sunlit external settings had not lodged in my mind. Somehow the Earle, that cavernous, dilapidated hotel, with its air of morbid hopelessness and slow decline, had taken over my recollection of the film.

One thing that was obvious on this rewatching was that the interior of the Hotel Earle represented Barton Fink's subjective state, an exteriorized projection of his own rapidly decaying mind. Or at least a mind about which he could not be certain as to whether or not it was decaying. And it became clear to me too that one of the reasons I had reacted so strongly to the film was that it was the Coen brothers' own version, their reimagining, of *The Wizard of Oz*. Barton, as much as Dorothy, is stuck in his own mind. The world is, for him, as it is for her, a projection, a dream that has been quite pleasant to this point, but which now, for whatever reason, has turned ominous and sinister. Of course, Dorothy is a child. She can be forgiven for projecting her inner state onto the cosmos at large and allowing it to obscure her view of objective reality. Or, if not forgiven, at least understood. Barton is not only an adult but an artist, a playwright who writes, as he would tell you himself, *realistic* plays about *real* people. The depiction of reality, of his beloved "common man," is his business. We can't say that Barton's livelihood depends on his ability to perceive reality accurately; perhaps no artist's livelihood ever has. Illusions are so much easier to sell than truths. But his integrity as an artist surely does depend on that ability. He himself, one imagines, would be the first to say so.

*

According to Plato, we inhabit a realm of illusion. We are, in his famous allegory, like people chained in a cave, facing forward, staring at a wall. Reality is the world outside the cave. And all we can see— unless and until we manage to achieve enlightenment by breaking those chains and leaving the cave—is shadows on the wall before us, cast by a fire behind. We can't even see the fire, just the shadows. Which we take, of course, to be reality, not realizing that the world revealed to us by the senses is nothing but illusion.

I suppose I don't have to point out how much the whole setup resembles a movie theater.

The philosophers of the modern era tended to agree with Plato that the realm of the senses was a realm of illusion, though they were not always as optimistic as he was about the ability of the intellect to penetrate it, to put us in touch with reality. In my first year of university I read the *Meditations* of René Descartes. In his first meditation, Descartes presents a variety of arguments to show that we cannot be certain of anything that comes through the senses, or indeed of anything at all. We can't really know that the world is as it appears to be, or even that there *is* a world outside our own minds. The remaining meditations are meant to overcome this initial outlay of skepticism, establishing that God exists and that, because God exists, we can be confident in our knowledge. For surely a good God would not let us walk around deceived all the time.

The problem is that while the skeptical arguments of the first meditation are powerful and persuasive, the arguments for the existence of God, on which all the rest depends, are profoundly unconvincing. Descartes's *Meditations* do the opposite of what they were meant to do and are likely to plunge the unsuspecting reader into an abyss of skepticism.

At any rate, that's what happened to me. I swallowed the arguments, I was mortally convinced by them, and for a period of three weeks or so I was so depressed I was barely able to get out of bed. (It was, if nothing else, an early demonstration of the power of philosophical argument.) I did not, could not, know whether anything in my life was real. Maybe it was all just a vivid dream, or some other species of illusion. I couldn't get it out of my head, this fear that the world might be entirely in my head.

*

If people in Hollywood films seem simultaneously both more real and less real than people in "real life," it is because they are the objective realizations of aspects of people that, in the actual world, are kept hidden and beneath the surface. People in movies look, speak, and act like the people we know ourselves to be on the inside. This is why we believe in them so strongly, even though they are often unbelievable. There is no chasm, as there is with us, between the publicly visible exterior and the private, concealed interior. Characters in film are all surface. Even their depths are laid out on the surface. A cinematic person is, in that splendid phrase of John Ashbery's, "Not / Superficial but a visible core."

Similarly, environments in films—rooms, landscapes, the various spaces in which characters move—are very often external realizations of inner states of the characters. This is obviously and oppressively so in *Barton Fink*, where the most vivid and memorable of the environments are external realizations of Barton himself. As *Barton Fink* progresses, it, and Barton, seem to descend into solipsism. We, the audience, find ourselves less and less certain whether we are witnessing "real" events or a dream or hallucination being had by the title character, and become increasingly unnerved, uncertain as to whether any of the other characters even exist or whether Barton has simply made them up. Like Barton, we find ourselves fearing that the people he encounters are real and also fearing that they might not be. That what we feared was actually inside Barton, or inside us, all along. We are not confident about which possibility should frighten us more.

In horror films, rendering the internal external is a means of producing terror. Few things are more frightening than being confronted

284

with what is ordinarily hidden away, what is normally kept inside. Most obviously, horror films put blood and gore on display, frightening us by making visible and external what ought to remain unseen. To take outside the skin what belongs underneath, a kind of disquieting, transgressive border crossing. In *Barton Fink* it is the border between reality and fantasy itself that is threatened, pierced, and violated so profoundly and pervasively that we feel unable to establish any sort of grip on the distinction.

Consider how thin are the walls of Barton's hotel room, as evinced by the noises they are unable to shut out. Barton's skin too is thin, and easily penetrated. Consider the mosquito that plays such a prominent role. In its own tiny and familiar way, it performs the essential functions of the horror film, piercing the crucial yet fragile boundary of one's skin, moving the blood from where it is felt to belong—inside the body, where it is literally a part of you—into the outside world, where it becomes alien, something that confronts you, something you would almost certainly rather avoid. Blood, the very stuff of life, becomes one more thing we do not control, one more thing to be afraid of.

*

Barton Fink spends a good deal of the film at his desk, struggling to write a screenplay. It's supposed to be a wrestling picture, a genre he knows nothing about. So he ends up staring at a postcard tacked to the wall above his typewriter, a postcard that depicts an attractive young woman in a swimsuit sitting on a beach, staring out at the ocean. It seems to be a source of solace for him, if not of inspiration.

The film's final scene finds him walking on a beach. He seems dazed, and he may well be homeless; the last time we saw the Hotel Earle, it was on fire. Beyond that, I won't try to summarize the various bizarre and implausible events he has witnessed and endured. I won't venture an opinion as to whether these experiences have demolished him as a person or whether in some way they have woken him up from his solipsistic slumber. I will just say: Barton is on the beach.

All that space—the big sky, the open ocean—it might almost suggest a kind of freedom. It's a wide, empty landscape, not entirely unlike Kansas. But there is no hint, in this final scene, that Barton might

285

escape. He is never getting out of Los Angeles. There are no ruby slippers that will whisk him back to Manhattan. If anything, all that openness merely amplifies his vulnerability. The Hotel Earle, for all its must and deterioration, was a shelter. Now, like Lear wandering on the heath, he is unsheltered, unhoused.

If Dorothy had not been able to return from Oz, would she eventually have come to believe that it was Kansas she had dreamed up, that Oz was the only reality? And how long would it have taken for her belief in her former home to fade away? The Chinese sage Chuang Tzu, it is said, wondered, on waking from a nap, whether he was a man who had just dreamed that he was a butterfly or a butterfly who was dreaming that he was a man. The thought apparently amused and intrigued him. He was a sage, after all. Whereas when I find myself dwelling on our inability to know such things, I find myself growing anxious and afraid, suffering a kind of epistemic vertigo. It frightens me that I cannot really know what I am. Or where I come from. Or when I am dreaming. Or what dream I am having.

Perhaps, as Dorothy says, there really is no place like home. Home is no place, the nonexistent. A pleasant thought we had once, like the thought of being a butterfly. Perhaps Barton too will one day decide that a place like Manhattan could only exist in pictures or in dreams. Didn't the film, after all, begin on a theatrical stage, during the performance of a play? One of his plays, a product of his imagination, something that came from his head. Or rather, it begins behind the stage, a place we might have presumed to be real. It likely occurs to us at this point that at the beginning of *Barton Fink* the film's title character is, quite literally, the man behind the curtain.

*

In the final scene, Barton carries a package. It's about the right size to contain, say, a bowling ball. Or a human head. It quite likely does in fact contain a human head, a fact of which Barton is well aware. Heads, I should say, feature prominently in this film. People keep bringing them up. Charlie Meadows in particular—Barton's next-door neighbor at the Earle, played unforgettably by John Goodman. He says things like "Well, ain't that a kick in the head!" and "Where there's a head, there's hope" and "Things have gotten all balled up at the head office" and "Can't trade my head in for a new one." It's too bad Charlie can't trade his head in, for there is indeed something wrong with his: he has an ear infection that keeps him in constant discomfort. But there is probably something else wrong with his head too, given the fact that, as it turns out, he is alleged to be a serial killer who enjoys cutting off the heads of his victims. (As an investigating police detective says to Barton, with terrifying understatement, "He's a little funny in the head.")

On the beach Barton encounters a young woman. The screenplay tells us, "She looks much like the picture on the wall in Barton's hotel room." Like the noises that penetrate the walls of the Hotel Earle, like the blood that fed the mosquito—like Barton himself, adrift in the alien realm of L'Oz Angeles—the woman, previously confined to a postcard, seems to have transgressed boundaries, to have shown up where she does not belong. "What's in the box?" she asks. He replies, "I don't know." "Isn't it yours?" she asks, and meets the same response. She considers, nods, turns away.

"You're very beautiful," Barton says. "Are you in pictures?" Her reply is the film's devastating final line: "Don't be silly." Then she turns to look out at the sea. In doing so she adopts the exact pose of the woman in the postcard that Barton, and we, so frequently stared at. She gazes at the sea. He gazes at her image. So do we.

*

You don't listen! Charlie Meadows screams at Barton. And indeed Charlie has repeatedly tried to tell his stories to Barton, only to be repeatedly silenced, dismissed, and ignored. *You think the whole world revolves around whatever rattles inside that little kike head of yours*, the anti-Semitic Jewish studio head Jack Lipnick (Michael Lerner) tells him not very long afterward. Again, the accusation sticks. Barton has no actual curiosity about other human beings; he lives in fear of them and mostly tries to avoid them. Is Dorothy also afraid of other people? Both, after all, spend a good deal of time inhabiting made-up interior mental worlds, populated by cartoonish figures they themselves have constructed, figures that are only superficially and intermittently human.

The novelist Harold Brodkey once wrote that "the 1939 MGM movie *The Wizard of Oz* is the archetypal modern American movie that shows us the real structure and source of popularity of American movies." *The Wizard of Oz*, in Brodkey's account, is "a charming account of an entirely solipsistic adventure arising from a blow to the head of the heroine. In its chief sections it is dreamed. It has only one 'real' character, the dreamer. . . . We expect it in an American movie that the star's is the only life." Rather than a story of complex interaction between independent minds and wills, Hollywood, again and again, gives us a single character to identify with—our onscreen avatar—as he (nearly always a male, especially until recently) goes on a quest, a hero's journey, in which every other character has an allotted functional role, defined relative to the needs and journey of the protagonist. Brodkey goes on to draw illuminating parallels with fascism, the way all significance is drained from the individuals, now regarded as disposable, who compose the masses, to be assigned to or installed in the quasi-divine leader, who alone matters and who alone carries the mass project forward.

*

Just before that final scene set on the beach, Barton goes to visit his big boss, the tyrannical studio head, for the last time. (He is already, in this scene, carrying the package that might contain a head.) Jack Lipnick has indulged Barton to this point, patiently accepting his refusal to produce, or even describe, his screenplay in progress, telling him that at his studio, Capitol Pictures, the writer is king. At times his expressions of respect have bordered on the obsequious. Now, however, Barton has exhausted Lipnick's tolerance. He has at long last submitted the screenplay he struggled to compose, and Lipnick, having obtained a glimpse inside the mysteries of Barton's head, is most displeased with what he has found there. He explodes, delivering a tyrant's tirade, and informs Barton of his punishment: he will continue to work for the studio to which he is contractually bound, he will continue to write movies, and none of those movies will be produced. He will not be able to leave Los Angeles, to return to his former life. His life, his own person, his own mind, no longer belong to him. The contents of his head are now the property of Capitol Pictures.

The terrifying fact that the contents of his head are no longer his, and perhaps never were, is one that has been dawning on Barton, slowly, painfully, over the course of the entire film. In a sense, Lipnick's angry speech simply confirms the fear Barton, and we, have vaguely felt for some time. That his ideas are the property of a major Hollywood studio, on the other hand, might be news to him. But then again perhaps not. If Barton has read his Marx—he has, to be sure, pretensions to being a leftist intellectual—he might have recalled certain relevant fragments. For instance:

> The worker puts his life into the object; but now his life no longer belongs to him but to the object. Hence, the greater this activity, the greater is the worker's lack of objects. Whatever the product of his labor is, he is not. Therefore the greater this product, the less is he himself. The alienation of the worker in his product means not only that his labor becomes an object, an external existence, but that it exists outside him, independently, as something alien to him, and that it becomes a power on its own confronting him; it means that the life which he has conferred on the object confronts him as something hostile and alien.

Just as Dorothy is confronted with her own fantasies, objectified and made alien to her—the position Descartes feared we were all in, a possibility he was unable to convincingly vanquish—the contents of Barton's head, having shifted in ownership, now "confront him as something hostile and alien." Just as the mosquito has removed Barton's blood, transforming it into an external object and source of disquiet and fear, Lipnick and Capitol Pictures have taken away his ideas, the essence of his art, objectifying them and making him their prisoner. "Capital is dead labor," Marx famously wrote, "which, vampire-like, only lives by sucking living labor, and lives the more, the more labor it sucks." Blood, labor, inspiration, ideas, our most intimate possessions, are removed from us and moved through the borders that protect the integrity of the person, with the ultimate result that we ourselves, we humans, find ourselves objectified and commodified:

> Labor produces not only commodities: it produces itself and the worker as a commodity . . . Labor's realization is its objectification. In the conditions dealt with by political economy this realization of labor appears as loss of reality . . .

If Barton had at the appropriate moment recalled the phrase "loss of reality"—as concise and accurate as any for the condition he has been plunged into—it might have reminded him of the passage in which Marx wrote, "In reality, the laborer belongs to capital before he has sold himself to capital." Which may remind us, in turn, of Lipnick's description of the fate he has chosen for Barton Fink: "Anything you write is going to be the property of Capitol Pictures. And Capitol Pictures is not going to produce anything you write."

*

Why does Lipnick react to Barton's screenplay with such rage? Presumably because Barton, rather than merely reproducing the clichés of the wrestling genre, has tried to write the truth. Those who don't want to hear about reality have always been afraid of those who want to puncture the fragile skin of their illusions. And the latter have just as much reason, if not more, to fear the former. Plato knew this. He imagined a man who was able to escape from his allegorical cave. Leaving the cave, he finds himself on the surface, where he is at first blinded by sunlight. When he goes back into the cave, his eyes having adjusted to the sun, he will again seem to be blind. The others in the cave, still chained, still enjoying the shallow show they take to be real, will laugh at the one who has returned, mock him, and refuse to take him seriously. They won't listen when he tries to explain that they are imprisoned, oppressed, and deluded. He could grab one of them and try to drag him up to the surface. But, Plato says, the response of the cave denizens, who prefer the comfort and familiarity of their dim prison to the unknown terrors of reality, was entirely predictable. Terrified at the prospect of discovering the truth, of being confronted by the actual world, these people would resist the one who was trying to free them from their illusions. If necessary, they would kill him.

*

The word *reality*, as it happens, is not uttered either in *Barton Fink* or in *The Wizard of Oz*. Barton speaks once or twice of a "real theater," of "something real" forged out of "everyday experience." The most telling deployment of a cognate of *real* is found in a line from the screenplay that didn't make it into the film. Early on, when Barton expresses hesitation about Capitol Pictures' offer to put him under contract, the screenplay has his agent reply, "I'm only asking that your decision be informed by a little realism—if I can use that word and 'Hollywood' in the same breath."

In *The Wizard of Oz* screenplay, the word *real* occurs four times. One, unsurprisingly, occurs at the end, as Auntie Em tells Dorothy that Oz was merely a dream and Dorothy insists that it was "a real, truly live place." The other three usages of *real* all occur in the scene in which the characters confront, and unmask, the Wizard. *You promised us real things!* the scarecrow protests. *A real brain!* To which the Tin Man adds, *A real heart!* And the Cowardly Lion, *Real courage!*

"We need more heart in pictures," Jack Lipnick tells Barton Fink when he first meets him. But is it real heart that he wants? When a man like Jack Lipnick talks about *heart,* just what could he possibly mean? A real brain—is that what Barton is carrying in his package, tidily tied up with string? Is that what is inside the skull that sits on his own shoulders? And if so, is it his? How could he be sure? Real courage—is that what Barton displays when he quietly endures Lipnick's rage, insisting that the screenplay Lipnick hates is the best work he has ever done? Saying to Lipnick, "I tried to show you something beautiful—something about all of us"? Perhaps Barton, or the Cowardly Lion, have made the mistake of thinking that real courage is the absence of fear. But no: the ability to display real courage and the ability to feel real fear are so closely connected as to be in essence inseparable. If the Cowardly Lion really does come away from his adventures having at last achieved "real" courage, he will now know, possibly for the first time in his life, what real fear feels like.

*

Something else I had forgotten since first seeing the film: the sound of the ocean in the final scene. Violently, frighteningly loud, so loud that it almost overwhelms the dialogue. At first, indeed, Barton and the young woman can't hear each other above the crashing waves. It's only the second time in the film that we hear the ocean. The first, much earlier, occurred in a single shot of crashing waves that separated the brief New York segment of the film from the main body, set in Los Angeles, thus representing Barton's transition from successful Manhattan playwright to oppressed and struggling Hollywood screenwriter. There is, structurally speaking, a strong echo of *The Wizard of Oz* here, with a powerful, elemental natural phenomenon—the ocean in one case, a tornado in the other—representing the shift from initial reality to a less plausible, possibly fantastical alternate realm. Like the tornado in the Coens' 2009 film, *A Serious Man*—which echoes the one in *Wizard* while also calling to mind the whirlwind out of which God speaks in the book of Job—the ocean in *Barton Fink*, which dwarfs the human figures in the foreground, has the air of a malevolent divinity. It could so easily spill its bounds, washing away not only the beach but the entire city of Los Angeles and all the souls contained therein.

Wandering the beach, wide-eyed and stunned, Barton Fink looks as if he has just emerged from Plato's cave. Is this, the beach, the real world at last? Is the sun that hangs over that landscape the same sun that, in Plato, represents reality, blinding those who escape the confinement of the cave? All that space—the big sky, the open ocean—it might almost suggest a kind of freedom. Particularly after his confinement in the claustrophobic environs of the Hotel Earle. Dorothy is, I suppose, similarly stunned when she first emerges in Oz, after her long incarceration in black-and-white Kansas. But the terrifying clamor of those waves silences any thought that we might view this as a liberation. If Barton were to suddenly find himself in a comfortable bed, surrounded by loved ones relieved at his miraculous recovery, would he insist that the place he had just returned from was real, that the dream factory of Hollywood was not a mere figment of his imagination? Perhaps. It doesn't matter, really. This Dorothy isn't ever going back.

The Consequence
Quintan Ana Wikswo

AUTHOR'S NOTE

What follows is drawn directly from the primary source Colonial ranger report of a Shawnee engagement of my ancestral grandmother, her husband, her infant, and her three daughters. The family had been warned of a coming fatal consequence by the local Shawnee. The husband—a ranger—intentionally violated the law of boundaries; the wife discouraged him violating the treaties and multiple laws and agreement with the Shawnee. Her husband, enthusiastic with his peers to violate these well-established laws, built a small settlement well inside the Shawnee lands. In the years that followed the subsequent violent engagement, those who survived became the progenitors of our multiracial/transracial in The Shenanadoah Valley of Virginia.

* * *

BRIEFE AND TRUE REPORT OF THE NEW FOUND LAND OF VIRGINIA OF THE COMMODITIES AND OF THE NATURE AND MANNERS OF THE NATURAL INHABITANTS BY MEMBERS OF THE COLONY IMPLOYED IN DISCOVERING THAT PART OF THE WORLDE LATE IN THE YEERES AFTER VOYAGES HAVING BEEN THITHER MADE AND SUNDRIE TIMES AT HIS MAGESTY'S GREAT CHARGE IN THE FUTURE LIFE OF SOWEGE GLIDING SWAN MARY ELIZABETH CASSEL

HE TELLS ME that we will go west, just a bit west, where there is a spring. I tell him that the goldenrod whispered no, whispered no, but it was the Others at the riverbed, hip deep in the mud and roots, cleaning blood, who said no, no, you can't go there, that's beyond the

293

boundary. Beyond what's allowed. The blood carries down the stream, dry clots and bits of hair, is it that time of month already? No, there was a birth. No, there was an attack by Shawnee, by White Tassel The Hunter no no they call my man Did Many Die. The "savage" is the husband who did not hear no, no, and the red is the blood of the dead settler girl one land grant over. It is a birth, we argue to the goldenrods, dancing in the wind, but there are clumps of scalp on the water. The long blonde hair on the scalp is lovely in the late summer sunshine, wet and glowing, a trail of red, the yellow and the red and the clear water, her name was Susannah, she will finally be clean and they will hang her hair from a tree in their village that we were told we were settling too close to, and this is the consequence.

I tell him, no, not this time, we have the girls, it's not allowed, it's not allowed. Soon enough we have a wagon and oxen and he is laughing for we are over the treaty boundaries, past the lines, he and the men are fierce in their pride of watching, of walking the fences, musket fire into the copperheads he calls whatever men live here before us and we have been warned, Chief Keighttugh Wua Shawnee and the baby kicks, it is not right, my belly is fat with child, says the Chief. My husband planted it in me, the men say, each child a fence in the wilderness, a cornstalk in the wilderness that will suckle me on land forbidden to us and my man says to me we will make more, our babes will grow to cover the land so pale so pale, blue eyes, he plants them in me, our babes, and he makes them to cover the land as we move deeper into this continent and the baby rolls to the side of my hip and whether or not this is what the babe wants, this is the consequence.

No, say the Shawnee, their black locks hanging down, copper bodied, and they talk of the King of England and its Queen and meetings and agreements, and they talk of treaties, and I keep the girls Mary and Felty, they carry water from the spring, says my husband, now hidden because the rangers, our men who walk the boundaries and then step over, step over, step over them, I don't know what to do with them, with us, what they may do to my girls. Their father will not listen. The Others whisper the coals in the fire the Others will take them and your husband will get you killed whisper the coals but nonetheless we are in the wagon, and we are crossing the border, my husband, my belly of child, me, my daughters, Mary and Felty, and at night he watches with brandy flasks and black powder from a built height of sticks and branches to protect us from the death he says are the Others I say is him, is him, we do not belong we are the others, not them. I saw the Other girls at the riverbed washing their dark babies dead of disease and they said what light in the sky of death did you bring here to us and I look up and curse the star that will kill us all. And they tell me the babes in their villages are all dead, all with sickness, and so I sleep with an extra deerskin around my belly as though it might make some difference, the doe we killed and ate surely feels no need to safekeep me. This baby about to be. Nor should it. That is the consequence.

And they come, the Others, and my back is turned but my eyes in the back of my head see the hatchet cleave his head in half, the white bone splitting, a chicken egg, a skull of spray of pink halo, Christ child, and the scalp of my husband is gone and his cranium sizzles on the fire it's venison no it is my lawfully no longer wedded. And the Others tell me to quiet down to be quiet we did this to ourselves and now I think who is wrong here, we should have left, and then I think they have rights but they have no rights not for this and I reach my hands into the fire and hurl at them burning coals and I scream tavern words in rage that they made good on their warnings and they say we warned you and I say yes but this but this. They say talk to your King George and I curse them curse the king curse my dead man curse the red blood unnecessary in one more continent where the men cause the consequence and we bring more babies, always more babies into nation after nation of blood and where are we to be safe if this, this is always the consequence.

My girls already dragged to the edge of our land. The goldenrod screams not your land, not your land. The men remain to stare at me. I scream, I utter curses, how dare they, how dare they, this is our home and the goldenrod shrieks we told you not to come, this is not your land, this is the consequence.

Quintan Ana Wikswo

I must be alive as they tie my man's scalp around my face, the heat
of his body pressed against my mouth and nose. I cannot breathe, I
have lain with this hair that was my man he settled his weight on
me this head on my face before but with eyes and a nose, a mouth
and a mind, he settled his weight and made this child they now cut
from me. I want to go home I confess to the goldenrod. As we said
you should, as we said you wouldn't says the goldenrod you have no
home. I can still see as the Other men dash the baby's skull against
the side of this cabin and she stops screaming or is it me, which one
of us cannot breathe, when we said no, no, we cannot cross that line,
it's their land, and yet we did. My daughters disappear into the
distance, and one day will be the palest of all the wives and one will
try to return carrying her golden babe and her father's last name and
the family will say no, you have the wrong drops in your blood, and
they will not own of her, she will not be writ in the family Bible
where our blood goes back to the Highlands our roots, they will
deny her our roots and blood with her Other husband and their
golden child are not of our roots they will say, not of our blood,
Sowege Gilding Swan Mary Elizabeth Cassel and the Childe Kattee
Bird Heliziknoope Ounaconua and where will my girl belong? Blue
Sky Mary The Others are saying ask King George, yes, ask your
King George who said you shouldn't leave blood here these are not
your roots and down my throat is filled the muck blood, their
father's flesh and blood and the root of his very hair and this, then,
is the consequence.

Door

Ann Lauterbach

1.

The Said closes, is closing, has closed the door.
John said, *I am the Door.* Who closed it?

And who will open it, if it is not shut
Forever. This is the other question, called

From the balcony by the young Marine
In uniform, before the matches flame

And the entire arena is lit and flickering
With its own memory. Who is there?

These lights, knocks, hands,
Faces, crowds, surges. Who

Is there? The street flares again
In the mind's geography,

Cascading out from the numerical
So everyone is passing, countless.

Anonymity caresses its dream
And you were there, inside me,

Where no story can be told, but for
The passivity of the mute child.

2.

Is the door a wound?
Farther still, the hall is dark,

And a stranger is passing
Across the threshold, entering under

Rugs or blankets pulled across the small rusty
Cot. She stood in the pond, her body drenched.

And the girl said, *Don't you wash your face
Before bed?* They were naked on the grass

When the iris bloomed, and the mother turned
Away. There were other masks, another time,

Perhaps by the sea, perhaps on the stairs,
Where the scent of balsam and lavender pulsed.

Why be concerned? As if invited to share
A secret. The one behind the door?

There is nothing behind the door; there is only
Door, a condition, a prospect, a

Perception in which a gap occurs, or might
Occur, and you can step into or across, you

Can leap or fall, you can turn away, go back.
It's an open-shut choice; it's a dare.

3.

The story is always a dare. What sorrow
We have made. Earth wounded, ready to quit.

Where is the circle loved as we
Went around on the great horses, riding up

Down, down up, preparing. All the lit
Matches; all the weak lights flickering

In the auditorium, the blasted church,
The Tree of trees. We knew the words

To the song; *Go down, Moses,*
Way down to Egypt's land, tell old Pharaoh

To let my people go. Gaunt branch forked
Upward; juncos scavenging the hard ground.

There's no one in this clearing. And the deer?
Gone from the hill, onto yesterday's

Horizon. Some final animation presses down
As at the end of a novel, and everyone

Weeps for the mute child, for the dead deer.
The flames are lavender and gold

Licking at the charred edge of a log
As if there were no urgency.

When can I use my gun? When can I shoot?
An urban noise unsettles the plain.

4.

A drone tumbling across the sky
Flagging its intent, and the unfolding

Wings of a telescope. Flap, flap, hoarding space
Only to crash into a holiday postponed

For eternity. Good we have this word
So the gigabyte and its multiplication

Can endure, the motherboard
Go dim without consequence. I

Will name my start-up
Terminal Eternal.

She got up from the bunk, damp,
And walked across the field

Ann Lauterbach

As the sun broke over a high ridge
And its splinters radiated outward

Like transparent blades
And the air became alive with atoms

Of her previously intact reception,
Her limbs and hair, her open mouth,

Now only luminous breath
Precocious and atavistic as a spell.

5.

So those remaining
Will forage for their facts

Under the wood ash and the bones
Of the putrid carcass decaying

In the underbrush.
The observed world will rescind

Its rights to observation,
Transitioned into the aperture

Of an uncanny, sightless eye
Careering through space

With its lidded wings
And enormous, engorged desire.

Where do we go? We dissolve,
Ashes to dust, dust to an infinite

Atmosphere turning its particulates
Into noise, contamination, grace.

And then there are no numbers
To calculate infinity; there is only infinity.

6.

Please do not address me as Team.
I am not a Team; I have not joined a Team.

Please do not address me as Friend.
I am not your Friend. I have never met you.

Please find another way of
Counting on me other than by asking

For money. I don't understand
Money. It frightens me.

Power frightens me.
I am not much good to you

Dear faceless voiceless
Bodiless thing of the ask, dear

Solicitous encounter with no one.
One hundred and six ships

Backed up in the harbor and no market
For the mediocre; only

The latest and greatest will do.
I'm still waiting for

Christmas ornaments. Five cards
Command: *Scratch & Win.*

7.

Forgotten discursive threshold.
Queasy opacity above, slick below,

Fool's gold of the chronic impasse
Between what is and what is not.

Marauding ravenous jays
Wearing the uniform of the sky

Plummet downward onto stones.
Was the father a bluejay, dead on the attic floor?

There was no early warning, no sea breeze.
Now the future condemns

All our heralds to chiding,
Indignant as crows. And the wind

Thrashes at our stare, and something leaks
Into the pond, some stain

Found in the old metal cage, the saw's ragged
Edge. In winter, all the tools are silent.

8.

I know, such reading perpetuates
A stranded vocabulary,

Before the listing algorism
Tested our mutability in exchange

For knowing the instrumental tally
Of our accumulated dread,

Our daily dead. The face changes. The heart
Stumbles onto a clearing, as in

A painting whose surface
Is a pattern rendered

As brilliant debris echoing across
The landscape, carrying our beliefs.

The layers are like a translucent cloth
Flowing outward, sailing almost,

Into the deep folds of a sunset,
Its bloods spreading their wonder.

And this is thought, also, one
Under another, waiting, colliding,

Carrying all the partial images
As on a breath; phantom, until said.

9.

Mirage, smoke and mirrors, tricks.
What ails? What makes us want to stay

Asleep forever, rather than awaken
To morning's fortune, as the door closes

On our skit of promise, our fabled
Enchantment, when we marched,

Hands outstretched, singing,
Onto the field, and the words spilled

Into the air like so many vagrant seeds
Carried across, and down, and into

The river's bright agenda. Now flow coils
into an obsidian hole, and an old rake

Hangs on the side of the fence
As if to entice us back into an alignment,

As if to alleviate the scheme's
Reckless anomaly, its mute consent,

Passed from one to another
Like a masked kiss between lovers.

10.

Tenuous, the wire or thread or single line
Drawn across, edge to edge,

Or down to the strip between
Frame and floor like a slip of moon,

An apparition where the footsteps
Blur through and whatever is visible

Retreats into the animate whispers
Of fear. Who is there?

Turning away, or toward,
Not answering the door, not ever

Knowing who went out, came back,
Went out, came back, went,

Never came back. Tenuous, the sign
With the name, the false resemblance.

Waiting is a form of thought. Thought
Turns away, unable to name its ancestry.

11.

Begin this imagining, pull together
Whatever is unspoken, trace, enigma,

Ghost plurality: the near and the other,
The mongrel and the brute brokers

Of unspeakable acts. Is speech action?
Still the question haunting time,

Just when ——
Please conduct me to a place

Ann Lauterbach

Where there are no calibrations and no outcomes.
I can hear the wind. It sounds the way

I imagine an aura might sound, hovering just
Over sense, like an underpainting

Never to be discovered but which is alive
With crimson, a wound, or a mouth; a smile

On the face of a stranger. The wind is louder now
But it has no language and so no origin.

How to name a sound? Call it John, call it Door.
I know what comes next; I know the tune.

NOTES ON CONTRIBUTORS

Named one of *Variety*'s 2021 "10 Storytellers to Watch," MATTHEW BAKER is the author of the story collections *Why Visit America* (Henry Holt) and *Hybrid Creatures* (LSU Press). Born in the Great Lakes region of the United States, Baker currently lives in Tokyo.

One of the major voices in contemporary Mexican poetry, CORAL BRACHO is the author of *Firefly under the Tongue: Selected Poems* and the forthcoming *It Must Be a Misunderstanding* (both New Directions), translated by Forrest Gander.

MICHAEL HARRIS COHEN's work includes the novella and short story collection *The Eyes* (Mixer Publishing) and the forthcoming *Effects Vary* (Off Limits Press). He lives and teaches in Bulgaria.

MONICA DATTA's work has appeared several times in *Conjunctions'* print and online editions as well as in *Blackbird, The Collagist/The Rupture,* and *The Evergreen* (Scotland).

KATHRYN DAVIS's most recent novel is *The Silk Road* (Graywolf). Her memoir, *Aurelia, Aurélia,* from which "Fluke" is excerpted, is out from Graywolf this spring. Among her many awards are the Franz Kafka Prize for fiction by an American woman and both the Morton Dauwen Zabel Award and the Katherine Anne Porter Award from the American Academy of Arts and Letters.

Longtime contributor JULIA ELLIOTT is the author of the story collection *The Wilds,* a *New York Times Book Review* Editors' Choice, and the novel *The New and Improved Romie Futch* (both Tin House Books). Elliott was the recipient of a Rona Jaffe Writer's Award in 2012, and her stories have been anthologized in *Best American Short Stories* and *Pushcart Prize: Best of the Small Presses.*

Contributing editor BRIAN EVENSON is the author of over a dozen books of fiction, most recently the story collection *The Glassy Burning Floor of Hell* (Coffee House). His work has won the World Fantasy and Shirley Jackson Awards, and he has been a finalist for the Edgar Award and the Ray Bradbury Award.

JEFFREY FORD's most recent books are the short fiction collection *Big Dark Hole* (Small Beer Press); a retrospective collection of his stories, *The Best of Jeffrey Ford* (PS Publishing); and the novel *Ahab's Return* (Morrow/Harper Collins).

FORREST GANDER's translation of *It Must Be a Misunderstanding* by Coral Bracho is forthcoming from New Directions. *Twice Alive: An Ecology of Intimacies* (New Directions) is the most recent collection by Gander, a Pulitzer Prize–winning poet.

HENRY GLOVER is a London-based painter and ceramicist who won the Saatchi Art Rising Star award in 2020, naming him as one of the top thirty-five artists around the world under thirty-five years old. His debut solo exhibition, *Take Me Somewhere Nice*, was hosted by the Liliya Art Gallery in the spring of 2021.

BRANDON HOBSON's most recent novel is *The Removed* (Ecco). His novel *Where the Dead Sit Talking* (Soho) was a finalist for the National Book Award.

TROY JOLLIMORE's books include the poetry collections *Earthly Delights* and *Syllabus of Errors* (both Princeton University Press) and *Tom Thomson in Purgatory* (Intuit House), which won the National Book Critics Circle Award. As a philosopher, he is the author of *Love's Vision* (Princeton University Press) and *On Loyalty* (Routledge).

STEPHEN GRAHAM JONES is *The New York Times* bestselling author of nearly thirty novels and short story collections, as well as a number of novellas and comic books. His most recent books are *The Only Good Indians*, which won the Ray Bradbury Prize for Science Fiction, Fantasy & Speculative Fiction; *My Heart Is a Chainsaw*; and the forthcoming *Don't Fear the Reaper* (all with Saga). He lives and teaches in Boulder, Colorado.

AKIL KUMARASAMY is the author of the story collection *Half Gods* (Farrar, Straus and Giroux). She is the 2021 recipient of the Bard Fiction Prize, and her debut novel, *Meet Us by the Roaring Sea* (Farrar, Straus and Giroux), is forthcoming in August 2022.

MARY KURYLA's collection *Freak Weather: Stories*, published by the University of Massachusetts Press, received the AWP Grace Paley Prize in Short Fiction. Her debut novel, *Away to Stay*, was published by Regal House Publishing. She is a screenwriting and film studies professor at Loyola Marymount University.

ANN LAUTERBACH's eleventh collection, *DOOR* (Penguin), is forthcoming in 2023. She is Schwab Professor of Languages and Literature at Bard and has been a contributing editor of *Conjunctions* since 1982.

REBECCA LILLY has published several collections of short poetry and haiku with Red Moon Press, most recently *Aporia*. Her latest collection of prose poetry is *Creatures among Us* (Broadstone Books), 2019.

TORI MALCANGIO's story "There I Said It" was included in Best Small Fictions 2021 (Sonder Press). She is the winner of the William Van Dyke Fiction Prize and the American Literary Review Fiction Prize, among others. Malcangio lives in San Diego and is at work on a novel.

SHANE McCRAE's latest books are *Cain Named the Animal* and *Sometimes I Never Suffered* (both Farrar, Straus and Giroux), a finalist for the Maya Angelou Book Award, the T. S. Eliot Prize, and the Rilke Prize. He has received a Lannan Literary Award, a Whiting Writer's Award, and an Anisfield-Wolf Book Award, among others.

RICK MOODY is the author of six novels, including *Hotels of North America* and *The Ice Storm* (both Little, Brown), three collections of stories, a volume of essays on music, and two memoirs, including *The Black Veil* (Little, Brown). He's at work on a new novel, *52 Descriptions of Flag Burning*, and teaches at Tufts University.

KRISTINE ONG MUSLIM has published nine books of fiction and poetry, including *The Drone Outside* (Eibonvale Press), *Black Arcadia* (University of the Philippines Press), *Meditations of a Beast* (Cornerstone Press), *Butterfly Dream* (Snuggly Books), and *Age of Blight* (Unnamed Press). She coedited the British Fantasy Award–winning anthology *People of Colo(u)r Destroy Science Fiction!* (Lightspeed) and *Ulirát: Best Contemporary Stories in Translation from the Philippines* (Gaudy Boy).

BRONKA NOWICKA is an interdisciplinary artist and lecturer at the National Film School in Lodz, Poland. Winner of the Nike Literary Award for her book *To Feed the Stone* (Biuro Literackie), she was made a laureate of the New Voices from Europe project, realized as part of the Literary Europe Live platform to offer support to outstanding European writers after their debuts.

Longtime contributor JOYCE CAROL OATES's latest books include the novel *Breathe* (Ecco) and *Night, Neon: Tales of Mystery and Suspense* (Mysterious Press). She is the 2019 recipient of the Jerusalem Prize and the 2021 recipient of the Cino Del Duca World Prize.

BIN RAMKE's most recent book is *Earth on Earth* (Omnidawn). He teaches at the University of Denver.

JESSICA REED's forthcoming chapbooks are *Still Recognizable Forms* (Laurel Review/Greentower Press) and *World, Composed* (Finishing Line Press).

ELIZABETH ROBINSON is the author of the forthcoming poetry collection *Being Modernists Together* (Solid Objects) and *Thirst & Surfeit* (Threadsuns Press).

ELENI SIKELIANOS, who provided the frontispiece for *Fear Itself*, is the author of the forthcoming *Your Kingdom* (Coffee House Press).

BENNETT SIMS's novel, *A Questionable Shape*, and short story collection, *White Dialogues*, are both available from Two Dollar Radio. His work has received the Bard Fiction Prize and the Joseph Brodsky Rome Prize from the American Academy in Rome. He teaches fiction at the University of Iowa.

TERESE SVOBODA has two books forthcoming: *Roxy and Coco* (West Virginia University Press) and *Dog on Fire* (University of Nebraska Press). Her seventh book of fiction, *Great American Desert* (Mad Creek Books), was published in 2019.

KATARZYNA SZUSTER-TARDI's recent translations include *To Feed the Stone* by Bronka Nowicka (Dalkey Archive Press), *Polish Literature and Genocide* by Arkadiusz Morawiec (Routledge), and the chapbook *Codex of the Insane* by Bronka Nowicka (Toad Press/Veliz Books). She earned her MA in English studies from the University of Lodi, Poland.

BARBARA TOMASH's five books of poetry include, most recently, *PRE-* (Black Radish Books) and the chapbook *Of Residue* (Drop Leaf Press). In the poem "Of Illness," which is part of the "Twelve Nightmares" sequence published here, the lines in italics are from Søren Kierkegaard as paraphrased by Ernest Becker in *The Denial of Death*.

GENEVIEVE VALENTINE is the author of *Mechanique* (Prime), *The Girls at the Kingfisher Club, Persona,* and *Icon* (all Simon & Schuster). Her short fiction has appeared in over a dozen *Best of the Year* anthologies including *Best American Science Fiction & Fantasy* (HarperCollins).

ROB WALSH's stories have appeared in *BOMB, NOON,* and previous issues of *Conjunctions.* He presently lives in Seoul, Korea.

QUINTAN ANA WIKSWO is the author of the collection *The Hope of Floating Has Carried Us This Far* (Coffee House Press) and the novel *A Long Curving Scar Where the Heart Should Be* (Stalking Horse Press).

What Is Now Known Was Once Only Imagined: An (Auto)biography of Niki de Saint Phalle
Nicole Rudick

Known best for her exuberant, often large-scale sculptural works that celebrate the abundance and complexity of female desire, imagination, and creativity, Niki de Saint Phalle viewed making art as a ritual and a performance—a process connecting life to art. This unconventional, illuminated biography, told in the first person in Saint Phalle's voice and her own hand, dilates large and small moments in Saint Phalle's remarkable life as an artist who pointedly challenged taboos.

In a kind of collaboration with the artist, Rudick has assembled a gorgeous and detailed mosaic of Saint Phalle's visual and textual works from a trove of paintings, drawings, sketches, and writings, many rare or previously unpublished. *What Is Now Known But Was Once Only Imagined* is an erudite, insightful, and generous construction of Niki de Saint Phalle's life that, despite the recognizability of her work, has remained mostly obscured, until now.

$45 · Hardback · 268 pages · full color throughout · **www.sigliopress.com**

siglio

uncommon books at the intersection of art & literature

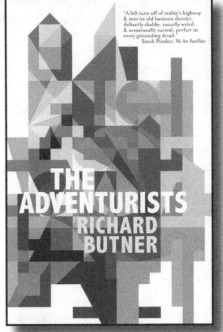

NEW ENGLAND REVIEW

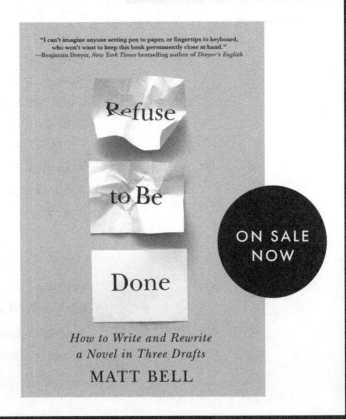

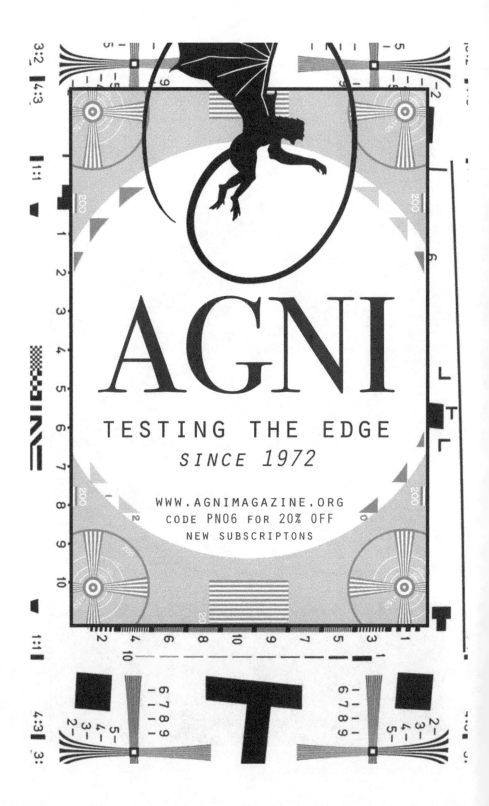

AGNI

TESTING THE EDGE

SINCE 1972

WWW.AGNIMAGAZINE.ORG
CODE PN06 FOR 20% OFF
NEW SUBSCRIPTONS

Donate to *Conjunctions*

We are very proud that *Conjunctions* celebrated
its 40th anniversary last year.
During these past four decades, *Conjunctions* has
brought together writers and readers who share the
same vision of a literature that transcends expectations,
abolishes boundaries, embraces the breadth of the possible.

Now, as we press forward into the future, we need your support
to continue providing a home for the pathbreaking fiction,
poetry, criticism, drama, art, and interviews
that have set the standard for a generation and more.

Whether you give $50 or $5,000, or any amount you can
comfortably afford, your fully tax-deductible donation will help
ensure that *Conjunctions* can continue publishing
the best in contemporary literature.
Will you make a donation?

Please donate by credit card today at
http://annandaleonline.org/supportconjunctions
or send a check to
Conjunctions, Bard College, Annandale-on-Hudson, NY 12504.
For more information contact our managing editor,
Melynda Fuller, at mfuller@bard.edu or (845) 758-7054.

Read Dangerously, Give Generously

Our Donors

Publishers Circle ($2,500 & up)

Hyman Abady   Lawrence Bank, *in honor of Jerome Bank*
Barbara Grossman & Michael Gross
Jay Hanus, *in memoriam*   Peter Straub

Benefactors Circle ($1,000 & up)

Jackie & Kate Douglas
Theresa Fadul, *in memory of*
William F. S. Orner
Beth L. Herstein

The Morris Foundation
Joyce Carol Oates
Richard Powers & Jane Kuntz
Anonymous (1)

Friends Circle ($500 & up)

Mary Caponegro & Michael Ives
Catherine A. Imbriglio, *in memory of*
Reginald Shepherd & C. D. Wright
Nancy Leonard

William Mascioli
Motoyuki Shibata
Cole Swensen
Anonymous (2)

Supporters Circle (up to $500)

Kristina Una Amadeus
Rae Armantrout
Mary-Kim Arnold
Rick Ayre
Shane Ryan Bailey
Mary Jo Bang
Peter Beatty
Susan Bee & Charles Bernstein
Martine Bellen
Jennifer Breen
Susan Love Brown
Leslie Bumstead
Karen Burnham
Jay Cantor
J'Lyn Chapman
Maxine Chernoff
Karen & Sara Cinquemani,
    class of 2002
Mark Cohen
Peter Cole & Adina Hoffman
Elizabeth Collison
Robert Crawford
Kathryn Davis
Michèle Dominy
Cecelia Shalini Dsouza
Tyson Duffy
Henry Dunow
Rikki Ducornet
Rachel Blau DuPlessis
Elizabeth Ely & Jonathan Greenburg
Margaret Fisher & Robert Hughes
Forrest Gander
Frieda Gardner
The Estate of William H. Gass
Ian Gill
Diane Glancy
Eli Gottlieb
Christine Graham
Tara Hadid
Jeff Hanson
Elizabeth Logan Harris
Marina Hatsopoulos

Brenda Hillman
Brandon Hobson
Amy Holman
Tim Horvath
Mark Irwin
Sharon Johnson
Stephanie Joyce
Paula Joyner
Karen Kaczmar
Vincent Katz, *in honor of Ada Katz*
Chris Kearin
Jared Killeen
Megan Kincheloe
Mary Kuryla, *with Isaac Yelchin,*
    class of 2019
Byron Landry
Alison & John Lankenau
Sylvia Legris
Henry Ledwith
Christin Lee
Literary Hub
Anthony Madrid
Michael J. Maresca
Luna Mari
Thomas J. Marnocha
Carole Maso
Peter McCabe
Theodore McCombs
James McCorkle
Kelly McKisson
James M. McLachlan
Daniel McMinn
Jon Miller
Nicolas Minutillo
Roger Mitchell
John D. Morgan
Richard Murphy
Stephen E. Myers
Betty Joyce Nash
New Directions
Patricia O'Sullivan
Andi & Lance Olsen

Toby Olson
Suzanne Paola
Aikya Param
Michael D. Parker
LJ Pemberton
Debra Pemstein
David Perry, *in memory of*
W. Dixon Powell, class of '66
Hope Polidoro
David A. Poole
Melissa Pritchard Schley
Roseanne Giannini Quinn
Jessica Reed
Jane Rosenthal
Karen Russell
Laurence Ryan
Cara Schlesinger
Janet Schlesinger
Kirstin Scott
Michael Sheehan
Margaret Shuhala
Eleni Sikelianos & Laird Hunt
Margot Singer
Angelica J. Smith
James B. Stewart
Meredith Stricker
Arthur Sze
Rebecca Thomas
Barbara Tomash
Andrew Touhy, *in honor of*
Daniel Touhy
Lily Tuck
Rachel Tzvia Back
Enrique Urueta
G.C. Waldrep
Jeffrey Wertheimer
James B. Westine,
in memory of Peggy Brady
Thomas Wild
Ros Zimmerman
Anonymous (95)

This project is supported in part by awards from the National Endowment for the Arts, the New York State Council on the Arts with the support of Governor Kathy Hochul and the New York State Legislature, Community of Literary Magazines and Presses, and the Whiting Foundation.

NATIONAL ENDOWMENT for the ARTS
arts.gov

 NEW YORK STATE OF OPPORTUNITY.

Council on the Arts

[clmp]
COMMUNITY OF LITERARY MAGAZINES & PRESSES
www.clmp.org

 whiting
FOUNDATION